Contents

C000179261

How to Use This Guide

Order of Entries

London appears first and is in alphabetical order by **establishment name**. Listings outside London are in alphabetical order by **location** within divisions of England, Scotland, Wales, Channel Islands and the Isle of Man. See contents page for specific page numbers and the index for individual entries.

Types of Establishments

Categories such as **Hotel, Restaurant, Pub, Tea Room** are printed within the header for each establishment. If a hotel features in our *Hotels & Restaurants Cellnet Guide 1993* then it is given the % grading from that Guide; several private house hotels, more modest London hotels and country inns (many of which include 'hotel' in their title) also feature in both Guides but are not given a grading as their range of public rooms is limited; nevertheless, good facilities for families are offered in all establishments.

Hotels

Prices given are high season rates and are accurate at the time of research but may well have changed by the middle of 1993. We urge readers to ask about weekend break prices as many hotels that fill up with business people during the week offer reduced prices at weekends; family facilities may also be extended for weekend periods. The price quoted in the header for each establishment entry is for a double room (occupied by two adults) with private en-suite facilities and a cooked breakfast; children's beds and cots may well attract an extra charge. The percentage shown is an individual rating arrived at after careful testing, inspection and calculation according to Egon Ronay's Guides' unique grading system. **The size of a hotel and the prices charged are not considered in the grading.**

Only in those hotels that feature a separate entry for their restaurant do we specifically recommend the food for adults; children's meals are considered separately and, where information has been provided, details are given. Where a hotel's brochure says 'Egon Ronay listed' this does *not* automatically include the restaurant; there are many hotels in the UK where the food continues to fail to live up to the standards of accommodation. Children may be easily satisfied with homely offerings such as fish fingers and baked beans but once they are safely tucked up in bed their parents have a right to expect higher standards.

Chain hotel groups are listed only under a separate section at the rear of the Guide; they are not plotted on the maps but are listed in county order.

Pubs

We include establishments where our team of professional inspectors found good-quality bar food. Reference may also be made to the pub's restaurant, but our chief concern has been with bar food and facilities for families, both inside and outside. Typical dishes are usually listed, with prices valid at the time of our visit. Prices may, however, have risen a little since then. We indicate when bar food is served and also any times when food is not available. Times of restaurant meals may differ and are then listed separately.

Where a pub offers accommodation suitable for families we give the relevant statistics at the end of that establishment's story. The price quoted is for a double room with en-suite facilities and a cooked breakfast. If residents cannot check in at any time during the day then we print the appropriate check-in times; if it's advisable to arrange a check-in time (say, out of pub hours) when booking, we print *by arrangement*.

Pubs recommended as pleasant or interesting places for a drink rather than for their bar food or accommodation have very short entries and no statistics for bar food times or accommodation. Invariably these offer outdoor areas where children can let off steam and are thus included as useful stopping places.

Restaurants

Wherever possible we have given an indication of a restaurant's attitude towards children; some obviously attract families like bees to a honey pot, others have a menu, room layout and staff attitude that offer more subtle attractions. Prices given in the header are for two people and include a *three-course meal for two including one of the least expensive bottles of wine, coffee, service and VAT*. Set-price menu prices quoted often do not include service, usually exclude wine and may not necessarily comprise three courses. Many restaurants and hotel dining rooms now offer *only* a set-price menu, although this will usually include a choice. Vegetarians should inform the establishment of their requirements when booking. Facilities such as the provision of high-chairs and children's cutlery have been listed where known.

Map references

Entries contain references to the map section at the rear of the Guide (before the index). **Map 8 C2**, for example, refers to map square C2 on page 8 of the maps. Use this section to help select establishments in areas you wish to visit.

Credit Cards

We list credit cards currently accepted by each establishment. If it is vital to your visit that an establishment take a particular credit card then we suggest that you always confirm this information at the time of booking as credit card facilities sometimes change after we have gone to press.

Symbol

   Outstanding facilities for families.

Introduction

This edition of *...and Baby Comes Too* sees a Guide greatly expanded since its inception in 1990. We have collated information from the whole year's research work of our team of professional hotel and restaurant inspectors, including family-friendly establishments from throughout *Egon Ronay's Hotels & Restaurants Cellnet Guide 1993, Pubs & Inns MLC Guide 1993* and *Just a Bite Guide 1993*. In addition to this research we have included the findings of an experienced team of parents and their children (not just mums and toddlers as in previous years) who can relate tales of hotels that banish children to their rooms by offering children's food via room service only and restaurants that suffer children only because they want their parents' business. So, for families who want to travel around Great Britain with their children in tow, we now offer a more diverse choice than ever before of establishments in which to stay and eat.

We continue to exclude family chain restaurants such as *McDonald's, Harvester, Old Orleans, TGIF, Garfunkel's* and *Deep Pan Pizzas* as they are, in general, well marketed and in the most easy-to-find locations. We make no excuses for not 'filling in the gaps' in certain geographical areas where there is a paucity of quality establishments (Glasgow, for example) as there are often many burger and pizza chain outlets around with admirable family facilities, if not exceptional food. As always there are exceptions to the rule and we have included a few chains, namely *Browns* (who most recently opened in Bristol), *Littlejohn's* in Scotland, *Pizza Express* (outside London) and several pubs in the *Brewers Fayre* group – all of whom we feel are above the ordinary. Chain hotel groups are listed at the rear of the Guide in county order but do not appear on the maps.

Off The Beaten Track

Egon Ronay's Guides' aim, as ever, is to single out establishments – from tea rooms to trattorias and homely hostelries to posh palaces – where effort and quality are in evidence, however off the beaten track; this year we have even included the wonderful *Kilberry Inn* in Strathclyde, Scotland, which is at the end of a 16-mile, winding, hilly single-track road – but well worth the drive. Similarly, it may be easier to stop off at a *Little Chef* or *Happy Eater* by the side of the A1 when heading north, but it will be ultimately more rewarding (and probably more healthy) to drive on for a while and find the unusual *Ram Jam Inn* in Stretton, Leicestershire.

Awards

Once again we have singled out exceptional establishments by awarding them a duck symbol. At these places we feel that children are likely to be treated as valued customers rather than tiresome, noisy irritants to other diners or residents. It has been impossible to visit every establishment listed with children, but our inspectors have kept a watchful eye on how proprietors have reacted to families during their visits for all the Egon Ronay's Guides. In addition, we have requested details from all establishments with regard to the provision of high-chairs, baby utensils, children's menu and changing facilities (it's not easy for a gentleman inspector to inspect the Ladies!) in restaurants, and cots, extra beds, baby-listening/sitting, baby baths, potties and even nappies in hotels. Where there is particularly good access for prams and push-chairs, storage for both, or a private area for nursing or nappy changing we emphasise this in the text; although these facilities are the ideal, we accept that even some of the best establishments cannot be all things to all families!

Eating out with youngsters under the age of five can so often be hell, but when you walk in to a place like *Blubeckers* in Shepperton, Middlesex and find a high-chair reserved for your 2-year-old, a balloon and crayons and a children's menu (for ordering and colouring) produced within minutes, it's a relief; when there's a quality and quantity of food on offer to satisfy both young *and* old then it's a real bonus. Equally, a Chinese restaurant offering dim sum can be of similar interest to junior diners with its mix of steam baskets, chopsticks and unusual food. Those hotels that provide early evening high teas and supervised crèche and play facilities during adult meal times are on the right track, making life easier for everyone all round.

Change In Character

The things that don't make life easier all round are weekend wedding parties and weekday conference groups that dominate a hotel's or restaurant's facilities, thereby completely changing the character of the establishment. Proprietors who put families (or single mothers and their children) in rooms a long way from lifts and stairs may be trying to maintain the equilibrium ("peace") of their hotel but may inadvertently be making life intolerably awkward at the same time. Invariably it is people that count – staff can so easily make up for lack of facilities; this has been proved time after time and we thus include many establishments that may seem to be short on facilities but which are certainly not lacking the right attitude.

In the course of research it should be noted that many establishments have stated a wish not to be included in the Guide; thus, while many readers may think they have found a delightful family retreat and have written to tell us about it, it may be missing from this Guide because of the proprietor's wishes.

Your Views

We thank all those who have sent us their readers' comments forms during the last year and hope that new readers will use the forms provided at the back of this year's Guide. Readers' comments form an essential part of our research and help keep the information we provide as up to date as possible. There is still a dearth of French-style family restaurants where all the family can enjoy a homely meal together in comfort; burgers and fries, pizza and other fast food outlets are all too often the easy option. If *your* local restaurant transforms into a haven for little ones at weekends and you can bear sharing the news with other readers then please write and tell us about it.

Andrew Eliel
Managing Editor

FOREWORD

Heinz is delighted to sponsor Egon Ronay's Guide ... *and Baby Comes Too* for the fourth successive year.

We believe that the Guide has now established itself as an indispensable friend to parents travelling with young children.

Heinz Babyfoods come in a huge variety of flavours and textures, from the more traditional favourites like Chicken and Ham Dinner, to the more exotic Apple & Mango fromage frais. They are ideal for parents out and about with a baby.

Heinz Babyfoods in cans are ideal for travelling as they are light to carry and unbreakable. They now have a ring-pull opening making them easier to open, without having to take a can opener too. Heinz Babyfood jars can also easily be opened and closed when you are out.

Another plus when you are away from home is that Heinz Babyfoods can be fed to your baby without heating first. This is because they are cooked in the can and jar and so need no further cooking and are perfectly safe to feed unheated. This makes them ideal for use when travelling and for outings and picnics. Take a Heinz can and jar and baby's spoon and that's all you need!

The Heinz range includes a delicious array of meals, both meat and vegetable based, as well as fruits, yoghurts and fromage frais desserts. Value for money and convenience make Heinz Babyfoods the natural choice when you are away from home.

...and Baby Comes Too
Family Hotel of the Year

Crieff Hydro
Crieff, Perthshire, Tayside, Scotland PH7 3LQ
Telephone 0764 65555

An imposing red stone Victorian hotel built in 1868 as a hydro with elegant proportions and extensive grounds, between St Fillans and Perth. Now self-styled as 'Scotland's favourite family hotel', they ably demonstrate that 'happy children mean happy parents'. Catering for families with children of all ages – from donkey rides for the youngest to football for teenagers – the Crieff Hydro is a family hotel *par excellence* (there's even a doctor's surgery on site).

During mealtimes there is 'parents' peacetime' when a supervised nursery looks after children over 3; dances are held three times a week in the ballroom. The one thing you won't find here, though, is a bar; drinks are only served with meals in the dining room.

The wide variety of accommodation includes family rooms with bunk beds, suites with interconnecting bedrooms, 'Executive' rooms (some with views over the Vale of Strathearn), duplex studio suites in an annex and self-catering wooden chalets (where family pets are welcome) on the wooded hillside above the hotel.

There are enough leisure facilities – both indoor and outdoor – to keep even the most energetic family busy, including many ball games (9-hole golf course, 5 tennis courts, squash and badminton), an outdoor paddling pool and a riding school. If the weather takes a turn for the worse then there's a 20m indoor swimming pool (complete with large splash pool and refreshment area) in the Lagoon Leisure Complex, a cinema, table-tennis and playroom plus bounteous beauty facilities for parents. Kennels are provided for dogs and children can let off steam by walking them in the large gardens; proud parents can perambulate their babies in a traditional pram provided by the hotel. Special terms for children under 10 can include three meals in the nursery (with adjoining playroom), where high-chairs and baby food are provided for the very young.

Although families predominate in high season, out-of-season periods can see a higher proportion of conference and 'Golden Age' guests and the character of the hotel can change accordingly. Nevertheless, with its outstanding range of family facilities, the Crieff Hydro is a worthy winner of our 1993 Family Hotel of the Year award.

...and Baby Comes Too
Family Restaurants of the Year

Smollensky's on the Strand
105 Strand London WC2
Telephone 071-497 2101

What can a whole apple do that a half apple can't? Look round! The jokes on the 'fun at Smollensky's' children's menu may be old hat but the food is guaranteed to please. Smollensky's mix of American-style menu, friendly staff and entertainment is a successful blend of burgers and steaks, late-night jazz and weekend lunchtime jollity.

Immensely popular with families, booking at weekends has become almost essential. A supervised play area with slide, seesaw and 25 or so large, indestructible toys (bikes, tractors, hoovers) helps the under-7s through the cooking times of their parents' main courses. Colouring sheets, badges, pens and cartoon videos help, too. Best of all is the positive attitude of the staff towards children. There are heaps of high-chairs and booster seats available; a changing mat is in the toilet and a manager's office for breast-feeding in privacy.

Every weekend sees an entertainer or two, with clowns, balloons, a show and a popular children's dancing session. Live music regularly features in the evenings, with dancing on Friday and Saturday evenings; live jazz and light music every other evening (including Sundays when there's a £3 charge). A sensibly-priced Brasserie menu (with no minimum charge) is offered at lunchtimes Mon-Fri in the gallery section. Happy Hour 5.30-7pm.

Smollensky's Balloon Bar & Restaurant
1 Dover Street London W1
Telephone 071-491 1199

How does an intruder get into a house? Intrude a window! The jokes are the same at this original branch of Smollensky's (now in its 7th year) and so is the weekend kids' menu – koktails (£1.55 with freshly-squeezed orange juice as an option), main courses (£3.95) including hot dog in a bun, hamburger in a bun, bangers, mash and beans, spaghetti and meatballs, chicken nuggets, tender steak and fish fingers. Kids dessert konkoktions (£1.95) complete the picture with the likes of gingerbread men with vanilla ice cream, knickerbocker glory and super milkshakes. The choice is generally smaller at other times of the week.

Along with an extensive American-style menu for adults, a 'pre-fix' menu of £9.85 offers a choice of four starters or salad followed by entrecote steak, sauce, French fries and a glass of house beer or wine. Adult diners are encouraged to 'surrender the impulse to be virtuous' and tuck in to the likes of Grandma Smollensky's peanut butter cheesecake or Erna's chocolate mousse (served from a giant goblet plus free second helpings for trainee trenchermen) for dessert. A bottomless cup of coffee completes the transatlantic picture.

A lunchtime brasserie menu is served Mon-Fri on the upper floor area and offers plenty of variety – from smoked haddock fish cakes with tartare sauce to chicken and broccoli lasagne with garlic bread; no minimum charge.

Between 12 and 3 at weekends, families are kept amused by entertainers offering table-side magic and fun music videos on the television monitors; computer games nuts can even have a go with the latest Nintendo software. At 2.30, parents have half-an-hour's peace while children are taken to a separate end of the restaurant for a puppet, magic show or both – there may be a jester on a horse, a stilt-walker or even a fire-eater! The over-7s are particularly well catered for and a takeaway Smollensky's balloon puts the icing on the cake for the under-7s. There is a children's urinal for wee ones in the Gents, a baby-changing area in the Ladies and there are high-chairs and booster seats galore – a veritable parents' paradise!

There is no cover charge but, unusually, an 8% service charge is automatically added to your bill, but, as they explain on the menu: 'The English are renowned for not complaining. We hope that we won't give you cause to complain, but if we do, please make an exception in our case. We really do care and we really do want to know if anything goes wrong.' Enough said.

Cellnet makes more of the cellphone.

With the technological expertise and financial support of our parent companies – BT & Securicor – Cellnet has played a key role in developing the UK mobile telecommunications market.

Today, we are acknowledged industry leaders with an unrivalled innovation record.

Having first developed the most comprehensive range of services for the business user, Cellnet has now made it possible for everyone to enjoy the benefits of the mobile phone with Lifetime – the new low cost tariff for the less frequent user.

Offering considerable savings over standard business rates for people who make the majority of calls in the early morning, evenings and weekends, it's perfect for the occasional call – when you just have to get hold of someone. And, of course, it enables your friends, relatives and customers to get in touch with you. Anytime. Anywhere.

cellnet
The nearest phone.

The siting of our transceivers and aerials is critical, if we're to ensure the best possible radio reception for Cellnet users.

The higher, the better – is the rule for cellular equipment.

To this end we sometimes take advantage of the most unlikely sites – Ely Cathedral, for example, and even Manchester City's football stadium.

Better coverage – nationwide.

Embracing over 98% of the UK population, Cellnet's quality and reliability standards are assured by a sophisticated national network which includes exclusive coverage of the Channel Islands and the Isle of Man.

With around 30,000 voice channels operating through more than 800 cellular radio stations throughout the UK (over 1000 during 1993), Cellnet has network capacity in reserve, ensuring first time success with the vast majority of calls, anywhere in the country.

Handportables are the preferred choice of 70% of all new subscribers. Already offering unrivalled handportable coverage, Cellnet is now investing over £30 million in a network development programme which will include the commissioning of over 230 new cellular stations during 1993.

cellnet
The nearest phone.

Cellnet gives you more choice.

Recognising that different users have very different needs, Cellnet offers two tariffs for the business and less frequent user. Now you can choose the service which best suits your lifestyle.

Lifetime – The new low cost tariff for people who tend to use a mobile phone outside the peak period: before 8am, evenings after 7pm, and at weekends. It offers savings of up to 50% on standard business rates for callers making less than 25 minutes of calls a month. Calls can be made at anytime but are charged at a higher rate during the peak period.

This exciting new package gives you access to intelligent messaging services, and answering systems*. No ordinary answering services, these take messages when your cellphone is engaged or switched off and play them back when your phone is free.

Primetime – A tariff for the business user and people who use a mobile phone frequently during the day. The fixed costs are higher than Lifetime but calls are cheaper during peak hours: 8am to 7pm. Primetime offers a comprehensive range of services including intelligent messaging and answering systems, international calls, CallAccess and dedicated information services.

Now, when you come to consider mobile communications, you'll have two decisions to make. The network it will run on. And the tariff that suits your needs best.

Choose Cellnet, and you'll be connected to the network that is really geared to your needs.

*Using these services will incur extra charges.

1993 Duck Awards

London

Benihana **NW3**
Newtons **SW4**
Rock Island Diner **WC2**
Smollensky's Balloon Bar & Restaurant **W1**
Smollensky's on the Strand **WC2**
Spices **N16**

England

Alfriston Toucans Restaurant
Blackpool Pembroke Hotel
Borrowdale Stakis Lodore Swiss Hotel
Bournemouth Swallow Highcliff Hotel
Bradford on Avon Woolley Grange Hotel
Branscombe Bulstone Hotel
Brightling Jack Fuller's
Brighton Dig in the Ribs
Brighton The Dove Hotel
Bristol Browns
Bristol Café Première
Cambridge Browns
Camelford Lanteglos Country House Hotel
Carlisle Hudson's Coffee Shop
Carlyon Bay Carlyon Bay Hotel
Castleton Moorlands Hotel
Chale Clarendon Hotel & Wight Mouse Inn
Chester Francs
Eastbourne Grand Hotel
Harome Star Inn
Harrogate Bettys
Harrogate West Park Hotel
Hythe Hythe Imperial Hotel
Ilkley Bettys
Kingscote Hunters Hall Inn
Kington Penrhos Court
Langdale Langdale Hotel
Leeds Salvo's
Lincoln Moor Lodge Hotel
Lytham St Anne's Dalmeny Hotel
Marlborough Polly Tea Rooms
Northallerton Bettys

Odiham Blubeckers Mill House
Over Stratton Royal Oak
Oxford Browns
Richmond The Refectory
Rochester The Knowle
St Martins St Martins Hotel
Saunton Saunton Sands Hotel
Shanklin Hambledon Hotel
Shepperton Blubeckers Eating House
Skipton Randell's Hotel
Stafford Soup Kitchen
Stow-on-the-Wold Fosse Manor Hotel
Stretton Ram Jam Inn
Studland Bay Knoll House Hotel
Swindon Blunsdon House
Thurlestone Thurlestone Hotel
Wantage Vale & Downland Museum
Westerham Spinning Wheel
Whitby Magpie Café
Willerby Grange Park Hotel
Woolacombe Woolacombe Bay Hotel
York Taylors Tea Rooms

Scotland

Banchory Raemoir House
Crieff Crieff Hydro
Largs Nardini's
New Abbey Criffel Inn
Peebles Peebles Hotel Hydro
Selkirk Philipburn House

Wales

Abersoch Porth Tocyn
Llanarmon Dyffryn Ceiriog West Arms Hotel

Channel Islands

St Brelade's Bay St Brelade's Bay Hotel

London

W1   Arisugawa   £60
Tel 071-636 8913	Restaurant

27 Percy Street W1   Map 18 D2

Just a few steps off Tottenham Court Road. The first choice of many
Japanese diners, this smart modern, basement restaurant has a menu
of more than usual interest. Western palates can play safe with familiar
favourites, or venture into unknown territory like sea-urchin roe
sashimi. While there are no specific facilities for children the staff are
patient and friendly and will gladly help with choosing dishes, clearly
describing each one (children should try the tempura); the food
is delicate, fresh and beautifully presented. The decor, is sophisticated
and chic and it's certainly not a place for anything less than best
behaviour from baby-san. *Seats 100. Parties 100. Private Room.
L 12.30-2.30 D 6-10. Closed L Sat, all Sun, Bank Holidays, Xmas/New
Year. Set L from £6.50 Set D from £15. Access, Amex, Diners, Visa.*

N1   Anna's Place   £44
Tel 071-249 9379	Restaurant

90 Mildmay Park Newington Green N1 4PR   Map 16 D2

Chatty Anna Hegarty is a constant presence in her tiny and noisy place
with its close-set tables and summer conservatory. Her native Sweden
is the main inspiration for the menu, which includes home-cured
herring served in dill and light curry sauces, broccoli and lemon soup,
gravlax or a hefty Janssen's Temptation (a creamy mixture of baked
potatoes, anchovies and onions). Salmon fishcakes with sorrel sauce,
a daily special fish dish, game in season and hotpots are typical of the
style. Saturday lunchtime is perhaps the best time to visit. Childrens
portions of most dishes are available and puddings like chocolate
truffle cake are especially child-friendly. There is one booster seat. The
atmosphere is rather grown-up in the evening although children are
welcome at any time. No specific baby-changing area. *Seats 45. Parties
30. L 12.15-2.15 D 7.15-10.45. Closed Sun, Mon, 2 weeks Xmas,
2 weeks Easter, all August. No credit cards.*

EC2   Barbican Centre, Waterside Restaurant
Tel 071-638 4141	Restaurant

Barbican Centre EC2   Map 20 B1

The Waterside is a self-service Justin de Blank restaurant on level
5 of the Barbican Centre, and benefits from a large terrace open in the
summer. The daily-changing menu offers hot and cold dishes of good
quality, all cooked on the premises: pumpkin and cheese soup £2.35,
chicken and ham gougère £5.95, salmon fishcake £6.95, vegetable
curry £5.35, vegetable terrine with salad and bread £5.60. There's
an interesting selection of cheeses, and customers cut their own slices
from a central display of loaves. The balcony café on level 6 is open
12-8 Sun, 10-8 Sat and 5-8 Mon-Fri, serving a slightly cheaper
menu. A simpler café, also on level 6, has tables and chairs spread
along the balcony. *Seats 230. Open 12-8. Access, Amex, Diners, Visa.*

SE3   Bardon Lodge Hotel   £74
Tel 081-853 4051 Fax 081-858 7387	Hotel

Stratheden Road Blackheath SE3 7TH   Map 17 D5

Convenient for the open spaces of the Heath and within walking
distance of the maritime attractions of Greenwich, this modern

conversion of two solid Victorian houses has much family appeal with
its lovely rear patio and enclosed garden for use in fine weather. Now
under new owners, meal times have been sensibly extended (though
closed Sunday nights) and the two high-chairs should come in handy
for breakfast. Family bedrooms provide a choice of bunk beds or cots,
and there's a standard baby-listening service via the internal phone
system. The Lodge and the Vanburgh (its 30-bedroom annex nearby)
are more geared to businessmen's needs during the week, so there are
some good deals on offer for families at weekends. Five family
bedrooms; £5 cot charge for under-5s. *Rooms 37. Access, Amex, Visa.*

SW3	**Basil Street Hotel**	71%	£170

Tel 071-581 3311 Fax 071-581 3693 — Hotel

Basil Street SW3 1AH — Map 19 C4

An Edwardian English atmosphere pervades this privately-owned
hotel just a few steps from Harrods. Public areas have a country house
feel, from the antique-lined corridor leading to the dining room to the
spacious lounge in sunny yellow with rug-covered polished parquet
floor. Up a broad staircase are well-kept bedrooms, usually with
a sitting area, traditionally furnished and decorated with understated
good taste. Most have equally roomy private bathrooms. If money
is no object then families should opt for a suite with interconnecting
rooms. Old-fashioned standards of courteous and obliging service
include shoe cleaning, servicing of rooms in the evenings and 24hr
room service. Children under 16 stay free in parents' room. *Rooms 92.
Access, Amex, Diners, Visa.*

The Dining Room   £50

Matching the rest of the establishment in every way, the space
is strong on Edwardian nostalgia. The cooking also tends towards the
traditional, epitomised by roast rib of beef served from the trolley.
Speedy pre-theatre dinners; children's portions. The dining room is not
suitable for children at night but meals may be eaten in the lounge
or bedroom. Good wines at kind prices. *Seats 90. Parties 15. Private
Room. L 12.30-2.30 D 6.30-10 (Sat & Sun to 9.30). Closed L Sat.
Set L from £14.50.*

NW3	**Benihana**		£75

Tel 071-586 9508 — Restaurant

100 Avenue Road NW3 3HF — Map 16 B3

Upwardly mobile toddlers will love Benihana, an American-Japanese
restaurant which goes out of its way to cater for families. All food
is cooked on a large griddle with showbiz flair by knife-flailing chefs
at hibachi tables. There is a children's menu but most children will
enjoy sharing with their parents from the main menu. To top it all
off there's children's entertainment on Sundays. There are plenty
of booster seats for toddlers but no high-chairs; this probably
isn't a very suitable place to take a baby, given the amount of high
drama and cooking at the table. Also Benihana is distinctly pricy –
count on £30 to £40 per adult for a family meal, although lunchtime
specials (not Sunday) are particularly good value at £6.50 and £10.25.
Children's menu selection (£4.75-£5.50): seafood splash-prawn
appetizer, corn on the cob, fish fillet, rice, ice cream or sorbet; side
orders of chips, frankfurter sausages and tempura. Non-alcoholic
cocktails (snow white, melon pussy, Shirley Temple, super B-kid)
from £1.75. 12½% service charge is added to all bills. The entrance,

which isn't easy to find, is next to the Hampstead Theatre in Swiss Cottage. *No-smoking area.* **Seats** *112.* **Open** *12.30-3 (Sat & Sun from 1) & 6.30-12 (Sun to 11).* **Closed** *L Mon, 25 Dec. Access, Amex, Diners, Visa.*

SW3   Big Easy

Tel 071-352 4071	Restaurant
334 Kings Road Chelsea SW3	**Map 18 B6**

Rough, dark wood liberally decorated with American memorabilia helps create a characterful, buzzy ambience. A wide selection of enjoyable popular American classics described with gusto and include starters such as buffalo fried shrimps with blue cheese can celery dip (£3.45) seafood gumbo available by the cup (£1.05) or bowl (£2.75). Steaks are certified Angus beef and seafood is fried in cholesterol-free polyunsaturated vegetable oil. Crab claws steamed in garlic butter (£6.90), BBQ chicken (£4.95) half-pound Bayouburger (£5.75). A two course set meal available from noon till 8pm at £4.95 represents good value. with the likes of spicy chicken creole, chargrilled trout or minute steak served with trimmings. **Seats** *150.* **Open** *12-12.* **Closed** *25 & 26 Dec, 1 Jan. Access, Amex, Visa.*

E1   Bloom's

Tel 071-247 6001	Restaurant
90 Whitechapel High Street Aldgate E1 7RA	**Map 16 B1**

For over 70 years, the Bloom family have dispensed authentic Beth-Din supervised cooking at this large Kosher East End institution. Chopped liver (£2.50), tzimmas (£1.50) and gedempte meat-balls (£5.90) are familiar favourites, but the salt beef (£7.90) is still the one to go for. Service from suitably sardonic staff is so slick you can order course by course if you wish. Great fun. Childrens' portions and take-away service available. **Seats** *130.* **Open** *10-9.30 (Fri to 3, 2 in Winter).* **Closed** *D Fri, Sat, 25 Dec, Jewish Holidays. Access, Amex, Diners, Visa.*

NW11   Bloom's

Tel 081-455 3033	Restaurant
130 Golders Green Road Golders Green NW11 8HB	**Map 16 D3**

Sibling establishment to the East End version. Similarly Kosher and equally vibrant with the menu running the gamut of comfortable Jewish cooking. Dishes include chopped herring (£2.30), gefilte fish (£2.50) and lockshen pudding (£2.20), with childrens' portions and a take-away service also available. Useful late opening on Saturday evenings. **Seats** *70.* **Open** *10am-10.30pm (Fri to 3, 2 in winter), Sat 1 hour after Sabbath to 4am.* **Closed** *D Fri, L Sat. Access, Amex, Diners, Visa.*

NW1   Bournes

Tel 071-482 0640	Fish'n'Chips
1-3 Pratt Street Camden Town NW1	**Map 16 C3**

Green-hooded wall lamps and a ceiling fan add a touch of luxury to a Cypriot-run fish and chip restaurant just off Camden High Street. Aside from the take-away counter are seats for 24 at properly laid tables, plus outside tables (cooler but not very peaceful) in hot weather. Decent quality fish and chips (cod £5.20/£6.60) plaice (£8.15) have the grill as an alternative to the deep-fryer. Taramasalata,

made on the premises, is a good starter (£1.95 with pitta bread) and
if you've still got room there are some homely desserts – apple pie,
steamed pudding (£2). Note that it's open on Sunday – unusual
for a fish and chip restaurant. *Seats 24.* *Open 11.30-10.15.* *Access,
Amex, Diners, Visa.*

W6   The Brackenbury

Tel 071-748 0107	Restauant
129 Brackenbury Road off Goldhawk Road Shepherds Bush W6 0BQ	**Map 17 A4**

Formed from two adjacent shops, The Brackenbury is run by partners
Kate and Adam Robinson, who offer a short menu that changes
at each session and manages to encompass much of what is best
in London's current simple, modern cooking style at reasonable prices;
many would call it "trend-setting". Start with roast beetroot salad, sour
cream and chives (£2.50), cullen skink (£2.50) or rocket, baked
tomatoes and olives (£3). Six or so main course choices usually
include a fish dish (grilled grey mullet, couscous and mint dressing
£6) and dishes such as spinach dumplings, tomato sauce and salad
(£5), poached chicken breast with leeks (£6.50), roast aiguillette
of beef bordelaise (£7.50) and ox tongue, carrots and horseradish
(£6.75). An apricot and almond tart, bowl of greengages or plum
crumble and custard (all £2.75) to follow. Wines are carefully chosen,
as realistically priced as the food and almost all offered by the glass.
Tables on the pavement in the summer. Simple fare, expertly
executed; deserving of success, not only because of the extremely
sensible prices. No high chairs are provided, so take your own.
The loos are down a steep staircase, but if you're prepared to make
the effort then the Robinsons will look after you well. *Seats 55.*
Open 12.30-2.45 & 7-10.45. *Closed L Sat & Mon, D Sun.* *Access,
Amex, Visa.*

SW18   Brady's

Tel 081-877 9599	Fish'n'Chips
513 Old York Road Wandsworth SW18 1TF	**Map 17 B5**

Fresh fish from Grimsby or Cornwall is prepared without fuss or frills
in Luke Brady's simple, uncluttered restaurant. With grilled
or battered fish (main courses around £5) come good chips and
various flavoured mayonnaises. Starters could include smoked salmon
(£3.50) or half-a-pint of prawns (£2.50), and there are regularly
changing specials among the main course. Treacle tart is a popular
pud. *Seats 38.* *Open 12.30-2.30 (Sat only) & 7-10.45 (Fri to 11.15).*
Closed D Sun, last 2 wks Aug, 10 days Xmas/New Year. *No credit cards.*

WC1   British Museum, de Blank Restaurant

Tel 071-636 1555	Restaurant
British Museum Great Russell Street Bloomsbury WC1	**Map 18 D2**

Pass through the Book Shop on the ground floor of the British
Museum to Justin de Blank's self-service licensed restaurant and
adjacent *Café de Blank*. The restaurant menu is on the blackboard and
covers a wide selection of salads, home-made soup (£2.10), up to three
hot dishes (steak and kidney pie £5.50) and home-made desserts
(walnut tart £1.60), cakes and pastries. Children's portions and high-
chairs provided. The separate Café serves sandwiches, cakes, and
pastries. Parent and baby room is through the Egyptian sculpture

exhibition. No smoking. **Seats** *Restaurant 160, Café 80.* **Open**
Restaurant 12-4.15 (Sun 2.30-5.30), Café 10-3 (Sun 2.30-5.15).
Closed *5 days Christmas. No credit cards.*

SW1   Café de Blank

Tel 071-730 6400	Café
General Trading Company 144 Sloane Street SW1X 9AY	Map 19 C5

Convenient for the Sloane Square shopping area, Justin de Blank's café
at the 'GTC' is popular for breakfast, lunch, tea or early evening snack.
Reached through the shop during the day or down the basement steps
in the evening, the daily changing blackboard menu offers specials
such as carrot and coriander soup (£2.95), aubergine and pine nut tart
(£6.25), or chicken and grape salad with chervil dressing (£6.50). Set
menus are served from 6pm: 2-course £12.25 or 3-course £14.95 –
pork rillette with walnut toast, pan-fried whitebait, roast poussin with
cider and apples, salmon fishcakes with Hollandaise sauce, apple gratin,
iced chocolate pecan pie. From 9 till noon, the Café de Blank breakfast
(£4.50) has a choice of croissants, brioches or breads, freshly squeezed
orange juice and unlimited cafetière coffee, or there's the choice
of toast with scrambled eggs and flat-capped mushrooms (£3.50)
or sausages and bacon (£3.50). For weary shoppers, a cream tea
is available in the afternoons (£2.75). A garden table is often preferred
in summer. Babies eat free and under-12s for half price (booster seats
supplied). **Seats** *52 (plus 20 in garden).* **Open** *9-9 (Sat to 6 – closes Sat
about 4 in winter).* **Closed** *Sun, between Christmas and New Year. Access,
Amex, Visa.*

SW14   Café Coco

Tel 081-878 4800	Restaurant
361 Upper Richmond Road West Sheen SW14	Map 17 A5

A clean, clean-lined neighbourhood café at the rear of a takeaway
bakery/patisserie with grey marble tables, tiled floor and prints on the
walls. Enjoy a good, strong espresso or freshly-squeezed orange juice
with a selection of croissants (from 80p), pastries and pannetone.
Sandwiches or baguette, ciabatta or granary bread (from £1.70) and
main course salads (£3.50) are joined by hot pasta dishes – lasagne,
tagliatelle, tortelloni (some vegetarian) – and a daily special, perhaps
lamb and apple curry (£4.95). Ices, frozen yoghurts and various
pastries and gateaux to finish. Filled jumbo Yorkshire puddings
(£4.25) make a novel Sunday lunch. **Seats** *30.* **Open** *9-6.*
Closed *25 & 26 Dec, 1 Jan. No credit cards.*

WC2   Café in the Crypt

Tel 071-839 4342	Café
St Martin-in-the-Fields Duncannon Street off Trafalgar Square WC2	Map 21 B3

As its name suggests the café is found underneath the beautiful vaulted
arches of Trafalgar Square's historic church, St Martin-in-the-Fields and
has original gravestones on the floor. It's a stylish, spacious café with
black metal tables, classical music, espresso bar and self-service. Open
for morning coffee with croissants and Danish pastries; lunchtime
choices include soup of the day, vegetarian pasta £5.50 or chili £5.75
and to finish a fruit crumble or bread-and-butter pudding. Half
portions on request. Spare toilet for changing or feeding. Guide dogs
only. No-smoking area. **Seats** *180.* **Open** *10-3.15 & 5.30-9 (Sun 10-6).*
Closed *25 Dec, some Bank Holidays. Access, Amex, Diners, Visa.*

SW6   Café Flo

Tel 071-371 9673

676 Fulham Road SW6   Map 17 B5

Cheerful, bustling all-day eating place occupying the corner site where
once Tall Orders traded. The split-level interior and large central bar
remains in what is now a very French café complete with posters
on the walls and daily newspapers on sticks. A feature of the menu
is the excellent and good value selection of set meals and specials.
There's a daily plat du jour such as pan-fried pork escalope with potato
galette and glazed apple (£7.75), fish of the day was a square
of chargrilled squid and endive with a delicious coriander, plum and
tomato salsa (£7.50). L'idée Flo at £6.95 comprises either a soup of
the day such as red lentil with caramelised onions or mixed salad,
followed by either steak with fries or fish with fries, which could
be pan-fried grey mullet, or an omelette, then filter coffee. Breakfast
ranges from a café complet £2.95 – orange juice, croissants, baguette,
preserves plus tea or coffee – to a full English (meat £4.25, vegetarian
£3.95) and stacked pancakes with streaky bacon and maple syrup
(£4.25). *Seats 100. Open 9am-11.30pm (Sun to 10.30). Closed 25 &
26 Dec, 1 Jan. Access, Visa.*
Also at:
Islington 334 Upper Street Islington N1 Tel 071-226 7916   **Map 16 D3**
Kensington 127–9 Kensington Church Street W8 Tel 071-727 8142   **Map 18 A3**
Converted pub opposite & *Clarke's* bakery
NW3 205 Haverstock Hill NW3 Tel 071-435 6744   **Map 16 B2**
Next door to Screen on the Hill cinema
WC2 51 St Martins Lane WC2 Tel 071-836 8289   **Map 21 B3**
Close to the Coliseum (English National Opera). Closed Bank Holidays
Richmond 149 Kew Road Richmond Surrey Tel 081-940 8298   **Map 17 A5**
Outside Richmond centre, on the road to Kew Bridge

SW18   Calico

Tel 081-947 9616   Café/Restaurant

573 Garratt Lane Wandsworth SW18 4ST   Map 17 B6

White paper squares over red check cloths and a bare-board floor set
the tone at this informal café/restaurant in the same stable as Gavin's
in Putney, The Depot at Barnes and Ciao, Fulham. Spinach and bacon
salad (£3.10), moules provençales (£3.10), chargrilled chicken breast
(£7.25), aubergine moussaka (£7.25) and various pasta dishes (from
£4.95) show the range. A lunchtime special offers pasta, side salad,
garlic bread and a glass of house wine for £4.95. There's a short
children's menu and a courtyard with tables for summer eating.
*Seats 70. Open 12-3 & 6-11 (Sun to 10.30). Closed 25 & 26 Dec.
Access, Amex, Diners, Visa.*

W1   The California Pizza Company

Tel 071 486 7878   Pizzeria

6 Blandford Street W1   Map 18 C2

A young, vibrant company out to change the way we eat pizza. King
prawn and goat's cheese (£7.90) and tandoori chicken masala (£6.90)
are but two examples. A new, expanded menu also embraces
American food from burgers (£6.30) and ribs (£6.70) to mesquite-
grilled cat fish (£6.90), as well as equally inventive salads (the Pier 39
mixed seafood version is £6.60) and pasta (Szechuan beef, broccoli
and spring onion £5.90). Desserts (all £2.90) include pecan pie and
chocolate brownies. 'Happy time' between 5 and 7 pm brings main

course prices down to £3.80. Children up to 12 eat free until 5pm. Mostly no smoking. Tables outside. Exclusively Californian wines. *Seats 130.* *Open 11.30-11.15.* *Closed Sun, 25 Dec, 1 Jan. Access, Amex, Diners, Visa.*

E2   Cherry Orchard

Tel 081-980 6678	Restaurant
241 Globe Road Bethnal Green E2 OJD	**Map 16 D3**

The Buddhists in charge of this informal vegetarian restaurant have made changes, notably an end to evening openings. Cakes (coffee, sugar-free flapjacks, carrot with orange icing) are priced between 75p and £1 and accompany an excellent range of teas. Hot specials (around £3.35) on offer at lunchtime could include paella or broccoli and almond filo pie. On the cold front there are salads (houmus salad plate £1.75). Children's portions. Two high chairs are available and staff will gladly heat baby food or bottles. Unlicensed (£1 corkage when you bring your own wine). No smoking inside but allowed at the seven garden tables. *Seats 55.* *Open 12-3 (Tues, Wed 12-7).* *Closed Sat, Sun, 1 week Christmas/New Year. Access, Visa.*

WC2   Chicago Meatpackers

Tel 071-379 3277	Restaurant
96 Charing Cross Road WC2	**Map 21 A2**

Huge, successful American theme restaurant with slick management, motivated staff and a winning formula of favourite American foods. A rationalised menu means prices are actually cheaper than last year – a half rack of ribs £7.25, burgers from £5.20, swordfish steak £8.95 – with starters such as Caesar salad (£2.25), skins (£2.95 a small portion) and crab cakes (£3.25). Indulgent desserts include a brownie ice cream sandwich (£4.50). No-smoking section. Children-friendly with menu colouring-in competitions and face painting on the first Sunday of each month. *Seats 300.* *Open 11.45-11.30 (Sun 12-10.30).* *Closed 25, 26 & 31 Dec. Access, Amex, Visa.*

W1   Chicago Pizza Pie Factory

Tel 071-629 26691	Pizzeria
17 Hanover Square off Oxford Street W1R 9AJ	**Map 18 C2**

Huge framed posters of Chicago cover the brick walls, a TV by the bar shows endless American football games and the lively sounds come via WJMK Magic 104FM in Chicago. It's a very busy and popular place that's almost as much a London institution as the Hard Rock Café. Enormous deep-dish pizzas are the main attraction, served with tasty toppings that include 'spinoccoli' (from £7.80), 'everything & the pan' (from £11) and the speciality cheese and sausage (£8.40 regular for 2 persons, £12.70 large for 3-4 persons). A choice of hamburgers, chef's salads (£5.95), lasagne (£5.95), stuffed mushrooms (£2.95), 5-way chili beef (£5.75), cheesecakes (£3.10) and a selection of sundaes. Recent additions to the menu include bruschetta (£2.25), aubergine Parmigiana (£4.95) and stuffed pizza with ricotta cheese (£4.75). The beer may be served in frosted glasses, but it's Hobson's choice of not-so-authentic Chicago Old Gold (brewed in England). Reservations for parties of 8 or more. Popular venue for children on Sundays when entertainment, children's menu, balloons, crayons, booster seats, clip-on and high chairs, and nappy-changing facilities are provided. No smoking area. **Seats** *250.* **Open** *11.45-11.30 (12-10.30 Sun). Access, Amex, Visa.*

SW7   Chicago Rib Shack

Tel 071-581 5595	Restaurant
1 Raphael Street Knightsbridge Green SW7	**Map 19 C4**

Very lively, very friendly, and very busy, this is a place where you can really relax and join in the fun, usually after a short wait in the long wooden bar where the sixteen or so cocktails(£3.95-£4.40) include 'Between the Sheets', 'Grasshopper', and the famous 'Sloe, Comfortable Screw'. Waiters will tie a plastic bib around your neck once you've ordered, and by the end of your meal you'll probably be thankful for it. Spare ribs with barbecue sauce (£7.25 half rack) are the favourite order, along with barbecued chicken (£7.25), 5 way chili (£6.45), giant salads (from £5.95), onion loaf (£3.75) and stuffed potato skins (£2.80). Favourite home-made American desserts include Key lime pie (£3.75), pecan pie (£3.75) or mud pie (£4.75). Happy Hour 5.30-7.30 (Mon-Sat). Popular with children at weekends with a special menu, balloons, crayons and clowns provided. No smoking area. **Seats** *260.* **Open** *11.45am-11.45pm (midday-11pm Sun). Access, Amex, Visa.*

WC2   Chicago Rib Shack II

Tel 071-839 4188	Restaurant
17 Bear Street Leicester Square London WC2	**Map 21 A2**

A newly opened branch which is conveniently located in Leicester Square. On Sundays, one of the rooms is turned into a children's playroom with toys and balloons, supervised by a member of the staff. Children have their own menu of barbecue ribs, chicken wings or beef sandwich and glass-bottled Coca-Cola, mud pie or ice cream for £3.95. At the back of the menu, they can draw anything they see and enter the drawing competition. The inspiration is easy as the red painted walls are covered with images of cattle and hogs. Pity the restaurant is in the basement (a bar is at street level) with difficult access and no changing facilities. High-chairs and booster seats provided. Expect to wait for a table on Friday and Saturday nights. No changing facilities. **Seats** *240.* **Open** *11.45-11.45 (Sun 12-11).* **Closed** *25 Dec. Access, Amex, Visa.*

W1   Chuen Cheng Ku

Tel 071-437 1398	Restaurant
17 Wardour Street W1	**Map 21 A2**

One of the fixtures of the Chinatown eating scene, Chuen Cheng Ku is a vast place stretching through the block to Rupert Street and up a couple of floors. In an atmosphere that's often reminiscent of a bustling bazaar local Chinese and Westerners make their choice from a very long Cantonese menu. Best value for snackers is provided by the dim sum (£1.65-£3.30), which are served from little metal wagons steered along the tables by reserved but not unfriendly waitresses. One prepares and dispenses noodle soup, another carries a payload of fried items, others deal in bamboo steamers filled with pork, beef and prawn dumplings. Busy with Chinese families at weekends. **Seats** *350.* **Open** *11am-midnight.* **Closed** *24 & 25 Dec. Access, Amex, Diners, Visa.*

W9	Colonnade Hotel	60%	£80
Tel 071-286 1052 Fax 071-286 1057			Hotel
2 Warrington Crescent W9 1ER			Map 18 A2

A Victorian Grade II listed building in residential Little Venice, close
to Warwick Avenue underground station. The bedrooms are spacious
and comfortable and staff offer a genuinely warm welcome to families,
which if you are staying for any length of time, is more valuable
than a city centre location. There is a spacious family suite with a four-
poster bed, two sofas and space for two extra beds. A nearby agency
supplies baby-sitters, and there are two extra cots plus storage space for
pushchairs in the lobby. At mealtimes there are high-chairs, children's
portions, baby food and baby bottles; all this and a garden too.
Off-season specials for families. The whole hotel has been recently
refurbished and 19 rooms are now air-conditioned. Under the same
ownership for over 40 years, the style is straightforward with a variety
of bedrooms – from singles to suites and four-poster rooms, some with
whirlpool baths. Families are well catered for. *Rooms 49. Access,
Amex, Diners, Visa.*

SW5	Concord Hotel		£55
Tel 071-370 4151			Hotel
155 Cromwell Road SW5 0TQ			Map 19 A5

Budget bed and breakfast hotel with some family-size bedrooms.
Handy for Earls Court, Olympia and the South Kensington museums.
Unlicensed. No dogs. *Rooms 40. Access, Amex, Visa.*

W8	Costa's Grill		
Tel 071-229 3794			Restaurant
14 Hillgate Street Notting Hill Gate W8			Map 18 A3

This two-roomed restaurant has long been popular for its friendly
service and reliable cooking of Greek dishes at very low cost. A short
wait in line is sometimes necessary but always worth it. In summer,
the garden offers a pleasant option for al fresco eating. Classic dishes
include kleftiko (£4.50) and souvla (£4.50). Amongst the chargrilled
choices are fish specials (£6-8). *Seats 70 (plus 35 in garden).*
*Open 12-2.30 & 5-10.30 (Sat to 10.30). Closed Sun & Bank Holidays.
No credit cards.*

W2	Craven Gardens Hotel		£66
Tel 071-262 3167 Fax 071-262 2083			Hotel
16 Leinster Terrace W2 3ES			Map 18 B3

Comfortable, well-kept bed and breakfast hotel just off Bayswater
Road, handy for Kensington Gardens, Paddington Station and the
cosmopolitan appeal of Queensway. No dogs. Cots and extra beds
provided but otherwise basic facilities. *Rooms 43. Access, Amex,
Diners, Visa.*

W1	Deals West		
Tel 071-287 1001			Restaurant
14 Fouberts Place off Regent Street W1V 1PB			Map 18 D2

Styled as an American dealing room with cream-painted wood, mock
gaslights, TV and a bar running the length of the room. There should
be something on the long menu to suit most people, be it a T-bone

steak (£13.50), fish and chips (£5.50) or salads (Californian salad
£5.75). An Eastern influence is also evident (Thai curries – chicken
£6.25, and Gado Gado Indonesian salad (£5.50) and the wide choice
is supplemented by a blackboard Dealer's Choice that changes daily (it
might be chicken florentine or Vietnamese stir-fry). On the standard
menu dishes range from tasty spring rolls stuffed with the catch of the
day and served with a sweet and sour chili relish (£3.50), or rather
average quality burgers (including a vegetarian version) served with
fries or baked potato (£4.95-£5.50) to Jamaican jerk (£6.95) and
Singapore Fried Noodles (£5.25). Desserts are mainly American, with
the likes of chocolate mud (£2.95), New England apple pie (£2.75)
or home-made waffle (£2.95) with extra topping at 50p. Live music
from 9.30 onwards on Friday and Saturday evenings (jazz or steel
band). Afternoon tea served 3-7.30 (scones with jam and cream
£2.50). No smoking area. Tables on pavement in summer. *Seats 160.*
Open 12-12 *(Sun to 5). Access, Amex, Visa.*
Also at:
SW10 Deals Chelsea Harbour SW10 OXD. Tel 071-376 3232.   **Map 19 B6**
Packed at weekends with families but inconsistent cooking of the
same menu as above. Easy parking. No changing facilities, but
nursing mothers should ask for a booth seat (which afford a little
privacy).

SW7	**Eden Plaza Hotel**	£72
Tel 071-370 6111 Fax 071-370 0932		Hotel
68-69 Queen's Gate SW7 5JT		Map 19 B5

Neatly kept bed and breakfast hotel a short walk from the South
Kensington museums. Accommodation ranges from singles
to quadruples. Children up to 14 stay free in their parents' room.
No dogs. *Rooms 63. Access, Amex, Diners, Visa.*

SW1	**Elizabeth Hotel**	£65
Tel 071-828 6812		Hotel
37 Eccleston Square SW1V 1PB		Map 19 D5

Friendly privately-owned bed and breakfast hotel in a garden square
near Victoria station. Bedrooms range from singles to family-
size; a few are without private facilities. No dogs. *Rooms 40.*
No credit cards.

WC2	**Fatboy's Diner**	
Tel 071-240 1902		Restaurant
21 Maiden Lane Covent Garden WC2		Map 21 B2

A classic 40s' diner imported from the States after being restored to its
gleaming original state. The friendly banter of the staff is as much part
of the character as the colourful decor, burnished stainless steel, the
background music and the vinyl-upholstered bar stools and banquettes.
Food here is mostly a choice of burgers (from £3.95) or hot dogs
(£3.25) but be prepared to be cajoled into trying a host of extras – all
worthwhile – like the fat fries (£1.30) or crisp onion rings (£1.50).
Unlicensed but the soda fountain milk shakes (all £2.45) are good and
thick. *Seats 42. Open* 11am-midnight *(Sun to 10.30)* *Closed 25 &*
26 Dec.

E8   Faulkners

Tel 071-254 6152	Fish'n'Chips
424 Kingsland Road Hackney E8 4AA	**Map 16 D3**

The take-away trade is the major part of the business, but there are
seats for 16 to eat in at this very popular fish and chip restaurant
in a parade of shops. Groundnut oil is used to fry generous portions
of fresh fish, from traditional favourites like cod (£5.55) and rock
salmon (£5) to halibut and Dover sole (£9.10). Jellied eels and
rollmops among the starters; children can have scampi and chips, a soft
drink and ice cream (£2.95) or a half-portion of cod and chips.
*Seats 16. Open 12-2 & 5-10 (Sun 12-9). Closed Bank Holidays, 10 days
Christmas. No credit cards.*

W1   Fenwicks Terrace Café

Tel 071-629 9161	Café
New Bond Street W1	**Map 18 D3**

Popular at lunchtimes, but later in the day a peaceful spot for self-
service meals, though the choice by then may be somewhat limited.
Modern, uninspired decor is a bit worn and at odds with the smart
surroundings of the rest of the store. Salads, like turkey and ham pie
(£4.95) and cottage cheese with fresh fruit (£4.25), and hot dishes
limited to baked potatoes with the usual fillings. Daily specials are
more exciting – ham, cheese and tomato platter (£5.25), curried beef
(£5.25), vegetable crumble (£4.95) and lemon sole (£5.25). Large
selection of bought-in pastries (from 95p) and cakes, particularly sticky
Danishes. Speciality teas. High chairs for children. No smoking area.
Seats 100-120. Open 9-6 (Thu to 7). Closed Sun. No credit cards.

N16   La Fin de la Chasse   £60

Tel 071-254 5975	Restaurant
176 Stoke Newington Church Street N16 0JL	**Map 16 D2**

A long, narrow restaurant with a small paved garden to the rear
and a menu of largely familiar modern dishes given a slight twist
(breast of duck with lemon compote and raspberry juice, fillet
of salmon with a seaweed mousse on a glazed mushroom sauce, cider
syllabub with *langues de chat*). Not an obvious choice for dining out
with children, however, owners Robbie and Carol Richards insist
to the point of printing it on the bill that children are welcome. The
finery is best suited to adults with portable newborn babies or older
children. One high-chair is provided. No-smoking area. *Seats 40.
Parties 18. Private Room. L 12.30-2 D 7-10.30. Closed Sun & Mon,
Bank Holidays, 2 weeks Xmas, 2 weeks Sep. Set D £14.50. Access,
Amex, Diners, Visa.*

W8   Geales

Tel 071-727 7969	Fish'n'Chips
2 Farmer Street Notting Hill Gate W8 7SN	**Map 18 A3**

For longer than most of the locals can remember Geales has been *the*
place for fish and chips. Fresh fish is delivered daily, and the choice
is listed on a big board – haddock, cod, plaice, sole, rock salmon and
salmon fish cakes are sometimes joined by more exotic offerings such
as deep-fried clams or shark from the Seychelles. The batter's crisp,
cooking (in beef dripping for the fish, vegetable fat for the chips) spot
on, and two will dine in style for around £12. Drinks are paid for

separately. No bookings, so the occasional wait is necessary. You can leave the buggy at the entrance as there are three high-chairs and two booster seats. Upstairs you will find a room that doubles as an unofficial playroom on Saturdays and can be used for breastfeeding or changing. *Seats 100. Open 12-3 & 6-11. Closed Sun, Mon, Bank Holidays, 2 weeks Aug-Sep, 22 Dec-5 Jan. Access, Visa.*

SW1	The Goring	79%	£190
Tel 071-834 8211 Fax 071-834 4393			Hotel
17 Beeston Place Grosvenor Gardens SW1W 0JW			Map 19 D4

Close to Victoria Station and Buckingham Palace, but in an enviably quiet location, a very English hotel in the old style, "loved and nurtured" by the Goring family since it was built in 1910. Behind the impressive Edwardian facade is a high level of service and elegant, busy day rooms with polished marble, paintings and leather sofas. Bedrooms are individually decorated, but with a traditional feel. Brass bedsteads often feature and bathrooms are particularly good, mostly fitted out in marble; 24hr room and evening maid turn-down services are offered. Fifteen family suites, fourteen family rooms and four cots available, baby-listening is provided and an agency will supply a baby-sitter to allow parents a worry-free evening out. Many rooms are air-conditioned and the best have balconies that overlook the manicured Goring garden (no access for guests); similarly, the Garden lounge and Garden bar have delightful outlooks. Private dining rooms cater for up to 70. *Rooms 82. Valeting. Access, Amex, Diners, Visa.*

Restaurant   £85

A traditionally elegant dining room with service to match. There's a good choice of dishes on both the table d'hote and à la carte menus, ranging from the classical roast leg of English lamb with onion sauce or braised oxtail to the more modern mousseline of guinea fowl and sweet pepper with cranberry chutney. Desserts from the trolley. Good all-round wine list. There are two high-chairs and the attentive staff will serve baby food and half portions with courtesy and charm. *Seats 75. Parties 52. Private Room. L 12.30-2.30 D 6-10. Closed L Sat. Set L £15.50/£18.50 Set D £24.*

SW19	Gourmet Pizza Company	
Tel 081-545 0310		Pizzeria
Merton Abbey Mills Watermill Way Merton SW19		Map 17 B6

A complex on the banks of the River Wandle provides a home to craft shops, small businesses and the Gourmet Pizza Company, which is set alongside the river just above a lock. The interior is cheerfully done, white-painted brick, green and white wood panelling, bare floor boards, wall lights of metal shaped like face masks, waxed cloths with the menu laid down as a place mat. Service is cheerful, friendly and professional, even on a busy Saturday night.The pizzas, as at other branches, can seem a long way from Italy but don't suffer too much in the transfer. Eclectic combinations like Chinese duck or tandoori chicken might solve the 'Indian, Chinese or pizza' question after the cinema, but more realistic combinations are those such as California vegetable, piled high with lashings of spinach, mangetout, baby corn, yellow peppers, avocado and salsa finished with mozzarella, or four cheese – mozzarella, smoked edam, goat's cheese and dolcelatte with tomato sauce, spinach and sliced onions. Prices range from £3.95 for a plain and simple up to £7.70 for Cajun prawn and chicken.

They're all huge, with crispy crusts and doughy (but not soggy) bases. Salads come in two sizes, for main or side dish, and are priced accordingly. Bought-in ices or cakes to finish. A fun place to go in groups or families – there are plenty of high-chairs stacked ready by the entrance. Terrace tables in the summer. *Seats 100. Open 12-12. Closed sometimes between 4-6pm). Access, Amex, Visa.*

NW8	**Greek Valley**	£40
Tel 071-624 3217		Restaurant
130 Boundary Road St John's Wood NW8		Map 16 B3

Children are definitely welcome at this Greek-Cypriot restaurant in St John's Wood. For toddlers with conservative tastes, Greek food may be rather too seasoned, but the husband and wife management team here are happy to make suggestions so that the whole family is happy. Most children will favour the standard dishes like moussaka, or lamb shashlik cooked on a charcoal grill. There are no high-chairs but the tables are suitable for a clip-on chair. Many of the dishes are taken from the familiar Greek/Cypriot repertoire, but the cooking at Greek Valley is much above average. Spicy pork or minced lamb sausages, stuffed vine leaves, kleftiko and grilled baby chicken are all excellent, and vegetarians have their own versions of moussaka and souvlaki. Reasonable prices, friendly owners who really put their hearts into the job, and always a convivial party atmosphere. *Seats 70. L 12-2.30 D 6-11.30. Closed L Sat, all Sun, 2 weeks Sep. Access, Visa.*

WC2	**Häagen-Dazs**	
Tel 071-287 9577		Café
14 Leicester Square WC2		Map 21 A3

At Häagen Dazs, ice cream is so nearly elevated to an art form that you can almost convince yourself that it is good for you. A totally natural product, with no artificial additives, it is practically wholesome; how bad can full cream and cane sugar mixed with Swiss and Belgian chocolate be? However if you feel your arteries harden at the sight of the menu, the sorbets made with fresh fruit and carbon filtered water are light, refreshing and delicious. Stepping in from the bustle of Leicester Square, the pale wood decor is elegant and restful. The honey-coloured leather seats, beauties to the eye but beasts to the bottom must surely have been designed to encourage a quick turnaround of customers. High chairs are available and breastfeeding and nappy changing can just about be accomplished in the spotless Ladies. At off peak times children's parties can be accommodated in a cordoned off area. Branches now in Bath, Brighton, Heathrow Airport Terminal 1, Oxford and Windsor. *No smoking. Seats 65. Open 10am-midnight. Closed Dec 25.*
Also at:

NW1 75 Hampstead High Street. Tel 071-794 0646	Map 16 B2
SW3 138a Kings Road Chelsea. Tel 071-823 9326.	Map 19 C5
WC2 Unit 6 The Piazza Covent Garden. Tel 071-240 0436.	Map 21 B2

W1	**Hare Krishna**	
Tel 071-636 5262		Tea Room
1 Hanway Street W1 9DB		Map 21 A1

A newly refurbished vegetarian restaurant whose decor mixes representations of Krishna with flowery wall paper, crystal chandeliers and a green plant fountain. Dishes are freshly and skilfully prepared. Sautéed moist patras are served with chutney and lime wedges,

yoghurt is home-made, paratha arrives hot from the griddle, curries
(from £3.95) are light and carefully simmered with chosen spices and
Kadhai Undhiju, vegetables with spices and herbs are served sizzling
in a small frying pan. All the charm of a family run restaurant;
although it is a small restaurant, families are very welcome and they
have two high-chairs and storage for a pushchair. Dishes are prepared
to order and can be made according to the customers' taste and
in smaller portions (ideal for children). *Seats 44. Open 12-3 & 6-11.
Closed Sun, 25 Dec. Access, Amex, Visa (£10 or more).*

SW1   Harrods

Tel 071-730 1234	Café
87-135 Brompton Road Knightsbridge SW1X 7XL	**Map 19 C4**

Shoppers at this world-famous store have a wide choice of where
to enjoy a snack. The Westside Express concession (actually open
before the store, at 8.30) serves waffles, burgers, BLTs and the like; the
Café Espresso★ is found in the fruit and vegetable hall, the Bar
à Fromage★ next to the long cheese counter and the Ice Cream
Parlour★ in the Bakery department, just under the stairs. The Dress
Circle★, on the first-floor, is a self-service restaurant offering a variety
of hot and cold dishes, while up on the fourth floor – the children's
floor – there's the informal self-service Upper Circle, the conservatory
Terrace Bar, Way In Restaurant★ (a menu of light, imaginative dishes)
and the more formal Georgian restaurant, next to the children's book
department, serving lunch (12-2.45) and afternoon tea (3.45-5.15
£8.95). In the Georgian restaurant reservations are only taken for
lunch (from £12 minimum: carvery, cold buffet or à la carte) and
there are high-chairs provided; children under 12 eat for half adult
price. Finally, on the lower ground floor, are the oak-panelled Green
Man pub (pies and ploughman's) and the Health Juice Bar.
★No smoking. *Store open 10-6 (Wed to 8). Access, Amex, Diners, Visa.*

SW1   Harvey Nichols

Tel 071-235 5250	Café
Knightsbridge SW1	**Map 19 C4**

The top floor of Harvey Nichols is dedicated to food. Next to the new
food hall is the open plan café. The decor is mainly grey, enlighted
by powerful voltage and spots of colour from designer chairs and
bright T-shirts worn by the staff. Through a high structure of metal
and glass, Knightsbridge appears in the background. It is noisy,
dynamic, voguish and expensive. Cashing in on the Mediterranean
craze, pissaladière (£4.75), tortilla with mussel salad (£5.25), buffalo
mozzarella and truffle oil (£5.50), radicchio and wine risotto (£7.25)
are offered at high prices in diet-conscious portions. Croissant, muffins
or kedgeree (£5.75) are served from 10am and afternoon tea (£7.50)
between 3pm and 6pm. Certainly the most striking café of all
London's department stores. *Seats 110. Open 10am-11pm.
Closed 3 days Christmas. Access, Amex, Diners, Visa.*

SW6   Henry J Bean's Bar and Grill

Tel 071-381 5005	Restaurant
490 Fulham Road SW6	**Map 19 A6**

This is one of a chain of themed American bars created from former
pubs with a Mexican-influenced menu. A monitor displays 'chow-time'
when food orders are ready for collection. 'Loaded potato skins'

(£2.10 small), nachos (£2.50), chili flautas (flour tortillas) (£2.50) are starter choices, followed by fajitas (£7.95), spinach salad (£5.10), barbecued ribs (£6.25 half rack) and variations on hamburgers (from £5) served with relishes and chunky, crisp fries. Finally, try their mud pie (£3.25), ice cream (£1.50) or dessert of the day, if you've got any room left. Happy Hour is from 5.30-7.30 on weekdays when cocktails and spirits are half price. Cooked English breakfast plate (£4.75) on Sundays only between 11.30 and 4. The atmosphere is young and buzzy. Children's-size burgers (£3.40) also available. *Seats 85.* *Open* 11.45-11 (Sun 11.30-10.30). *Closed 25 Dec. Access, Amex, Visa.* Also at:

54 Abingdon Road off Kensington High Street W8 Tel 071-937 3339   **Map 19 A5**
Open 11.45-11 (Sun 12-10.30).

195 Kings Road Chelsea SW3 Tel 071-352 9255   **Map 19 C5**
Open 11.45-11 (Sun 12-10.30).

See also entries under **Aberdeen, (Scotland)** and **Manchester**.

SW5   Hogarth Hotel   59%   £92
Tel 071-370 6831 Fax 071-373 6179   Hotel
Hogarth Road SW5 0QQ   **Map 19 A5**

The Hogarth is a friendly, well-kept hotel just around the corner from the Earls court Exhibition Centre, the South Kensington museums and Kensington Gardens. Recent refurbishment has improved the bedrooms. Book in advance for a space in the basement car park. Families are well catered for, but the mechanisms for caring for families that are set up may need a bit of a kick start. When booking, if you make your requirements, such as a cot, a baby bath or a baby-sitter absolutely clear, you will be sure of a comfortable stay. It is also a good idea to tell the dining room if you need one of the two high-chairs. Children up to 16 accommodated free in their parents' room. *Rooms 86. Access, Amex, Diners, Visa.*

SE1   Horniman's
Tel 071-407 3611   Pub
Hay's Galleria Tooley Street London Bridge SE1 2HD   **Map 20 C3**

A modern Victorian pub built on the premises of Horniman & Co tea packing company right at the entrance of Hay's Galleria. The restaurant section has its own easy access through a ramp. Families are more than welcome and there's plenty of room around the tables for pushchairs. The Pantry offers a wide selection of daily dishes like turkey pie, lamb chasseur casserole, steak & kidney pie, broccoli and leek pie all served with chips and vegetables, with children's portions at £2.60. Triple-decker sandwiches and salads are also available. The upstairs galleria has a carvery serving traditional three-course lunches (£10.50, not Sat) with a roast, but no children's portions. *Seats Pantry 70, Carvery 60. Open 12-3 (cold food until 5). Closed Pantry evenings; Carvery all Sat. Access, Amex, Visa.*

W1   Inter-Continental Hotel, Coffee House
Tel 071-409 3131   Coffee Shop
1 Hamilton Place Park Lane W1V 0QY   **Map 19 C4**

Music with brunch on Sundays is a new feature of the Coffee House. From 12.30 to 3.30pm enjoy Caribbean food with a steel band, or New Orleans specialities with jazz, depending on the regularly changing theme. The daily extensive lunchtime (12-3) and dinner (6-11) buffet (£19 and £22.50 respectively) is particularly appetising –

salads, smoked fish, prawns, cold cuts, guacamole with nacho chips, curry with poppadoms and chutney, chicken teriyaki, steamed tofu, salmon coulibiac with tarragon sauce, roast beef and Yorkshire pudding, sushi, with a good selection of cheeses and impressive desserts (warm bread and butter pudding, apricots with caramel sauce). A choice of soups (£3.50), sandwiches (£7), hamburgers (£7) and salads (£6-7.50) can keep the price lower. The breakfast buffet (full £13, continental £10.50) is served from 7-11.30. Children enjoy the complimentary popcorn on Sundays. No smoking area. **Seats** *110.* **Open** *7am-11pm (Sat to 11.30). Access, Amex, Diners, Visa.*

W12   Jigsaw

Tel 081-746 0397	Restaurant
74 Askew Road Shepherds Bush W12	**Map 17 A4**

Hidden behind a dark smoked glass window is a charming candlelit restaurant with simple pink paper tablecloths and upside-down parasols on the ceiling. The menu appears on a large blackboard. Main courses are at £7.95, starters and desserts are one penny each. A clever marketing idea which is well complemented by fanciful dishes. Duck en croute is beautifully presented in a puff pastry chausson with an interesting Grand Marnier sauce, Jigsaw chicken is topped with Stilton, garnished with a fan-cut pear and a creamy sauce. There is always a vegetarian dish like assorted vegetables served in a crispy pancake. Starters are simple: cream of mushroom soup or moules marinière. Desserts might include profiteroles, fruit salad or a delicious cheesecake. Traditional roast on Sundays, when children under 12 eat for free! No high-chairs. Difficult to find better value for money. **Seats** *90.* **Open** *12-3 & 7-12 (Sun 12-11).* **Closed** *24 & 25 Dec. Access, Visa.*

W1   John Lewis, The Place to Eat

Tel 071-629 7711	Restaurant
Oxford Street W1A 1EX	**Map 18 D2**

A spacious third-floor restaurant with seven separate food counters. The choice is breakfast all day (full £5.85, continental £3.20), creperie (crepes from £2.65), crockpot (lasagne £4.75), cold table (fresh salmon salad £8), patisserie, seafood (£6-£9.50) and ice cream soda fountain (80p-£3.35). The breakfast of scrambled eggs with smoked salmon and a glass of Buck's Fizz is as popular as the fresh fish from the seafood counter. Pancakes and ice creams are generously laced with liquor. Convenient location. Children's portions. **Seats** *290.* **Open** *9-5 (Thur 9.45-7.30).* **Closed** *Sun, Bank Holidays. No credit cards.*

W1   Joy King Lau

Tel 071-437 1132	Restaurant
3 Leicester Street W1	**Map 21 A2**

Newly refurbished restaurant spread on four floors with a smart modern decor of Bordeaux and blue tones. The dim sum here are superb (from £1.40) and if you are prepared to fend for yourself childwise, you will have a pleasant, untroubled meal and no one will mind much if you make a noise or a mess. The restaurant is on several levels and if you have a pushchair, opt for the ground floor and stay put, as the loo (upstairs on the first floor) is too small to breastfeed or change a baby. Waiters will help (if pushed) with hot water, empty bowls and other requirements of a small baby. Come armed with

everything you may need (including a thick skin) and enjoy the
delicious food on offer. Melon pudding or egg custard tart should keep
older children interested all the way to the finishing line. **Seats** 200.
Open 11.30am-11.30pm (dim sum to 5pm). Access, Amex, Diners, Visa.

SW10   Ken Lo's Memories of China
Tel 071-352 4953	Restaurant

Harbour Yard Chelsea Harbour SW10   **Map 19 B6**

Best value at Ken Lo's airy restaurant overlooking the Marina
is provided by the bar snack menu. A plate of crispy fried dim sum is a
good way to start, followed by a large bowl of soup and one of the
main dishes – beef chow mein, chicken with cashew nuts, prawns
in hot black bean sauce, all priced around £3. A quarter of crispy duck
with pancake, plum sauce, spring onion and cucumber is very
reasonable at £4. There are several other menus available here, but
they're considerably more expensive. Parking is easy within the
Chelsea Harbour complex and a lift takes you direct to the restaurant
floor from the underground car park. **Seats** 100. **Open** 12-2.30 &
7-10.45, Sun 12.30-10. **Closed** 25 & 26 Dec. Access, Amex, Diners,
Visa.

W11   Kleftiko
Tel 071-603 0807

186 Holland Park Avenue Kensington W11   **Map 17 B4**

Straightforward Greek dishes are served among kitsch Greek-Cypriot
trappings in this 20-year-old, two-floor restaurant at Shepherd's Bush
roundabout, opposite the Hilton International Kensington.
Taramasalata is light and lemony, without the usual nasty pink look;
other well-known Greek dishes (stiffado, tava, sheftalia and souvla) are
all well prepared. The charcoal grill is used for most main courses
(mainly £5-£9) which always include market fresh fish – sea bass
(from £9) or halibut (£9). Meze (fish £15, meat £12.50) are
specialities. Good-value, three-course set dinner menus (£10.95 inc
coffee) and special offers at lunchtime. 12½% service is automatically
added to all bills. The latest addition to the Kleftiko chain is a
converted Victorian pub on the south side of Kew Bridge with a large
garden eating area. **Seats** 44. **Open** 12-3 & 5.30-11.30. **Closed** Sun, 25
& 26 Dec. Access, Amex, Diners, Visa.
Also at:
W4 163 Chiswick High Road Chiswick W4 Tel 081-994 0305   **Map 17 A4**
Open Sunday. Recently enlarged.
W5 7a The Green High Street Ealing W5 Tel 081-840 3297   **Map 17 A4**
Smaller, more intimate mews setting close to the Broadway Centre.
Kew The Kings Arms Kew Bridge Kew Bridge Rd Kew Surrey
Tel 081-940 3182   **Map 17 A5**
Live music Fri & Sat nights. Open-air eating in summer.

E1   Kosher Luncheon Club
Tel 071-247 0039	Restaurant

13 Greatorex Street E1   **Map 16 D3**

Located in the Morris Kasler Hall, this is the last survivor of the East
End tradition of the Kosher Lunch Clubs. A warm welcome awaits
you in the large white and blue refectory dining room. Everything
is prepared and cooked on the premises. The speciality here is fresh
fish, properly fried in matzo meal, steamed or grilled. Traditional hors
d'oeuvre include bean and barley soup (£1.80) and gefilte fish

(£1.50). Portions are extremely generous but if you're still hungry,
try the Lockshen pudding (£1.50). A membership fee of 50p and
service are added to the bill. Children's portions and caring waitresses;
high-chairs and changing table provided. Unlicensed. *Seats 140.*
Open 12-3. *Closed Sat, Bank Holidays, major Jewish Holidays.*
No credit cards.

W8	Hotel Lexham	£63
Tel 071-373 6471 Fax 071-244 7827		Hotel
32 Lexham Gardens W8 5JU		Map 19 A5

In a surprisingly peaceful garden square within walking distance
of Kensington's shops and museums, the Lexham has been in the same
family ownership since 1956 and provides good-value bed and
breakfast accommodation. Cheapest rooms are without private
facilities. Children free up to the age of three; cots and extra beds
(£10.50/£12.50) provided. No dogs. *Rooms 66. Garden. Access, Visa*

W1	Lok Ho Fook	
Tel 071-437 2001		Restaurant
4 Gerrard Street W1		Map 21 A2

All the well-known Cantonese dishes here, including classics such
as special fried rice, sweet and sour pork, and lemon chicken (£4.40)
or the more unusual such as stuffed duck (£6.50). Dim sum served
until 6pm (£1.35-£2.55), with a helpfully pictorial list from wehich
to choose – gourmet children will be delighted! The restaurant,
on two floors, is located at the east end of pedestrianised Gerrard
Street, a main Chinatown thoroughfare. *Seats 150. Open* 12-12 (*Sun
11.30-11.15*). *Access, Amex, Diners, Visa.*

W1	London Hilton, Brasserie	
Tel 071-493 8000		Brasserie
22 Park Lane W1A 2HH		Map 18 C3

The ground-floor café/brasserie has a children's menu which
is reasonably priced, though adults must expect to pay typical Park
Lane prices plus a hefty 15% service charge (add that to £1.80
for a 180cl bottle of Coca Cola and try to make it sound
like a bargain!). Entrecote with French fries (£11.50), pan-fried
monkfish (£9.75), plus a help-yourself hors d'oeuvre (£7.95) and
desserts (£3.25) are typical offerings. Children can choose a soup
of the day (£2.50), grilled sausage'n'beans and spaghetti in tomato
sauce (both £4.95) or a mini burger, chicken fingers and finger lickin'
fish fingers (£5.20 all with chips). Just try stopping them tucking into
Häagen Dazs ice cream, fruit salad or chocolate cake for dessert.
Sunday brunch is served in the 28th-floor restaurant, Windows on the
World, at £27.50 for adults and half that price for children (who will
love the express lifts and fabulous views). *Open* 7 *days. Access, Amex,
Diners, Visa.*

W2	Maison Péchon	
Tel 229 0746		Patisserie
127 Queensway W2 4SJ		Map 18 A3

Few can resist the chocolate eclairs and cream slices at the family run
Maison Péchon, founded in 1925 by the current owner's grandfather.
Cakes are baked on the premises and staff are friendly and relaxed
when it comes to dealing with choosy toddlers. Although small and

crowded, turnover is fast so you shouldn't have to wait long for
a table. The highlight is the mouthwatering display counter with 100
different cakes and dozens of breads. Savoury items for lunchtime
snacking run from ham and cheese croissants (95p) and vol-au-vents
to spinach quiche (£1.15) and Cornish pasties. Breakfast served until
11am. Pavement tables. *Seats 35. Open 8-8 (Mon-Wed to 6).*

W8 **Malabar**	£40
Tel 071-727 8800	Restaurant
27 Uxbridge Street Notting Hill Gate W8 7TQ	Map 18 D3

On two floors, Malabar is a quiet, friendly restaurant, artistically
decorated with original paintings and simple still-life arrangements.
The lunchtime trade is very slow so you can take your time and relax
over your meal. There is a high-chair and staff are happy to halve
portions, otherwise there are no special facilities. Foodwise, tandoori
chicken is popular with children as is the barbecued chicken makhani
cooked with butter, cream and spices. Stuffed with almonds and
sultanas, the Peshwari nan is a favourite for all ages. Good-value
Sunday buffet lunch. *Seats 56. Parties 15. L 12-3 (Sun from 12.30)
D 6-11.15. Closed 4 days Xmas, last week Aug. Set meals from £11.50.
Access, Visa.*

NW3 **Manna**	
Tel 071-722 8028	Restaurant
4 Erskine Road Primrose Hill NW3 3AJ	Map 16 C3

Little has changed here since its inception in the late '60s. Varnished
pine trestle tables (non-smoking area at rear) and a very laid-back
atmosphere with enjoyable and filling vegetarian food – three courses
are almost impossible to complete. Laid-back staff treat children on a
par with everybody else. Apart from small portions there are
no special facilities but no hassle about spillages either. Only open
in the evenings so keen parents should turn up at 6.30 on the dot for
an early supper of green pea and coriander soup, couscous on a bed
of salad and excellent apple crumble. Typical offerings are crispy
falafels (£2.30), American lentil soup (£1.90) or feta and cashew paté
(£2.30) to begin with, followed perhaps by gado gado (£6.50) and
mushroom lasagne (£6.50). *Seats 60. Open 6.30pm-11pm.
Closed Lunch, 3 days Christmas. No credit cards.*

W1 **Marché Mövenpick**	
Tel 071-494 0498	Restaurant
Swiss Centre Leicester Square W1	Map 21 A3

The setting is the basement of the Swiss Centre, the layout a large
circle and colourful food stands in the centre surrounded by dining
areas of French, German and Italian atmosphere. Browsing through
the different stands is like being at a food fair, and queueing while
watching the cook prepare your dish is entertaining. Each counter has
its own speciality: salads, salami and Swiss cheeses sliced to order;
Bloomer, cheese, walnut and onion breads are kneaded and baked
on the spot. Rösti is prepared to order and served with the roast of the
day (£3.50). Pasta, freshly out of the pasta machine, is cooked
on demand and tossed in frying pans with fresh ingredients of the day.
Fondue (£7.90) and raclette are available in the evening from 6pm
and all day on Sundays. There is of course Mövenpick ice-cream
by the scoop and a special pastries counter with freshly baked strudel,

fruit squares or chocolate marbled cake (£1.20). Beer, wine, cocktail and Mövenpick's own brand of coffee served as espresso, cappuccino or the Swiss way with whipped cream and chocolate flakes. Designed for freshness, it is an important step forward in the concept of cafeterias. The ground floor bistro offers a breakfast buffet from 8 to 11am. High-chairs are provided, as are half-price portions for half-size diners. **Seats** 380. **Open** 8-midnight (restaurant from 11). **Closed** 25 Dec. Access, Amex, Diners, Visa.

NW3   Marine Ices

Tel 071-485 3132	Restaurant
8 Haverstock Hill Chalk Farm NW3 2BL	**Map 16 C2**

One part of the smooth-running operation is an ice-cream parlour, the other a good, conventional Italian restaurant with a minimum food charge of £5.50. There's a wide choice of pasta (fusilli, linguini, ravioli, panzerotti, etc.), pizzas, veal, chicken and calf's liver, and specialities include the last with coppa ham (£9) and a pizza with smoked salmon (£5.45). Superb ice creams and sorbets: try three scoops of ice cream topped with cassis, zabaglione or delicious espresso coffee for a real treat. Children's portions. **Seats** 90. **Open** 12-2.45 & 6-10.15, Sun 12-10.15. **Closed** Sun, Bank Holidays. No credit cards.

SW11   Mariners

Tel 071-223 2454	Fish'n'Chips
30 Northcote Road Battersea SW11 1NZ	**Map 17 B6**

Pristine premises decorated with brick-red laminate, wood-strip and mirror panelling together with red gingham tablecloths. Its selection of fried fish is a familiar one ranging from standard and large neatly filleted portions of cod (£3.40/£4.15), plaice and haddock as well as huss and scampi. Everything comes with a lemon wedge, a garnish of sliced tomato and lettuce as well as piping hot, crunchy *real* chips, rolls or French bread and butter, tartare sauce and the choice of pickled onions and gherkins – both sliced. Tea arrives by the pot and as well as flavoured ice creams they do a good homemade apple pie with custard. To accompany the meal there's a short, basic wine list as well as minerals. Half non-smoking. **Seats** 36. **Open** 12-2.45 & 5-9.45. **Closed** Sun, Mon, 10 days Christmas. No credit cards.

W1   Le Meridien Terrace Garden

Tel 071-734 8000	Restaurant
Piccadilly W1V 0BH	**Map 18 D3**

Four floors up, overlooking busy Piccadilly, is the lovely, leafy, conservatory-style restaurant, the front, lower section of which is reserved for non-smokers. The huge picture windows must once have displayed views of the whole of London, now they let in as much light as the overbuilt streets show. Beautifully kept plants and trees fill the restaurant and add to the bright outdoors feeling. Staff are very formal, so discreet they are almost invisible but they will materialise as soon as you need anything. In marked contrast to the bustle outside, the Terrace Garden Restaurant is peaceful and dignified. Open from breakfast until dinner, the menus offer a range from croque monsieur to a club sandwich and crème caramel. Grills, fish, soups and salads complete the picture. Fine wines by the glass from a Cruvinet machine. Piccadilly hotel prices but no one will hassle you if you want to nurse one course for a whole lunchtime. **Seats** 130. **Open** 7am-11.30pm. Access, Amex, Diners, Visa.

W8   Muffin Man

Tel 071-937 6652	Café
12 Wrights Lane off Kensington High Street W8 6TA	**Map 19 A4**

After the hurly burly of Kensington High Street, revive yourself with
hot leaf tea and light scones in this clean and tidy restaurant painted
pale white with framed pictures of flowers and hanging plants on the
walls. Once you've negotiated the narrow doorway, the other side
of which can be opened to accommodate pushchairs, you enter
a bright, if somewhat cramped tea room with rose patterned
tablecloths and friendly helpful staff. There is a high-chair or room can
be made at your table for a pushchair. Set teas, light lunches, first-rate
home-made cakes and sandwiches are available in adult or children's
portions. The toilets are located down treacherously steep stairs and are
inadequate for baby changing. No-smoking area. On display in the
window are wooden clocks, sweaters and sweets – all for sale.
Seats 60. Open 8-5.45. Closed Sun, Bank Holidays. No credit cards.

W11   Nachos

Tel 071-792 0954	Restaurant
174 Notting Hill Gate W11	**Map 18 A3**

Mexico meets Notting Hill in a lively 200-seat restaurant that's
banked its name on its nachos. These are warm, crispy tortilla chips
topped with cheese and onion (£2.25) spicy chicken or spicy beef
(£2.65) or served with dips. Other staples on the menu are quesadillas
(grilled tortillas), Mexican pizza, taquitos, tacos, burritos, fajitas and
chimichangas. Rooms available for large parties, half-price kid's
portions, children's entertainer 1pm-4pm on Sundays. *Seats 200.
Open noon-midnight. Closed 25 Dec. Access, Visa.*
Also at:
SW6 212 Fulham Road SW6. Tel 071-351 7531.   **Map 19 B5**
Wimbledon 36 High Street Wimbledon Village Surrey. Tel 081-944 8875. **Map 17 B6**

SW7   Natural History Museum, Waterhouse Café

Tel 071-938 9185	Café
Cromwell Road SW7 5BD	**Map 19 B4**

As we went to press Justin de Blank's Waterhouse Café was moving
to the ground floor of the museum in larger premises (nearer to the
mother and baby changing room). Children have always been well
catered for and little is likely to change by way of facilities: high-
chairs, children's portions (£2.50), baby food warmed, extended
children's menu during school holidays and so on. Sausage and mash,
chicken drumsticks and beans (£2.50) is the buffet style, with pastries
and scones for afternoon tea (3-5pm); almost all of the food is freshly
prepared on the premises. *Seats 90. Open 10.30-5 (L 12-2.30), Sun
11.30-5. Closed Dec 25, 26 & Good Friday.*

NW6   Nautilus

Tel 071-435 2532	Fish'n'Chips
27 Fortune Green Road West Hampstead NW6	**Map 16 B2**

Fine, fresh fish is served in this simple restaurant. Matzo meal flour
is used as standard (with an egg and matzo option) and only ground-
nut oil used for frying. 18 different types of fish are offered, including
cod or rock salmon(£6), plaice on the bone (£8) or grilled Dover sole
(£10). Simple starters include soup (£1), prawn cocktail (£3), fresh

melon (£2) and cod's roe (£1). Portions are enormous and the chips generously sized. Gherkins, peas, pickled onions and roll and butter charged extra (70p). Busy fish'n'chip take-away next door. *Seats 48.* **Open** *11.30-2.15 & 5-10.15.* **Closed** *Sun, 3 days at Christmas. No credit cards.*

WC2   Neal's Yard Bakery

Tel 071-836 5199	Café
6 Neal's Yard WC2 H9DP	Map 21 B2

Man cannot live by bread alone? Well try this, arguably the best bread in London, and die. Olive and garlic, three seed – with linseed, poppy and sesame rolled throughout the loaf – season herb with cheese or the standard whole wheat are made with organic flour, filtered water and co-operative care. Stairs lead up from the triangular courtyard, a Covent Garden retreat with wholefood shops and homeopathy centre, to the small vegetarian café above the bakery. Buy downstairs from a daily blackboard selection and eat upstairs where whitewashed walls, stripped rafters and pine tables create a laid-back atmosphere. Avoid peak times. One high-chair. Half portions. No smoking. **Open** *12-6.30 (5.30 winter), Sat 12-4.30.* **Closed** *Sun, Bank Hols, Dec 25-Jan 2. No credit cards.*

WC2   New Shu Shan

Tel 071-836 7501	Restaurant
36 Cranbourne Street WC2 7AD	Map 21 A2

Cantonese and Peking and spicy Szechuan dishes. Children will probably like the sweet and sour won tons as a starter, which are rather like crisps served with a tasty but not too spicy sauce. For main courses, chicken, fried noodles and fried dumplings will be popular with everyone, whilst Sichuan specialities like aubergine in garlic sauce and vermicelli minced meat will appeal to the more adventurous. Families are most often seen here for Saturday or Sunday lunch, but children are welcome at any time. **Open** *12 noon-11.30.* **Closed** *Dec 25 & 26. Access, Amex, Diners, Visa.*

W1   New World

Tel 071-434 2508	Restaurant
1 Gerrard Place Soho W1	Map 21 A2

Join several hundred others and enjoy a meal in one of Soho's most typical and traditional Chinese restaurants. Think of a Chinese dish and you'll probably find it on the vast menu. Dim sum start at £1.35 (choose from trolleys as they are wheeled round the table); there are long lists of seafood and vegetarian specials, 'popular provincial dishes' and chef's specialities. Popular with Chinese families at weekends and one of very few places where you can choose dim sum from the trolleys, thus perhaps a good place to introduce children to the idea of dim sum. *Seats 700.* **Open** *11am-11.45pm (Sun to 11).* **Closed** *25 Dec. Access, Amex, Diners, Visa.*

SW4   Newtons

Tel 081-673 0977	Brasserie
33 Abbeville Road South Side Clapham Common SW4	Map 17 C6

Two-course, weekday lunch menu at £11.95, the Saturday Club Menu and the Sunday Brunch are the best value at a brasserie-style restaurant on a corner of Abbeville Road that caters for the voracious Clapham crowd. As eclectic as its clientele, the set lunch menu may offer carrot and pumpkin soup or chicken satay with peanut dipping sauce followed by blackened halibut fillet with a shallot and prawn sauce or corn-fed chicken chargrilled with basil and tomato cream sauce and broccoli. An optional 12.5% service charge is added to your bill. The long Sunday brunch menu runs the gamut from spicy garlic mushrooms (£3), eggs benedict (£6.05), smoked haddock kedgeree (£6.05), roast beef and Yorkshire pudding (£6.50) or spinach crepe (£6.95). Several tables are outside on an attractive terrace. No smoking area. Weekends are popular with kids when a special children's menu applies and a clown provides the entertainment on Saturdays. *Seats 85 (plus 30 on the terrace).* **Open** *12.30-2.30 & 7-11.30 (12.30-11.30 Sat & Sun). Access, Amex, Visa.*

W1	**Park Lane Hotel**	77%	£195
Tel 071-499 6321 Fax 071-499 1965			Hotel
Piccadilly W1Y 8EB			Map 18 C3

Built in 1927, the hotel retains some of its distinctive art deco features, although the feel throughout the public rooms and bedrooms is very traditional. The Palm Court lounge, where afternoon teas are served, is brightened by a magnificent vaulted ceiling with arched art deco stained glass. Standard bedrooms are well sized but tend to look out on the dark inside courtyard. The best rooms are the suites: all air-conditioned, they look out on to the central court or Green Park and benefit from private sitting rooms and more luxurious bathrooms. Standard double rooms have space for a cot or an extra bed, and nappies and baby-sitters can be provided, with a nanny on request. But then in a hotel like this, you can't help feeling that you should be able to ask for a replacement child when yours gets on your nerves. Spacious lifts and public areas are fine for a whole flotilla of push chairs, but toddlers are not welcome in the haute cuisine restaurant. Most suitable is the Brasserie on the Park, which can provide high-chairs, baby food and small portions. Staff will warm bottles and do their best to make babies happy. The downstairs powder room is ideal for breast-feeding and nappy-changing. Parking in a covered garage for 180 cars. **Rooms** *330. Keep-fit equipment, solarium, beauty & hair salons, brasserie noon-11.30pm, garage. Access, Amex, Diners, Visa.*

W2	**Parkwood Hotel**	£65
Tel 071-402 2241 Fax 071-402 1574		Hotel
4 Stanhope Place W2 2HB		Map 18 C3

Small friendly bed and breakfast hotel in a town house that's quiet but handy for Hyde Park, Marble Arch and Oxford Street shops. Special rates for children under 13. Unlicensed. No dogs. **Rooms** *18. Access, Diners, Visa.*

SW1	**Peter Jones**	
Tel 071-730 3434		Restaurant
Sloane Square SW1W 8EL		Map 19 C4

Although the service is extremely efficient, queuing at lunch time has to be expected for a seat in the popular open-plan dining room on the fourth floor. The decor is simple: light green carpet and curtains, flowery plastic tablecloth ceiling fans and a beautiful view of London. The menu offers light healthy selections like salmon fishcakes on a bed

of spinach with watercress sauce. The warm daily topping home-made cakes like banoffi pie, Irish chocolate gateau, fresh fruit salad and individual summer puddings. They serve full English breakfast (£5.75) from 9.30am to 11.30am. Afternoon tea between 3 and 5 includes a selection of sandwiches, cake or pastry and a pot of tea or coffee (£4.75), or two scones, clotted cream and strawberry preserve with a pot of tea (£3.95). The mothers' room is on the third floor and there's plenty of room for push-chairs in the restaurant. Small portions for those under 11 and even peanut butter sandwiches served with crisps! **Seats** *150.* **Open** *9.30-5.*
Closed *Sun & Bank Holidays. No credit cards.*

SW1   Pizza on the Park

Tel 071-235 5273	Pizzeria
Hyde Park Corner 11 Knightsbridge SW1	**Map 19 C4**

Owned by Peter Boizot (of Pizza Express fame), this famous restaurant, along with *Kettner's* forms a new direction offering food and service a cut above his old operation. Familiar pizzas are still the mainstay but the choice is much wider with, from 8am, a full ham and eggs breakfast (£3.95), cereals, toast and muffins, then, from 11am onwards, sandwiches (£3.85), salads (£6.25 for niçoise), pasta (cannelloni £5.20) and some vegetarian versions, with afternoon tea served in the 'West Wing' from 3.30-5.30pm. The downstairs room becomes a jazz venue in the evenings (booking essential) with sets at 9.15 and 11.15pm and an entrance fee of between £8 and £15 depending on who's playing. Peroni is the only beer (Boizot is MD of the company that imports it). **Seats** *260.* **Open** *8am-midnight.*
Closed *25 Dec. Access, Amex, Diners, Visa.*

SW7   Prince Hotel   £71

Tel 071-589 6488 Fax 071-581 0024	Hotel
6 Sumner Place SW7 3AB	**Map 19 B5**

Two houses in an early Victorian terrace provide comfortable bed and breakfast accommodation near South Kensington underground station. Some rooms are without private facilities. One family room sleeps four. Chintzy lounge; plant-filled conservatory. No bar; breakfast is the only meal served. **Rooms** *20. Garden. Access, Amex, Visa.*

SW8   Queenstown Dining Rooms

Tel 071-720 6960	Restaurant
129 Queenstown Road SW8 3RH	**Map 17 C5**

A good local restaurant that has seen many guises over the last couple of years. Three high-chairs are provided and baby's food and bottles will be heated on request, so families are considered. Sunday is a good time for an outing when there's a fixed-price, 3-course lunch (£8.95) with the likes of a roast, kedgeree and always a vegetarian option. At other times the cooking continues in a home-from-home style executed with panache: chicken liver terrine (£2.95), asparagus and goat's cheese filo parcel (£4.75), cod and chips (£4.50), coronation chicken (£5.95), liver and bacon (£5.50), beef and ale pudding (£6.50) and Lancashire hot pot (£5.25). Apple crumble (£2.25), lemon syllabub (£2.25), treacle tart (£1.95) and Trinity burnt creams (£1.75) to finish. **Seats** *60.* **Open** *12.30-3, 7-10.30 (to 11 Sat).*
Closed *D Sun, 25 & 26 Dec. Access, Diners, Visa.*

N3   Rani

Tel 081-349 4386	Restaurant
7 Long Lane Finchley Central N3 2PR	Map 16 B1

Stylish red-and-white decor and smart glass-topped tables are not the
norm for Indian vegetarian restaurants, but neither is Rani the norm.
The style of cooking is Gujerati, and even normally mundane dishes
are transformed by interesting use of spices and fresh herbs. Different
days bring different specials, Friday's, for example, might be baby
cucumbers with potato topped with yoghurt sauce. Regular delights
on the menu include bhajias with wonderful coriander chutney
(£2.60), delicate aubergine and lima bean curry (£4.10) and ripe
bananas with fenugreek leaves and tomato curry (banana mehti
£4.40). Some dishes, like aloo papri chat (chick peas and potatoes
served on flat crispy pooris with tamarind, topped with yoghurt sauce
£3), and methi thapla (spicy fenugreek bread roasted and fried £2.40)
are near perfect and the prices could hardly be lower. No eggs, fish,
meat or animal fats are permitted on the premises. Set meals are
offered only on Monday evenings and all lunches (2-course from
£11.50). Children's set menu for £5. There's no service charge and
any money left behind as change or gratuities will be donated
to charity. No smoking area; Saturday is all no smoking. Book for
dinner (minimum charge £10 on Saturday evenings and £8 on all
other evenings). This is one of London's very best Indian vegetarian
restaurant in terms of both variety and cooking. *Seats* 90.
Open 12.30-2 & 6-10.30. *Closed L Mon, Tue, Sat. Access, Visa.*

SW11   Ransome's Dock

Tel 071-223 1611	Restaurant/Bar
35 Parkgate Road Battersea SW11 4NP	Map 19 B6

Located midway between Albert and Battersea Bridges as part
of a modern dockside development the restaurant enjoys some good
views and there's a conservatory at the front for fine weather. Decor
is bright and airy with cornflower blue walls and jade green
highlights. Brunch on Sundays sees items like kedgeree (from £4.50),
salmon fishcakes (£6.90), lamb and Toulouse sausage cassoulet (£7.50)
or spinach and parmesan soufflé (£6.50). Sweets range from Greek
yoghurt with acacia honey (£2.50) or apple crumble and custard
(£2.95) to waffle with maple syrup and vanilla ice cream (£3).
Drinks to accompany include Bloody Mary (£2.50), Ransome's Dock
rum punch (£3.50) or buck's fizz (£4). Lunch during the week
represents good value with a two-course set menu at £10.50. Evenings
and lunchtimes also see a modestly priced à la carte with mussels
in saffron and cream (£3.75), tagliatelle with pancetta and mushrooms
(£3.50), chargrilled quails with couscous and lemon sauce (£9)
or grilled cod steak with a creamy parsley sauce, broccoli and new
potatoes (£7.50). Excellent desserts include a warm, crisp apple strudel
with cold custard (£2.90). *Seats* 60. *Open* 12-11 (*Sat* 12-12, *Sun*
12-3.30). *Closed D Sun, all Bank Holidays. Access, Amex, Visa.*

WC2   Rasa Sayang

Tel 071-734 8720	Restaurant
10 Frith Street Soho W1	Map 21 A3

Malaysian/Singaporean restaurant. Portions are normally quite
generous, so don't over order dishes to stay within a budget: Char
Kway Teow (broad rice noodles, fried Singapore style, with mixed

vegetables £4.60), Ayam Limau (boneless chicken pieces cooked
in a tangy lemon sauce £5.90), Gado Gado (popular cooked vegetable
salad, garnished with spicy peanut sauce £4.20), Sotong Goreng (fried
squid with chili dips £4.90). Help-yourself lunchtime buffet
on Sunday and Monday – £5.90 (children half price £3.50).
Seats 200. **Open** *12-2.45 & 6-11.30 (Sun to 10).* **Closed** *L Sat.*
Access, Amex, Diners, Visa.
Also at:
W2 38 Queensway Bayswater. Tel 071-229 8417.   **Map 19 A3**

W1   The Ritz, Palm Court

Tel 071-493 8181	Tea
150 Piccadilly W1V 9DG	**Map 18 D3**

Taking your well-behaved child to tea at the Ritz is a very civilised
thing to do. Taking any other sort of child will entail a tactical
withdrawal of self and progeny, if only for the duration
of unpleasantness. Book at least a week in advance, ask for the sole
high-chair, and enjoy elegant tea sandwiches highly suitable for
children. A visit to the splendid Ladies downstairs is a must for mums.
Seats 150. **Open** *Tea at 3pm & 4.30pm. Access, Amex, Diners, Visa.*

W6   Riverside Studios Café

Tel 081-746 3771	Café
Riverside Studios Crisp Road W6 9RL	**Map 17 A4**

A small cafeteria located on the ground floor of the Riverside Studios
and convenient for exhibitions, theatre and cinema. A limited menu
offers a healthy straightforward selection of salads, home-made soup
(£1.50), hot dishes like spinach filo parcels (£3.40), sweet and sour
spare ribs (£3.65) and oven-baked potatoes (from £1.60). Carrot cake
and Danish pastries accompany the speciality teas. Very popular on
Saturdays, particularly before the children's matinées; no high-chairs.
Nice promenade on the river terrace nearby. Organic wines and beers
are available. The bar, adjacent to the cafeteria, is open from 6pm
to 11pm. *Seats* 60. **Open** *12-2.30 & 6-8.30 (snacks 9-8.30, Sun from
10).* **Closed** *Bank Holidays.*

W1   Rock Island Diner

Tel 071-287 5500	Restaurant
London Pavilion Piccadilly Circus W1	**Map 18 D3**

A gleaming '54 Chevrolet is suspended above diners at this whacky re-
creation of a 50s' American diner on the second floor (via an escalator)
of the London Pavilion. Bobby-soxed waitresses literally dance from
table to table to the sounds of an in-house DJ who plays requests (even
from little Johnny!) and revels in keeping a party atmosphere moving
along at a pace. Burgers, hot dogs, BBQ ribs, five-way chili, BLT
sandwiches, fried chicken salads, Winnie's chocolate brownies, banana
dream cake, waffles and ice cream sundaes are the order of the day and
everything stops occasionally as the guys'n'gals line up to do a quick
hand jive routine. It's a fun place, best suited to the over-5s who are
guaranteed to love it; they may not serve the 'best burgers in town'
but they certainly serve up enough entertainment to keep a kid happy
for an hour or so. Four high-chairs are provided and there's room
to leave a push-chair by the table cubicles or at the entrance under the
watchful eye of the greeter. Between noon and 5pm at weekends
a child under 10 eats free of charge if accompanied by an adult eating

a meal; over-10s have their own menu. Combine a bite here with
a visit to Madame Tussaud's rock'n'rolling Rock Circus next door
and the little darlings should consider a visit to the Big Smoke 'totally
awesome'. The integral bar area offers a happy hour from 5.30-7pm
(Mon-Fri). Enjoy! *Seats 160. Open Noon-11.30 (10.30 Sun).
Closed 25 Dec. Access, Amex, Diners, Visa.*

W2   Royal Lancaster Hotel Lounge

Tel 071-262 6737	Tea
Lancaster Terrace London W2 3PF	Map 18 B3

One of the rare hotels to welcome children for afternoon teas. They
are served in the roomy lounge, where sofas and armchairs are set
around low tables, just the right height for children. For younger ones,
high-chairs can be borrowed from the café. Their set tea (£9.75)
selection is pleasant but somewhat minimalist: five finger sandwiches,
a scone, clotted cream, jam and two pastries like strawberry tartelette
and petit chou stuffed with whipped cream. The lounge is on the first
floor with easy access via a lift; the anteroom of the toilet nearby
is perfect for changing or nursing. A pianist tinkles away on a white
grand piano while one indulges; ask him to play Teddy Bears' Picnic –
he's bound to know it. *Seats 80. Open 3-5.30. Closed 25 Dec. Access,
Amex, Diners, Visa.*

W1   SAS Portman Hotel, Bakery

Tel 071-486 5844	Brasserie
22 Portman Street W1H 9AP	Map 18 C2

Popping into a London hotel for a snack with your buggy may seem
a little adventurous, but not at this one: a doorman will direct wheeled
families through a side door, not the revolving obstacle, and there
is storage space by the restaurants. The menu in Truffles Restaurant
might be a little too grown-up even for some pre-teens. The Bakery
serves the sort of food children understand and they are happy to serve
small portions and heat your baby's food. There are four high-chairs
and baby bottles provided on request. Afternoon tea is taken in the
lounge, which is so recumbent it even has a low-level high chair. No-
smoking area. *Seats 40. Open 11am-midnight. Access, Amex, Diners,
Visa.*

SE16   Scandic Crown   £156

Tel 071-231 1001 Fax 071-231 0599	Hotel
Nelson Dock 265 Rotherhithe Street SE16 1EJ	Map 17 D4

A splendid hotel for families, with the added bonus of a borough
playground opposite the hotel entrance. Especially popular with
Scandinavian tourists as a London base, the hotel is a clever conversion
of the 19th-century Columbia Wharf, with glass walkways linking
a marvellous new development to the three bedroom blocks. An old
sailing barque moored in the dry dock between the buildings
continues the nautical theme, and the hotel has its own pier. Most
of the bedrooms have a river view and include mini bar, trouser press,
hairdryer and security locks. Sixteen rooms have double sofabeds (up
to two children under 12 years sharing the room are free). Cheerful
and helpful staff, and an excellent Scandinavian buffet breakfast, taken
in the restaurant beside the river terrace, starts the day off in fine
style; a good evening smörgåsbord spread is equally impressive. There
is a special play area on Sundays at the buffet lunch and jazz barbecue.

Children are charged £1 for every foot of their height. Separate
supervised leisure complex, games room and outdoor tennis court.
Rooms 390. *River terrace, indoor swimming pool, sauna, solarium, spa
bath, gymnasium, tennis, games room, snooker. Access, Amex, Diners, Visa.*

SW1   Seafresh Restaurant

Tel 071-828 0747   Restaurant

80-81 Wilton Road SW1   **Map 19 D5**

A restaurant for serious fish-lovers, where fish is flown in from
Scotland, on ice and not frozen. They are fried in peanut oil or grilled
on request. The decor is simple and comfortable: saloon chairs, fake
beams and decorative fishing nets. Cod (£6.45), plaice (£6.25), skate
(£6.75), rock (£5.75), king prawns (£9.45) and calamari (£7.75) are
fried in light batter, served in ample portions with real potato chips
and large slices of pickles. Chicken (£4.25), pork sausage (£3.15) and
spam fritters (£4.15) are also available. Cheerful service and take-away
counter. One high-chair is provided and there's plenty of storage for
push-chairs. **Seats 100. Open** *noon-10.45.* **Closed** *Sun, 25 Dec-6 Jan.
Access, Visa.*

NW1   Seashell Restaurant

Tel 071-723 8703   Fish'n'Chips

49 Lisson Grove Marylebone NW1 6UH   **Map 18 B2**

One of London's best-known fish and chip restaurants, coping
admirably with the crowds who come from all over town to eat in or
take away. The restaurant is on two floors, connected by a spiral
staircase, and is large, smart and comfortable, with a non-smoking area.
Prices may vary according to weight and availability, but cod and
chips costs about (£7.90), plaice (£7.50), haddock (£8.50), Dover
sole (£12.90). Set lunch (Mon-Fri £8.75) comprises soup, fish
of the day with chips, sweet and coffee. **Seats 180. Open** *12-10.30.*
Closed *Sun, 25 & 26 Dec, 1 Jan. Access, Amex, Diners, Visa.*

W1   Selfridges, Food Garden Café

Tel 071-629 1234   Café

400 Oxford Street W1A 1AB   **Map 18 C2**

Selfridges' Top of the Shop cafeteria has been completely refurbished
and restructured to create the Food Garden Café. A new style
of cafeteria, strongly inspired by the Marché Mövenpick in Leicester
Square, but undoubtedly less charming. In its first week of opening,
things were not going smoothly and needed major adjustments. If all
goes well in the future, the idea is attractive: pasta (£3.25) and
Oriental dishes (£4.65) are prepared in woks in front of customers'
eyes, steaks (£3.85) are grilled to customer's liking, crepes (from
£2.95) are made to order. Quiches, salads, spuds and pastries are well
laid out and look appetizing. Children are well catered for with
a special menu of sausage, chips, beans and eggs, crepes, and Häagen
Dazs ice cream. The decor is now wood, granite, and warm colours,
the dining room bright and airy; it is a big improvement from the
Top of the Shop and a step towards healthy cafeteria food. Small no-
smoking area. The best offering from the Brass Rail café on the
ground floor is the succulent hot salt beef sandwiches (£3.75), cut
to order from freshly cooked brisket and generously crammed
between slices of rye bread; half a sweet and sour pickled cucumber

adds the finishing touch. The mothers' room is on the third floor.
*Seats 350. Open 9.30-6.45 (Thu to 7.45). Closed Sun, 25 & 26 Dec.
Access, Amex, Diners, Visa.*

W1 Signor Zilli

Tel 071-734 3924	Restaurant
41 Dean Street Soho W1	**Map 21 A2**

Sunday lunch is the time to visit one of Soho's oldest restaurants, now
actively encouraging families with a traditional Sunday roast (three
courses £12.50) alongside the menu of Italian dishes. A children's
menu (£4.95) includes pasta dishes, sausages and mash, burgers or fish
with chips and beans, followed by mixed ice cream and chocolate
sauce, fruit salad or a banana long boat. There are bowls of Smarties
on every table for those who 'eat it all up' (or not, as is the case!).
Adults can choose a starter from the à la carte menu and desserts from
the trolley, to complement good roast beef served with Yorkshire
pudding. The basement room has a colour television, balloons, activity
books and coloured pencils, plus a magician who entertains diners
before the children's show (and/or disco) at 2.30pm. Owner Aldo
Zilli's young daughter is usually on hand to make friends and play
with visiting children. High-chairs are provided. *Seats 30. Sunday
lunch 12-4. Access, Amex, Diners, Visa.*

W1 Smollensky's Balloon Bar & Restaurant

Tel 071-491 1199	Restaurant
1 Dover Street W1X 3PJ	**Map 18 D3**

Opposite The Ritz, this hip basement restaurant attracts the young and
very young with its lively atmosphere. Along with an extensive
American-style menu, a 'pre-fix' menu of £9.85 is offered which
includes a choice of four starters or salad followed by entrecote steak,
sauce, French fries and a glass of house beer or wine. A brasserie menu
is served only in the bar and offers plenty of variety, from smoked
haddock fish cakes with tartare sauce (£2.95) and stuffed Sicilian pasta
shells (£2.85) to chicken and broccoli lasagne with garlic bread
(£4.50), hamburger, French fries and coleslaw (£4.75) and mini fillet
steak sandwich (£5.50). The focus is on children Saturday and Sunday
lunchtimes with a special menu – 'kid's koktails' £1.55, main courses
£3.95 and 'dessert konkoktions' £1.95. Between 12 and 3, families are
entertained with magic and fun at the tables and cartoons on the
monitors; computer games nuts can even have a go with the latest
software. At 2.30, parents have half-an-hour's peace while children are
taken to a separate end of the restaurant for a puppet or magic show.
There is now a baby changing area in the Ladies and high-chairs are
provided. Joint winner of our 1993 Family Restaurant of the Year
award. *Seats 220. Open 12pm-12am (12-10.30 Sun). Access, Amex,
Diners, Visa.*

WC2 Smollensky's On The Strand

Tel 071-497 2101	Restaurant
105 The Strand WC2R 0AA	**Map 17 C4**

Book it or forget it – this fashionable restaurant is immensely popular
with families. Its peculiar appeal consists of equal parts style and
inviting transatlantic menu. A play area with slide, seesaw and bikes
helps the under-7s through the cooking times of their parents' main
courses. Colouring sheets and pens and cartoon videos help, too. Best

of all is the positive attitude of the staff towards children. There are
heaps of high-chairs and boosters seats available; a changing mat is in
the toilet and a manager's office for breast-feeding in privacy. The
weekend brings clowns, balloons, a show and the very popular
children's dancing session. Live music regularly features at this branch
of Smollensky's: dancing on Friday and Saturday evenings; live jazz
on Sunday evenings in conjunction with Jazz FM; and live light music
every other evening. £3 music charge, whether dining or just
drinking. Discounted cocktails and spirits are offered during Happy
Hour (5.30-7pm) also benefiting diners who wish to drink at this
time. Joint winner of our 1993 Family Restaurant of the Year award.
Seats 240. **Open** 12-12 (Fri & Sat to 12.30, Sun to 10). Access, Amex,
Diners, Visa.

N16   Spices

Tel 071-254 0528	Restaurant

30 Stoke Newington Church Street N16 OLU   **Map 16 D2**

The perfume of burning incense hangs heavily in the air and with
dark, candle-lit tables and Indian music playing in the background
there's a suitably oriental ambience at this vegetarian restaurant
in young and trendy Stoke Newington. To the rear is a more brightly-
lit section with booths that seat four, most unusually, on floor
cushions – a novelty that most children seem to enjoy. This is an ideal
location for families as children are less likely to disturb other diners;
the booths also allow a measure of privacy for nursing. Though the
menu features a variety of spiced dishes made with specially imported
fresh herbs and spices, there are several items suitable for young
children such as plain popadums and pakoras (sliced potatoes and
vegetables dipped in gram flour paste and deep fried £1.70); the
waiters will be happy to point out those dishes that are popular with
chidlren. Two children can share a Bombay tiffin (£2.65) – a starter
assortment of delicately spiced gujerati savouries including samosas,
vegetable cutlets and aubergine slices topped with sour cream (malai
baigan). To finish there are home-made ice-creams with pistachio,
mango, almond or coconut (£1.90). A fresh, nutritious and delicious
drink is either banana or mango lassi (£1.40). Two high-chairs are
provided but a changing area is not; another plus for families is a car
park to the rear with easy pushchair access. **Seats** 65. **Open** 12-2.30,
6-midnight. **Closed** 25 & 26 Dec. Access, Amex, Diners, Visa.

W8   Sticky Fingers

Tel 071-938 5338	Restaurant

9 Phillimore Gardens off Kensington High Street W8   **Map 19 A4**

The walls of Bill Wyman's immensely popular American-style diner
are covered with Rolling Stones memorabilia, but other groups (even
including Abba!) get a share of the sound system. The food is served
in liberal portions by friendly, clued-up staff: starter helping of ribs
£3.85, guacamole and tortilla chips £3.65, cheeseburger £5.65, Cajun
chicken £6.95, steak sandwich £7.75, frozen yoghurt with fresh fruit,
honey and almonds £3.15. Half-price drinks during happy hour 5.30-
6.30. No bookings in the evening. **Seats** 160. **Open** 12-11.30 (Sun
to 11). **Closed** 25 Dec. Access, Amex, Diners, Visa.

SE1   Sweeney Todd's

Tel 071-407 5267	Restaurant
London Bridge Tooley Street London Bridge SE1 2QT	**Map 20 C3**

Located at the back of Hay's Galleria, across from the London
Dungeon, is this two-floor restaurant with access at street level. Not
just a welcoming restaurant for families but a haven for children.
A special menu for 'tax payers of tomorrow under 11' offers main
course, first fizzy drink and dessert for £3.25. Main courses include
BBQ ribs, chicken nuggets, cheeseburger, bean burger or pizzas,
sundaes, milk shakes or fruit juices – not exceptional quality but well
executed nontheless. Children are encouraged to draw their waiter
or waitress on the back of their place mat and may win a T-shirt.
Children's parties are particularly well catered for with balloons, hats
and streamers. Changing shelf in the Ladies. *Seats 280.* **Open** *11-11.*
Closed *25 Dec. Access, Amex, Diners, Visa.*

SW4   Tea Time

Tel 071-622 4944	Tea Room
21 The Pavement Clapham Common SW4	**Map 17 C5**

Yet another change of ownership but this institution on the east side
of Clapham Common continues to pull the crowds, particularly
at weekends. A window display full of tempting gateaux and pastries
whets the appetite for an all-day 'Tea Time special' (£6.95), a lavish
cream tea with sandwiches, cakes and a good choice of quality teas.
Breakfast, also all day, includes kedgeree (£2.95) and scrambled eggs
with smoked salmon (£4.95) while other savoury options include
sandwiches, plain, toasted (from £2.30) and double-decker (£3.85)
– a daily soup (£1.95) and hot specials, perhaps lasagne or lamb stew
(£3.95). Cosy, civilised ground and basement (no smoking) rooms
are served by cheerful waitresses. No bookings at weekends. *Seats 60.*
Open *10-6.15 (Sat & Sun to 6.45).* **Closed** *Bank Holidays.*
No credit cards.

N10   Toff's

Tel 081-883 8656	Fish'n'Chips
38 The Broadway Muswell Hill Broadway N10 3RJ	**Map 16 C1**

The Toffalli family's popular fish and chip restaurant is decorated with
Edwardian prints of Billingsgate market. Most of their fish now comes
from Peterhead, to be coated in batter or egg and matzo meal and
fried in ground-nut oil. Prices start at £7.25 (cod and chips), with
plaice at £7.50, skate at £9.50 and halibut at the top of the range.
Add £1 and allow a little more time for grilled fish. Side orders
include mushy peas. Set menu at £7.95 (not evening) offers soup, fish
and chips, ice cream and tea or coffee. Children's menu (Young Toff's)
features everything with chips (saveloy, pie, scampi, fishcake, veg
pastie – all £2.50-£3) plus mushy peas, salad, ice cream and cakes
from a trolley. *Seats 32.* **Open** *11.30-10.* **Closed** *Sun, Mon, 2 weeks
Aug, 1 week Easter, 1 week Christmas. Access, Amex, Visa.*

W4   Tootsies

Tel 081-747 1869	Restaurant
148 Chiswick High Road W4	**Map 17 A4**

Six branches of this popular burger chain share the same decor of can
bistro chairs and walls covered with enamel signs and colourful

mirrors. Aberdeen Angus beefburgers (from £3.60) are offered with
a choice of ten different toppings – from Mexican hot sauce
to mushroom in sour cream and white wine sauce or just a fried egg.
Salads are made freshly from good ingredients, chicken served
in grilled or in a sandwich and English breakfast (£5.50) is available
all day. 'Tootsies tots' under 10 are given balloons, special plates
and a menu of mini hamburger with cheese, egg or beans and fries;
small chicken sandwich or sausage, fries and baked beans; finish with
TT's ice cream (£1.15). Regular dishes can be shared with their
parents. Being so popular for so long with families, it is hard
to understand why none of the outlets offer changing facilities,
although high-chairs and booster seats will be found in all of them.
12½% service is automatically added to your bill, but you are invited
to complain should anything not be to your liking. Tables on the
pavement in good weather. *Seats* 72. *Open* 12-12 (Sun 12-11.30).
Closed 5 days Christmas. Access, Visa.
Also at:

NW3 216 Haverstock Hill Tel 071-433 3896.	**Map 16 B2**	
SW19 48 High Street Wimbledon Village Tel 081-946 4135.	**Map 17 B6**	
SW6 177 New Kings Road Parsons Green Tel 071-736 4023.	**Map 17 B5**	
W11 120 Holland Park Avenue Tel 071-229 8567.	**Map 17 B4**	

Special breakfast menu at weekends from 8am to noon, then open all day
as usual.

W11 115 Notting Hill Gate Tel 071-727 6562.   **Map 18 A3**

N1   Tuk Tuk   £30
Tel 071-226 0837	Restaurant
330 Upper Street Islington N1 2XQ	**Map 16 D3**

Don't be put off by the rather austere look of Tuk Tuk, it is
comfortable and the food is delicious. Thai food is ideal for sharing
and the range of dishes is wide enough to allow grown-ups to try the
hot, spicy dishes while children enjoy the milder ones. Satay and Thai
spring rolls are favourites with children and our three-year-old
inspector loved the rice and chicken in a clay pot. Customers are
invited to share dishes 'in the traditional manner'. There are no high-
chairs but there is room for a push chair by the larger tables. *Seats* 80.
Open 12-3 & 6-11.15. *Closed L Sat, all Sun, Bank Holidays. Access,
Amex, Diners, Visa.*

NW1   The Underground Café
Tel 071-482 0010	Restaurant
214 Camden High Street London NW1	**Map 16 C3**

Like its sister restaurant the Camden Brasserie next door, they have
no high-chairs. Nevertheless, the clientele of regulars will happily take
baby in on their laps and introduce him to serious cooking with
a strong Italian bent. The service is helpful and flexible enough
to accomodate any needs. Pasta is home made and served with
delicious combinations like roast aubergines, pesto and pine nuts.
Starters include char-grilled vegetables with pesto and herb polenta
or risotto of the day, main dishes are pungent combinations of chargrilled corn-fed chicken with a balsamic glaze or slowly braised osso
bucco served with red cabbage. Black and white chocolate mousse,
Häagen-Dazs ice cream or biscotti cantuccini (with vin santo for
adults) will take you past the finishing post. Popular with families
on Saturdays. *Seats* 80. *Open* 6-11 (Fri & Sat to 11.30). *Closed* all Sun,
23 Dec-1 Jan. Access, Diners, Visa.

N1   Upper Street Fish Shop

| Tel 071-359 1401 | Fish'n'Chips |

324 Upper Street Islington N1   **Map 16 D3**

Alan Conway set up shop here in 1981, and he's been in charge, with
his wife Olga, eversince. When the chips are down, it's quality that
counts, something well known to the crowds who come to sit down
and eat or take away. Besides the excellent fish and chips (cod,
haddock, skate, halibut, even sea bass among the daily specials – prices
start at around £6) there are some very tempting starters, including
smoked salmon paté and a skewer of deep-fried mussels (both £2) and
half-a-dozen Irish rock oysters for £4.75. Sweets, home-prepared like
everything else, are guaranteed to fill any remaining gaps: favourites
are bread-and-butter pudding and jam roly-poly. Unlicensed, so take
your own wine – there's no corkage. Buggies at tables during peak
periods may be frowned upon. *Seats 50. **Open** 12-2 (Sat to 3) &
5.30-10. **Closed** L Mon, all Sun, Bank Holidays and Sats before
and a week after, 3 weeks Christmas. No credit cards.*

W1   The Westbury   75%   £193

| Tel 071-629 7755 Fax 071-495 1163 | Hotel |

Conduit Street W1A 4UH   **Map 18 D3**

Built in the 1950s as sister hotel to the Westbury in New York, the
London version is just off New Bond Street. Sparkling chandeliers and
smartly liveried porters create a formal impression on first entering the
marble-floored lobby. The pine-panelled Polo Lounge (open 24 hours
for refreshments) and dark green Polo Bar boast polo murals and
memorabilia, inspired by original owners who had a passion for the
sport. Bedrooms vary in size from smallish singles through mini-suites
to 13 full suites and a penthouse; all share the same traditional-style
darkwood furniture with pleasing floral fabrics and many extras like
mini-bars. 20 of the rooms are suitable for families, with cots, funpacks
and baby-sitting available. No leisure amenities. Forte Grand.
Rooms 243. *Access, Amex, Diners, Visa.*

W5   Wine & Mousaka

| Tel 081-998 4373 | Restaurant |

30 & 33 Haven Green Ealing W5 2NX   **Map 17 A4**

A pair of Greek restaurants (with another branch at Kew) serving
sensibly priced favourites like taramasalata, houmus (£1.75 each),
dolmades (£5.25) and moussaka (£5.25). There's a four-course set
menu at £6.95 (weekdays); meze (£9.45) offers 10 dishes, grand meze
(£11.95) provides 12 dishes, dessert and coffee. *Seats 140.
Open 12-2.30 & 6-11.30. **Closed** Sun, Bank Holidays. Access, Amex,
Diners, Visa.*
Also at:
Kew 12 Kew Green Kew Surrey TW9 3BH. Tel 081-940 5696.   **Map 17 A5**
Closed all Sun.

W2   Winton's Soda Fountain

| Tel 071-229 8489 | Café |

2nd Floor Whiteleys Queensway Bayswater W2   **Map 18 A3**

One of the many fast food outlets on the second floor of this vast
multi-unit shopping complex. An ice cream soda fountain with
marble-topped tables, parquet flooring and a Wurlitzer juke box.

There's a range of flavours from a selection of suppliers from which sundaes such as Monkey Madness (£3.90), Milky Chocolate Fantasy (£3.90), Jolly Giant (£6.30 and Children's Delight (£2.30) are created. Also available are milkshakes (£2.80), cakes (90p-£1.70) and biscuits. *Seats* 100. *Open* 11-10 (10-10 Sun). *Closed* 25 Dec. *No credit cards.*

W1 Woodlands

Tel 071-486 3862	Restaurant
77 Marylebone Lane W1	**Map 18 C2**

One of three restaurants serving Southern Indian vegetarian cuisine. Fresh herbs and spices create clean, distinctive and subtle flavours. Thalis, the set meals, are copious (from £8.50) and give a good introduction to this type of food. From the menu, starters include rasa vada (lentil doughnut in spicy gravy) and idli (steamed rice cakes served with sambar and chutney £2.75). Main dish specialities are dosas (pancakes) filled with a variety of ingredients – potato and onion, spicy cottage cheese (£3.25-£4.50) – and uthappams (lentil pizzas) with different toppings (£3.50-£3.95). Minimum charge £5. *Seats* 70. *Open* 12-3 & 6-11. *Closed* 25 & 26 Dec. *Access, Amex, Diners, Visa.*
Also at:

37 Panton Street SW1 Tel 071-839 7238	**Map 18 D3**
Open 12-3 & 5.30-11.	
402 High Road Wembley Middlesex Tel 081-902 9869	**Map 16 A2**

life*time*™

Whatever life holds in store.

If the majority of your calls can be made outside peak business hours, Cellnet Lifetime is the service for you.

Giving you more flexibility to juggle business commitments, social responsibilities and your leisure pursuits, Cellnet's exciting new Lifetime service makes mobile communications more affordable for the less frequent user.

Ideal when there's a sudden change of plan, when you're running late – and in emergencies it really comes into its own.

With Lifetime you can always keep in touch. And what's more your friends, relatives and customers can always get in touch with you.

life*time*™ You'll wonder how you ever managed without it.

cellnet

The nearest phone.

For further details call Cellnet on

0800 21 4000

England

Abbotsbury   Flower Bowl

Tel 0305 871336	Tea Room
Market Street Abbotsbury Dorset	**Map 13 F3**

Unpretentious tea room found behind the local craft shop where you
can enjoy cream tea with home-baked scones (£2.25), ploughman's,
sandwiches or home-made soup. In summer sit in the garden, which
offers a view of Abbotsbury's 15th-century chapel. Children will
be kept amused by a variety of toys made available. *Seats 24.*
Open 10-6. Closed Christmas eve-Easter. No credit cards.

Alcester   Arrow Mill   £72

Tel 0789 762419 Fax 0789 765170	Inn
Arrow nr Alcester Warwickshire B49 5NL	**Map 14 C1**

The Arrow Mill was listed in the Domesday Book, when it was
a working flour mill valued at three shillings and sixpence! The
stream-driven mill wheel still turns in the restaurant, and day rooms
feature heavy beams and flagstones. Bedrooms of individual character
use light, attractive fabrics and pine furniture. There's parking space
for 200 cars, and a heliport. Dogs in kennels only. "Mainly a business
hotel" (with limited public rooms), but a useful place to stop over.
Rooms 18. Garden, fishing. Access, Amex, Diners, Visa.

Alfriston   Toucans Restaurant at Drusillas Zoo

Tel 0323 870234	Restaurant
Drusillas Park Alfriston East Sussex BN26 5QS	**Map 11 B6**

One mile north of the Brighton-Eastbourne road, Drusillas Zoo
continues to attract hordes of families and it is rewarding to see them
so well catered for when the little ones get hungry. Our 1991 Family
Restaurant of the Year was so popular on a recent Sunday lunchtime
visit that the place was almost overrun with children and the play
corner, designed to combat those long stretches of boredom that visit
children at mealtimes, was well attended. There are bright plastic
tablecloths, ample room for prams and push-chairs, excellent nursing
and changing areas, high-chairs galore; every facility is provided. The
staff are young, friendly and attentive and deliver maximum portions
of food with a minimum wait. Baby meals can be ordered here, bottles
heated and jars warmed. The 'Little Monkeys' menu offers the usual
array of children's favourites, from spaghetti bolognese to fish fingers
and chips. No smoking; no dogs. The Inn at the Zoo next door caters
well for adults (from 10.30-5), offering a short menu of good pub
food. *Open weekends and school holidays 10-6 (March-Oct to 5). Zoo
open every day (10.30-4 in winter); under-3s free. Closed Dec 25. Access,
Amex, Visa.*

Allendale   Bishop Field Country House   59%   £76

Tel 0434 683248 Fax 0434 683830	Hotel
Whitfield Road Allendale nr Hexham Northumberland NE47 9EJ	**Map 5 D2**

A mile out of Allendale on the Whitfield road, this former farmhouse
was converted in 1985 by Kathy and Keith Fairless and is now run
by them with their young daughter Bridget, who is also the chef.
There's a cheerful, relaxed atmosphere in the lounges, one of which
has a cocktail bar, the other is non-smoking. Bedrooms are
comfortable and rather pretty, light colour schemes contrasting well

with dark-stained furniture. Children are very welcome and although
there are not a lot of facilities for them, the friendly attitude of owners
and staff goes a long way to making a family stay a happy one. One
of the pretty bedrooms has three extra beds and a cot and all rooms
have neatly-fitted bathrooms (some with shower only). High tea
is available or small portions in the dining room. Baby-sitting can
be arranged. *Rooms 11.* Garden, game fishing, shooting. Closed 2 wks
Xmas. Access, Visa.

Alston   Brownside Coach House
| Tel 04343 811263 | Restaurant |
Alston Cumbria CA9 3BP — Map 5 D3

Those impressed by large plastic play areas will be disappointed whilst
those impressed by excellent home baking most certainly will not.
In fine weather you will readily locate this small restaurant by the
shouts of happy children playing outside, while parents watch from
the sunny tables. The coach house itself is small and has no special
facilities for children (no high-chairs or boosters) but staff are most
obliging, heating baby food or bottles and serving half-portions of any
menu items. The outside toilets are clean and well kept but too small
for any baby-business. No-smoking area. *Open 10-6. Closed Tues & all
Oct-Easter.*

Altrincham   Francs
| Tel 061-941 3954 | Restaurant |
2 Goose Green Altrincham Greater Manchester — Map 6 B2

A French-styled bistro in the heart of Altrincham offering a wide
selection of grills, crepes, fish, vegetable and casserole dishes
from a daily-changing menu. A special four-course family-style lunch
is on offer on Sundays for only £7.50 per person with children under
10 free. There is also a selection of vegetarian dishes ranging from pates
au pistou (vegetables, tomatoes and pasta with basil, garlic, white wine
and cream £4.25) to champignons fromagère (garlic sautéed
mushrooms topped with mild French cheeses and baked £3.25).
Pleasant outdoor eating terrace. *Seats 80. Open 12-3 & 6-11 (Sun
12-7.30). Closed 25 Dec, 1 Jan, Bank Holidays. Access, Amex, Visa.*

Altrincham   The French Brasserie
| Tel 061-928 0808 | Brasserie |
24 The Downs Altrincham Cheshire — Map 6 B2

A large bar-brasserie with Provençal-style French cooking; on the
opposite side of the road to the more expensive sister restaurant *The
French*. Typical dishes include mussels or garlic mushrooms and Brie
(both £2.95) and main courses like chicken with mustard or lamb
with haricot beans (both £5.95). For dessert choose from creme
brulée, tarte aux pommes, profiteroles or pear Belle Hélène (£2.50).
Between 5-7pm there is a shortened à la carte menu offering
tremendous value with 3 courses for £5.50. Children under 10 eat
free Sunday lunchtime and for adults three courses cost £6.95. Live
jazz Wed-Sun eves. *Seats 200. Open 12-12, (Thur-Sat till 2am).
Closed D 25 Dec. Access, Visa.*

Alveley   Mill Hotel   66%   £73

| Tel 0746 780437   Fax 0746 780850 | Hotel |

Birdsgreen Alveley nr Bridgnorth Shropshire WV15 6HL   Map 6 B4

Just off the A442, midway between Kidderminster and Bridgnorth.
Ten acres of landscaped gardens surround The Mill, a 17th-century
building sympathetically restored and extended to include a variety
of conference facilities. The mill workings can still be seen in the rustic
Mill Bar, and the lounge bar is large and well furnished. Bedrooms are
in a modern extension. No dogs. *Rooms 21. Garden, games room.
Access, Amex, Diners, Visa.*

Ambleside   Zeffirellis

| Tel 05394 33845 | Pizzeria/Café |

Compston Road Ambleside Cumbria   Map 4 C3

Zeffirellis is an unusual complex comprising a shopping arcade,
a cinema, a pizzeria done out in Japanese Art Deco style and a leafy
café. The pizzeria is open in the evenings only and is situated above the
café. The pizzas have wheatmeal bases rolled in sesame seeds and
vegetarian toppings; they come in two sizes (plus one for children):
Mexican chili pizza (£4.75/£5.20), cipolla (onion) (£4.45/£4.75).
You can also get pasta (from £5.65) and desserts. In the café, sweet
snacks (fudge brownies, banana cake, Linzertorte – £1.45) as well
as savoury (soup £1.65, jacket potatoes, salads, quiches, and a dish
of the day at lunchtime – broccoli and Stilton pancakes with sweet and
sour relish, or hazelnut roast £3.85) are available. Scones and jam are
provided at tea time. Children's portions. No smoking. *Seats 80
(pizzeria), 50 (café). Open Pizzeria: L (Sat & Sun only) 12-2 & 5-9.45.
Café: 10-5. Closed Pizzeria: L Mon-Fri, all Tue & Wed Nov-Mar.
Pizzeria and café: 25 & 26 Dec. Access, Visa (pizzeria only).*

Ashbourne   Ashbourne Oaks Lodge   66%   £78

| Tel 0335 46666   Fax 0335 46549 | Hotel |

Derby Road Ashbourne Derbyshire DE6 1XH   Map 6 C3

By the A52 Derby road, a mile south of the town centre, this new
redbrick hotel is lent some old-world style by rustic-designed public
areas. Bedrooms are neat and light but not over-large, although twelve
are suitable for families; five suites have interconnecting rooms. Cots
are provided and baby-sitting can be arranged. Children under five
accommodated free in parents' room. There's a playroom in which
children can work up an appetite for the children's menu in the all-day
brasserie; four high-chairs are provided. No dogs. Convenient for
Alton Towers and the American Adventure Theme Park. Country
Life Inns. *Rooms 51. Garden. Access, Amex, Visa.*

Ashford-in-the-Water   The Cottage Tea Room

| Tel 0629 812488 | Tea Room |

3 Fennel Street Ashford-in-the-Water nr Bakewell Derbyshire   Map 6 C2

Everything is home-made in Betty and Bill Watkins' tea shop – brown
bread, currant bread, sultana and cheesy herb scones, preserves and
cakes. Five different set teas are served on Mondays, Wednesdays,
Thursdays and weekends only: Afternoon Tea (£3.25), Derbyshire
Cream Tea (£3), Tea with Hovis (£2.50), Savoury Scone Tea
(£2.35) and Something Light (£1.75). There's also a choice of leaf
teas, herbal infusions and coffees. Coffee and light refreshments are

served weekend mornings. Children's drinks and portions available. Special cakes, preserves and low fat items are always provided for customers with diabetic or cardiac problems. Children's drinks and half portions available, or they can willingly share their parents' meal; bottles are heated on request. Nursing mums should ask Betty to use her private room if they require privacy for feeding or nappy changing. No smoking. **Seats** 20. **Open** 2.30-5, also Sat & Sun only 10.30am-noon. **Closed** Tue, Fri, 25 Dec, 1 Jan.

Ashstead   Superfish

Tel 0372 273 784	Fish'n'Chips
2-4 Woodfield Lane Ashstead Surrey	**Map 15 E3**

Part of a Surrey-based chain of above-average fish and chip restaurants. See Morden entry for more details. **Seats** 56. **Open** 11.30-2 (Sat to 2.30), 5-10.30 (Thu-Sat to 11). **Closed** Sun, 25 & 26 Dec, 1 Jan. Access, Visa.

Avebury   Stones

Tel 0672 3514	Restaurant
Avebury nr Marlborough Wiltshire	**Map 14 C2**

Still at the forefront of vegetarian cooking with an unstinting mission to improve the quality of the lives of those who visit, work for, and supply produce to this exemplary operation. Small local organic producers are nurtured, herbs and salads come from their own garden and staff are valued as much as customers. Hilary Howard and Michael Pitts have created their own monument to which the faithful flock at this World Heritage site, often serving over 1000 customers a day from spotless self-service counters in a gentle, civilised atmosphere. All day offerings include various home-made light savouries, quiches, salads (all £1.85), hand-made English and Welsh cheeses with own-baked breads and crackers and local unsalted butter (£1.85), scones with Stone's jam and Guernsey cream (£1.15), ginger people (40p), world-famous date slice (95p) and fruit salad (£2). Noontime choice widens to include delectable inventive soups with specially baked bread (£2.50), Megaliths, or hot daily specials (£4.75), the Mason's Lunch, a definitive ploughman's (£3.35) and various hot and cold desserts (£2). The inimitable afternoon tea (£2.95) is served from 2.30. Non-smoking area. No bookings (except for parties of 6 or more). Phone ahead in winter to check opening times. **Seats** 85. **Open** 10-6 (Sat & Sun only Nov-Mar). **Closed** mid Dec-mid Jan. No credit cards.

Bakewell   Chatsworth House, Carriage House Restaurant

Tel 0246 582204	Restaurant
Nr Bakewell Derbyshire	**Map 6 C2**

Behind the great House stands the old carriage house with courtyard and fountain. The high-ceilinged room has impressive hanging lights and is decorated with large pictures of the estate; the original arches have been filled in with plate glass. The 50ft long pine self-service counter displays the food in refrigerated shelves and uniformed staff are friendly and efficient. Amongst the choice are soup of the day (£1.05), assorted salads (from £2.90), cottage pie (£3.95), scones and cakes (75p-£1.25), gateaux and treacle tart (£1.40) and assorted ice creams (£1.95). There's a roast every Sunday (£3.45) and children's

portions are available. Four highchairs are supplied, baby food
is available and mums can change a nappy or breast-feed in a separate
room in the Ladies. Visitors to the estate are not obliged to visit the
main house in order to eat at the Restaurant, however a £1 car park
fee is charged. No smoking area. *Seats 250.* **Open** *10.15-5.30.*
Closed *Nov-mid March. Access, Visa.*

Bamford   La Dolce Vita

Tel 0706 350278	Restaurant
Norden Road Bamford Rochdale Lancashire OL11 5PN	**Map 6 B1**

Children's hour is from 6-7pm, when for £2.95 tinies in high-chairs
can tuck into fish or fresh chicken with chips, spaghetti bolognese,
burgers or mini-pizzas, with drinks and ice cream. Lunchtimes and
weekends are also popular with families but avoid late evenings: the
place is tiny and soon becomes crowded. Staff bring children's meals
swiftly while parents ponder over whether to have pasta or another
Italian speciality like scaloppine or calf's liver with sage. The toilets are
too small for anything other than their prime purpose but the office
may be used for changing or nursing. No-smoking area. *Seats 75.*
Open *12-2 & 6-11 (Sat 5.30-11, Sun 5.30-10).* **Closed** *25 Dec.
Access, Visa.*

Barking   Colonel Jasper's

Tel 081 507 8481	Wine Bar
156 Longbridge Road Barking Essex	**Map 11 B4**

Hard by Barking Station, below the 'Spotted Dog', this is one
of Davy's old ale, port and wine houses, with mahogany furniture,
a sawdust-covered floor and candle-light. Specialities are cod, chips and
mushy peas, Cumberland sausages with mash and baked beans (£4.95)
and charcoal grills. Children's menu. *Seats 100.* **Open** *12-3.30 &
5.30-11.* **Closed** *L Sat, D Mon-Wed, all Sun & Bank Holidays. Access,
Amex, Diners, Visa.*

Barnard Castle   Market Place Teashop

Tel 0833 690110	Tea Room
29 Market Place Barnard Castle Co Durham	**Map 5 D3**

Full of atmosphere and character, this stone-flagged tea room with
antique furniture offers much to taught with good quality home-
baking, and a very reasonably priced wine list. Carrot and courgette
bake (£2.50), steak pie (£2.75), quiche and salad (£2.70), sticky toffee
pudding and raspberry and apple pie (both £1.75) provide a flavour
of what to expect. Children's portions. *Seats 45.* **Open** *10-5.30 (Sun
from 3).* **Closed** *Sun Dec-Feb, 10 days Christmas. No credit cards.*

Barnard Castle   Priors Restaurant

Tel 0833 38141	Restaurant
7 The Bank Barnard Castle Co Durham DL12 8PH	**Map 5 D3**

With tastes to tempt even the most hardened carnivore, Mark Prior's
vegetarian counter-service restaurant and take-away continues to draw
converts and the faithful alike. A blackboard menu might include two
or three soups (spinach and courgette or cauliflower £1), red bean and
vegetable shepherd's pie (£2.65), leek and mushroom au gratin
(£2.65) or chick pea and apricot casserole (£2.65), with fruit crumble
(£1.25) or bread pudding (70p) to finish. There's always a variety
of interesting salads (95p) and sandwiches as well as cakes and tarts –

perhaps pecan pie or curd tart (both £1.45). A few tables outside
in fine weather. Good organic wines and beers. Young families very
welcome; high-chair, cushions, potty and changing mat are provided.
No smoking throughout. *Seats 45.* *Open* *10-5 (Sat to 5.30, Sun
12-5.30).* *Closed 25 & 26 Dec, 1 Jan. Access, Amex, Visa.*

Barnet   Pizza Express

Tel 081-449 3706	Pizzeria
242-248 High Street Barnet Hertfordshire	Map 15 E2

Formerly a car showroom, this Pizza Express benefits from 40 feet
of windowed frontage which is opened up in summer. Pizzas are
priced from £3.15 to £5.30; high-chairs. No-smoking area. *Seats 96.*
Open *11.30am-midnight.* *Closed 25 & 26 Dec. Access, Amex, Visa.*

Basingstoke   Pizza Express

Tel 0256 54439	Pizzeria
The White House Winchester Road Basingstoke Hampshire	Map 15 D3

A large restaurant next door to Basingstoke Football Ground, with
a terracotta floor, pine tables and chairs and Laura Ashley curtains.
A large conservatory at the front has two big settees and an armchair
for pre-dinner drinkers. Crisp, thin based pizzas and fresh topping
ingredients (around £5). No-smoking area. *Seats 200.*
Open *noon-midnight.* *Closed 25 & 26 Dec. Access, Amex, Visa.*

Baslow   Cavendish Hotel, Garden Room

Tel 0246 582311	Restaurant
Baslow Derbyshire	Map 6 C2

Set on the Duke and Duchess of Devonshire's Chatsworth Estate, the
building housing the Cavendish Hotel was rebuilt in the early 1970s.
Its original character was retained however and the Duchess herself
selected the decor and furnishings, some of which came from
Chatsworth House itself. Panoramic views from the Garden Room's
conservatory windows provide the backdrop and the comfortable
bistro chairs, yellow tablecloths, fresh flowers and gentle classical
music set the stage. From mid-morning, chef Nick Buckingham serves
'The Late Breakfast', followed by lunch, afternoon tea and finally
supper. Food is served in a less formal and more relaxed atmosphere
than in the main restaurant: tomato and basil bread with button
onions, mushrooms and tomato (£4.40), Castlegate black pudding and
liver served on bubble and squeak (£6.05), parfait of raspberry and
vanilla (£2.75). Tea offers finger sandwiches (£1.60 per round),
home-made scones or toasted teacakes (£1.50) and two choices of cake.
Children's portions available (½ adult price). Although not particularly
appropriate for very young children, there is one highchair. Guests can
eat on the lawn in summer where children can be kept busy with
mini-golf and swings. *Seats 32.* *Open* *11-11. Access, Amex, Diners,
Visa.*

Baslow   Derbyshire Craft Centre Eating House

Tel 0433 631583	Restaurant
Calver Bridge Baslow Derbyshire S30 IXA	Map 6 C2

Craft centre alongside the A623 north-west of Baslow. Paintings of the
Dales and Derbyshire's stately homes hang on the walls. Cakes, tarts
and pies are available throughout the day (lemon meringue pie £1,
Bakewell 95p), while savoury choices include chicken liver paté

(£2.95), nut loaf, pasta bake and quiche (all £4 with a good selection of salads). There's a playroom well stocked with toys. **Seats** *35.* **Open** *10-5.50.* **Closed** *weekdays early Jan, 25, 26 Dec & 1 Jan.*

Bath **Bath Hotel** 66% **£100**

Tel 0225 338855 Fax 0225 28941	Hotel
Widcombe Basin Bath Avon BA2 4JP	**Map 13 F1**

Mainly business hotel by the Widcombe Basin: ramped entrances, spacious reception and airy day rooms. Limited, but practical accommodation for families. **Rooms** *93. Access, Amex, Diners, Visa.*

Bath **Bath Puppet Theatre**

Tel 0225 480532	Coffee Shop
Riverside Walk Pulteney Bridge Bath Avon	**Map 13 F1**

Puppeteer owner Andrew Hume also turns his hand to a variety of wholesome vegetarian snacks in his coffee shop-cum-puppet theatre – large ploughman's (£3.45), baked potato with filling (£1.85), quiches (£1.95), pizzas (£1.95), toasted sandwiches (£1.80), all served with fruit and salad. Home-made cakes feature scones (in summer), coffee and walnut cake, chocolate cake, date slice, shortbread (85p-£1.20). There are daily performances at different times (usually block booked) and since everything takes place in the same room, visitors are likely to catch a performance while eating. Children's portions are available and on a fine day, there's outdoor eating on the terrace overlooking the river. Good value. Fun atmosphere. No smoking. **Seats** *40.* **Open** *11-5.30 (Summer to 8).* **Closed** *25 & 26 Dec. No credit cards.*

Bath **Café René**

Tel 0225 447147	Restaurant
Unit 2 Shires Yard Wilson Street Bath Avon	**Map 13 F1**

Situated in the trendy Shires Yard (former livery stables) alongside small designer shops, Café René is run by an Englishman but everything else about it aspires to be French. The café has its own bakery and patisserie which supplies its croissants, brioches, pains au chocolat and traditional French cakes (religieuse, millefeuille (both £1.50) and tartelettes. Continental breakfast (£2.95) is available from 8am and the self-service lunch offers light meals (filled potatoes from £3.20) as well as four hot specials daily: vegetable lasagne (£3.50), broccoli bake (£3.50), fisherman's pie (£3.85), chicken breast provençale (£3.85) or beef bourguignon (£3.85). There's a very large courtyard for alfresco eating which is popular in summer *and* winter. **Seats** *60 (inside), 100 (outside).* **Open** *8-5.30.* **Closed** *Sun (winter only), 25 & 26 Dec. No credit cards.*

Bath **Combe Grove Manor** 71% **£126**

Tel 0225 834644 Fax 0225 834961	Hotel
Brassknocker Hill Monkton Combe nr Bath Avon BA2 7HS	**Map 13 F1**

An elegant country mansion standing in 68 acres of landscaped woods and gardens, Combe Grove enjoys spectacular views across the Limpley Stoke valley, yet is just two miles from the city centre. Fine antiques and elegant fabrics are eye-catching features of sympathetically restored day rooms with bold floral patterns and hand-painted bathroom tiles lending some splendour to the manor house bedrooms. Housing the remaining rooms in no less spacious comfort, the newer Garden Lodge is adjacent to impressive leisure facilities where a crèche operates at weekends and public holidays. An all-day coffee shop derives character from its location in the manor vaults. No dogs. *Rooms 41. Garden, golf driving range, mini-golf, tennis, indoor & outdoor swimming pools, gymnasium, squash, spabath, sauna, solarium, beautician. Access, Amex, Diners, Visa.*

Bath	Fountain House	£120
Tel 0225 338622 Fax 0225 445855		Hotel
9 Fountain Buildings Lansdown Road Bath Avon BA1 5DV		Map 13 F1

A Palladian mansion run since 1986 as an all-suite hotel catering for families, tourists and business people. Each suite has a sitting room and a fully-equipped kitchen, with individual front doors and entry phones to ensure privacy. Room rates include continental breakfast (only), which arrives each morning with the paper. Facilities offered include secretarial services and lock-up garages. *Rooms 14. Access, Amex, Diners, Visa.*

Bath	Green Park Brasserie	
Tel 0225 338565		Brasserie
Green Park Road Bath Avon BA1 2JB		Map 13 F1

With free parking at the adjacent Sainsbury's the glass-arched former Green Park station contains a colonnade of craft shops and Andrew Peters' family-friendly brasserie under a single roof. Menus are all-encompassing from cappuccino to a three-course lunch (£7.95), with sandwiches, salads, snacks and fresh pasta available all day. Popular for a snack or starter is the fresh asparagus tartlet with onion sauce (£3.75): follow, perhaps, with fresh halibut in Stilton cream sauce (£6.50) served with French fries or bubble and squeak. English and Continental breakfast (with newspapers) and traditional roast lunch fill Sunday to the accompaniment of live jazz in a careful Victorian recreation of the old Midland Railways ticket office. *Seats 70. Open 10am-10.30pm (Sun/Mon/Tue to 3.30pm). Access, Amex, Visa.*

Bath	Number Five Bistro	
Tel 0225 444499		Bistro
5 Argyle Street Bath Avon BA2 4BA		Map 13 F1

A popular, relaxed bistro near Pulteney Bridge. The lunchtime menu changes daily, offering the likes of club sandwiches (£4.25), chicken curry and moules marinière. Wednesday evenings bring fish specials, and there's always something for vegetarians. The place is licensed, but on Monday and Tuesday evenings you can alternatively bring your own wine (no corkage). A selection of British cheeses changes each week. *Seats 40. Open 12-2.30 & 6.30-10.30 (Sat to 11). Closed L Mon, all Sun. Access, Visa.*

Bath	Pizza Express	
Tel 0225 420119		Pizzeria
1 Barton Street Bath Avon		Map 13 F1

On two floors, recently redecorated in the usual Pizza Express style of chrome, black and white. Crisp-based pizzas, fresh topping ingredients. *Seats 85. Open 11.30am-midnight. Closed 25 Dec. Access, Amex, Visa.*

Bath — Pump Room, Milburns

Tel 0225 444488	Restaurant
Stall Street Bath Avon	**Map 13 F1**

The famous Pump Room was built in the late 18th century and was
the haunt of fashionable folk when they came to take the waters. Now
the tourists are attracted in the same way since the tables overlook the
Roman baths and giant Corinthian columns stand guard all around
while a great chandelier hangs overhead. The hustle never stops and
chamber musicians play from a raised platform. The food ranges from
Continental breakfast (£3.75) to brunch (£6.75), Georgian Elevenses
(£3 – hot chocolate, Bath bun, cinnamon biscuits and Spa water),
lunch, snacks and four variations on the afternoon tea theme (clotted
cream tea £4, high tea £6.25). The lunchtime menu includes soups
(£2.70), pastas (£6.90), salads (warm trout salad £5.90), open-faced
sandwiches (salami and watercress with straw potatoes £3.75)
or breast of chicken with cream and fennel sauce (£7.90). Visitors are
asked to take either a starter with a side dish or main course
at lunchtimes. Mothers will find a pull-down baby-changing shelf
in the ladies loo. No-smoking area. *Seats 96. Open 10-4.30 (winter
to 4). Closed 25 & 26 Dec. Access, Visa.*

Bath — Sally Lunn's House

Tel 0225 461634	Restaurant
4 North Parade Passage Bath Avon	**Map 13 F1**

Sally Lunn's brioche-type Bath bun is an acquired taste; famous since
the 1680s, it's served today in her own 15th-century refreshment
house in any number of ways. Twenty of them listed on the menu
include savoury toasts with scrambled eggs (£3.28) or patum
peperium (£2.18), cold with salads of goat's cheese (£5.28), tuna and
egg (£4.98) or prawns (£5.48), and sweet ones with brandy
or cinnamon butter (£1.98) or strawberry jam and clotted cream
(£2.88). Alongside are winter soups (£2.08), apple pie, carrot
or banana cake (£1.85), multifarious beverages and speciality teas. The
basement kitchen museum is alone worth the trip. English candle-light
dinners from 6pm Tuesday to Sunday. No smoking. *Seats 55.
Open 10-6 (Sun from 12). Closed 25 & 26 Dec. No credit cards.*

Beckenham — Pizza Express

Tel 081-650 0593	Pizzeria
189 High Street Beckenham Kent	**Map 11 B5**

Formerly two shops and now one of the many pizza restaurants in the
popular chain. Archways were built in the shops' connecting wall
to give two dining rooms with picture windows, white-tiled floor,
marble-topped tables, plants, pictures and music regularly plays over
the loudspeakers. Crisp, thin pizzas (£3.15-£5.40) with fresh
ingredients are used for the toppings. No-smoking area. *Seats 86.
Open 11.30am-midnight. Closed 25 & 26 Dec. Access, Amex, Visa.*

Beeley — Devonshire Arms

Tel 0629 733259	Pub
Beeley nr Matlock Derbyshire DE4 2NR	**Map 6 C2**

The Devonshire Arms is a 17th-century country inn at the southern
end of the Chatsworth Estate. Two rooms are set aside for families and
the children's menu is varied. Bar food menu includes good

sandwiches, grills, pies and some vegetarian dishes. There is no high-
chair but most tables will accommodate a pushchair. Behind the pub
is a small enclosed garden reached by means of a narrow passage.
Nursing mums will find a chair in the Ladies. Adult menu selection:
smoked mackerel fillet with gooseberry chutney (£2.95), Stilton
stuffed pears with poppy seed dressing (£2.95), steak and ale pie
(£4.80), smoked Cumberland sausage (£5.50) and home-made
bakewell tart (£1.75). Children's menu: buttered cod fillet (£2.20),
cottage pie (£3), poached chicken breast (£3). No-smoking room.
Seats 120. **Bar Food** 12-2.30 & 7-9. **Closed** 25 Dec. Access, Amex, Visa.

Belton   Belton Woods Hotel & Country Club   72%   £115

Tel 0476 593200 Fax 0476 74547	Hotel
Belton nr Grantham Lincolnshire NG32 2LN	Map 7 E3

Just off the A607, two miles north of Grantham, a modern leisure
complex standing in 475 acres of grounds, with outstanding sports
facilities that are matched by equally impressive accommodation.
A spacious, high-ceilinged lounge leading off the main foyer is filled
with parlour plants and hanging baskets, and overlooks one of three
golf courses (two 18-hole and one 9-hole). The cocktail bar on the first
floor is more club-like, with easy chairs and rich decor. Spacious
bedrooms have good seating and working areas; plain painted walls
lighten up the use of contemporary fabrics. Ambassador rooms feature
extras like a mini-bar and settee. Excellent facilities for children
include a children's playground and swimming pool, cots and baby-
sitting. The Plus Fours all-day restaurant should be able to cater for
those out-of-hours hunger pangs from the children: cheeseburger and
fries, bangers and beans plus half-price portions of a few adult dishes
like tuna fish ravioli and sizzling hot chicken with cashew nuts.
Rooms 96. *Garden, indoor swimming pool, spa bath, sauna, steam room,
solarium, beauty salon, hairdressing, gymnasium, games room, snooker, golf
courses (9 & 18 hole), golf driving range, fishing, tennis, coffee shop
(7am-10.30pm). Access, Amex, Diners, Visa.*

Berkhamsted   Cooks Delight

Tel 0442 863 584	Restaurant
360 High Street Berkhamsted Hertfordshire	Map 15 E2

A paradise for vegetarians and vegans, both the ground-floor shop and
the restaurant above. Owners Rex and Khai-Eng Tyler, here for
12 years, are a mine of information on matters vegetarian, and lecture
dinners are held regularly. Organic produce is used throughout a menu
typified by apricot and sesame flan (£2.75), vegetable platter (£7.50)
or Malaysian curry with stir-fried vegetables and brown rice.
No smoking. Must book for Saturday night. *Seats* 40. **Open** 12-4 &
7-9.30 (Sat 9-4 & 8-12, Sun 1-4). **Closed** D Sun, all Mon, Tue, Wed,
25 Dec. Access, Visa.

Bexhill-on-Sea   Trawlers

Tel 0424 210227	Fish'n'Chips
60 Sackville Road Bexhill-on-Sea East Sussex TN39 3JE	Map 11 C6

Bexhill has a fairly aged population and as a result children are
a novelty and excite a good deal of fond attention. Trawlers does have
its fair share of small fry and caters for them well, offering a children's
menu, bottle-heating and a hearty welcome. All is scrupulously clean
and although there are no changing facilities or high-chairs there

is ample room for prams. *Open* 11.30-1.45 & 5-7 (7.30 Tues-Fri,
8.30 Sat). *Closed* Sun, Dec 25 & Jan 1. Access, Visa.

Bibury   Swan Hotel, Jankowski's Brasserie

Tel 0285 740695	Brasserie
Bibury Gloucestershire	Map 14 C2

A surprising find in a pretty Cotswold village, this is a genuine all-day
brasserie (rather smart too) with no minimum charge and a wide-
ranging menu that offers everything from poached quail's eggs with
spinach and mushrooms (£7.35), steamed mussels in white wine
(£3.25) and chargrilled wild boar sausage (£10.95) to Welsh rarebit
(£2.75), Spotted Dick and custard (£3.15) and toasted tea cakes. The
menu has both children's and vegetarian sections and there's espresso
coffee and a good range of loose-leaf teas. The courtyard, with
ornamental fountain, makes a good spot for al fresco eating. Friendly,
obliging staff add the final touch. *Seats* 60. *Open* 10-10. *Closed* 1 week
Christmas. Access, Visa.

Biddenden   Claris's Tea Shop

Tel 0580 291025	Tea Room
1-3 High Street Biddenden Kent TN27 8AL	Map 11 C5

The Grade 1 listed building (once called Claris House) dating back
to 1450 that houses Claris's Tea Shop was formerly part of a long row
of weavers' cottages. Owners Brian and Janet Wingham also run the
adjacent gift shop. The simple menu offers good home cooking: ham
(£1.65) and turkey (£1.75) sandwiches, tomato soup (£1.60),
creamed mushrooms on toast (£2), poached eggs on toast. They are
well known for their meringues (£1.90) and other cakes include
coffee walnut cake, fruit cake, lemon Madeira (all 90p) or Cointreau
cake (£1.90). Cream tea £2.50. Small patio for outdoor eating
overlooking a narrow south-facing garden. One high-chair; children's
portions. Unlicensed. No smoking. *Seats* 24. *Open* 10.30-5.30. *Closed*
Mon, 10 days Christmas. No credit cards.

Bingley   Bankfield Hotel   61%   £105

Tel 0274 567123 Fax 0274 551331	Hotel
Bradford Road Bingley West Yorkshire BD16 1TV	Map 6 C1

A castellated Gothic frontage that "wouldn't look out of place
on a Hollywood film set". Inside, handsome Victorian day rooms and
mainly modern, decent-sized bedrooms. Children under 15 stay free
in parents' bedroom. There are three family suites and six cots.
A supervised crèche is available on Saturday mornings as well as baby-
sitting and baby-listening services. High-chairs are provided in the
restaurant where there's a children's menu and small portions on offer.
Jarvis Hotels. *Rooms* 103. Garden, dinner dance (weekly). Access, Amex,
Diners, Visa.

Birmingham   California Pizza Factory

Tel 021-428 2636	Pizzeria
42 High Street Harborne Birmingham West Midlands B17 9NE	Map 6 C4

Wood-block floor, brick columns and wall panels and tubular
overhead air-conditioning lend a factory-like feel (and attendant
echoes) to a cavernous pizza house and take-away close to Harborne's
shops. Wood-fired pizzas from an imported Italian kiln are at the heart
of Gary and Tracey Perkins' new catering concept and the formula

seems to be working well. In just two minutes out come hot, crispy pizza bases with a hint of charcoal flavour and some notably imaginative toppings – from Greek goat's cheese (£4.75) to Hawaiian pineapple (£5.75), Thai chicken (£6.50) and Peking duck (£6.25). Top sellers are the four cheeses (£4.90) and Canadian bacon, lettuce and tomato (£4.95). To follow are imported American cheesecakes (£3.50), commendable home-made tiramisu (£2.75) and Häagen Dazs fudge sundae (£2.95). Californian house wine weighs in at under £7 a bottle (large glass £1.95). No-smoking areas. **Seats 110.** **Open** *noon-11pm (Sat/Sun from 11 am).* **Closed** *25 & 26 Dec. Access, Amex, Visa.*

Birmingham	**Chung Ying**	**£37**
Tel 021-622 5669		Restaurant
16 Wrottesley Street Birmingham West Midlands B5 6RT		**Map 6 C4**

The Chinese flock to this well-established, traditionally appointed restaurant for its long Cantonese menu. The choice extends to well over 300 dishes, from crispy fried chicken wings through assorted beef and pork to sizzling dishes and casseroles (braised brisket with spices, duck's web with mixed vegetables, eel with roast belly pork, lamb with dried bean curd). Seafood covers a very wide range, too, and there are more than 40 items on the dim sum list. Family dining is common and encouraged: to this end, Chung Ying provides at least 10 high-chairs. The tables are tightly packed so be prepared to struggle to your table if you have a pushchair with you. **Seats 220.** *Private Room. Meals 12-12. Closed 25 Dec. Access, Amex, Diners, Visa.*

Birmingham	**Chung Ying Garden**	**£37**
Tel 021-666 6622		Restaurant
17 Thorp Street Birmingham West Midlands B5 4AT		**Map 6 C4**

Sister and near neighbour of the original *Chung Ying*, this has more modern decor, with pillars, plants and murals. The menu is no less extensive and the chef's specialities include deep-fried chicken stuffed with banana, paper-wrapped fillet of beef, fried fish cake with mangetout and steamed pork pie with salted egg. Dim sum features on the menu, with a greater choice at lunchtime. Families are again much in evidence, especially on a Sunday when the restaurant really buzzes. Tables are well spaced so pushchairs are easily manoeuvred and plenty of high-chairs are provided. Decent-sized loo for changing your baby. **Seats 300.** *Parties 240. Private Room. Meals 12-12 (Sun to 11). Closed 25 Dec. Access, Amex, Diners, Visa.*

Birmingham	**La Galleria**	
Tel 021 236 1006		Restaurant
Paradise Place Birmingham West Midlands B3 IJH		**Map 6 C4**

150 yards from the Conference Centre, so do not be put off by the crush of businessmen and women at this Italian wine bar/restaurant under the same management for 25 years. The moment you step through the door with your buggy someone is likely to come forward to assist you. Smiling staff practically fall over each other to offer to keep a toddler amused while the parents study the blackboard menu and place their order. Fresh fish, pasta and pizzas plus daily specials make up the carte. Two high-chairs are provided and, although there is no children's menu, small portions will be served. The large toilets

are big enough for nappy changing. *Seats 160. Open 12-2.30 and
5.30-11 Closed Sun & Bank Hols. Access, Amex, Diners, Visa.*

Birmingham   Pizza Express

Tel 021-236 0221	Pizzeria

The Citadel Corporation Street Birmingham West Midlands   **Map 6 C4**

Popular with members of Birmingham's legal profession many
of whom occupy the Citadel. Crisp, thin pizzas with fresh ingredients
used for the toppings (£3.15-£5.30). Live jazz some evenings.
Seats 75. Open 11.30am-midnight. Closed 25 & 26 Dec. Access, Visa.

Birmingham   Rooftop at Rackhams

Tel 021-236 3333	Restaurant

Corporation Street Birmingham West Midlands   **Map 6 C4**

A popular shoppers' restaurant six floors up with plain wood tables,
paper flowers and no smoking. Amid a wealth of commercial patisserie
and bakery goods discerning Just-a-Biters will find good salmon
or rare beef salads, vegetarian quiches and fresh fruit salad, albeit
topped with aerosol cream. Cooked breakfast (from 99p) is a top
early-day seller, there's a popular daily roast (£6.50) and afternoon teas
from £1.99. Served by three ample lifts, the Rooftop is approached
by way of the children's wear and toy department, which might not
be necessarily good for harassed parents! *Seats 120. Open 9.30-5.45
(Thu to 7.45, Sat 9-5.30). Closed Sun, 25 & 26 Dec. Access, Amex,
Diners, Visa.*

Bishops Frome   Chase Inn

Tel 0885 490234	Pub

Bishops Frome Hereford & Worcester WR6 5BP   **Map 14 B1**

The warm reception for families makes the Chase Inn a welcome stop-
over for tired travellers. The menu is imaginative and well presented
and includes a sumptuous selection of locally made sweets. Children
can have small portions or choose from their own (less interesting)
menu. There is a separate dining room, one high-chair and a small
garden at the back. *Open 12-2.30 & 6-10. Closed Sun D, Dec 25 D.
No credit cards.*

Blackpool   Chequers Hotel   £63*

Tel 0253 56431 Fax 0253 500076	Hotel

24 Queens Promenade Blackpool Lancashire FY2 9RN   **Map 6 A1**

There's plenty of entertainment for children at this seafront hotel run
by Maureen and Jim Barton; in addition to quizzes, they have their
own dance spots on cabaret night. The lounge has four boxes of toys
and books. Unfussy modern decoration, and a very stated commitment
to service make for a comfortable stay for families. There is a single
family suite, and eight family rooms, sharing four cots. Toddlers like
the restaurant's children's menu, and many parents will appreciate its
no smoking policy. The restaurant has four high-chairs and feeding
cups. The hotel will hire additional equipment, and will help arrange
a baby-sitter. One child under 13 accommodated free of charge
if sharing with two adults; second child £10.50 per night. *Half-
board terms May-Aug, £2.50 supplement for rooms with a sea view;
reduced rates for stays of longer than three days. Rooms 47.
Closed 2-31 Jan. Access, Amex, Diners, Visa.*

Blackpool   The Cliffs Hotel   £88
| Tel 0253 52388 | Hotel |

Queens Promenade Blackpool Lancashire FY2 9SG   Map 6 A1

Auntie Lucinda has a special welcome for children staying at the hotel
and, parents will be glad to know, some very sensible rules for their
behaviour. In high season and some weekends in winter children can
be enrolled in the Cliffs Kids Club and enjoy supervised activities from
10 to 12 each morning (Mon-Fri), and from high tea at 5 until 8.30.
The hotel's Flippers Leisure Centre lists a 'tropical' swimming pool,
solarium and squash courts amongst its attractions. A lifeguard
is always on duty at the pool. The restaurant will accommodate
vegans, but the Buttery bar offers the children's menu. There are
15 high-chairs. As you would expect from a hotel that shows no sign
of stuffiness, breast-feeding is indulged in the restaurant and day rooms.
Although there are only six family suites, there are few rooms that
would not hold one of the 20 cots. Under-12s £10.50 d, b&b
including children's menu. **Rooms 163.** Access, Amex, Visa.

Blackpool   Harry Ramsden's
| Tel 0253 294386 | Fish'n'Chips |

60/63 The Promenade Blackpool Lancashire FY1 4QU   Map 6 A1

Few of our readers will not have heard of what may be the most
famous fish and chip restaurant in the world, but not so many will
know that they do a very reasonable children's meal. For those who
have not made the trip to Blackpool, Harry Ramsden's has a history
stretching back to 1928, and currently feeds one million people a year.
The queues are an inevitable result of its popularity, but the staff are
friendly and efficient, and the service is quick. Adult menu selection:
haddock fillet and chips £4.65 steamed ginger pudding £1.40.
Children's menu selection: small haddock fillet and chips, bread and
butter, ice cream, soft drink £2.95. Branches at: Guiseley (Leeds),
London Heathrow, Manchester, Newcastle and Glasgow. **Open** 11-11.
Closed 25 Dec. Access, Visa.

Blackpool   Pembroke Hotel   67%   £122
| Tel 0253 23434   Fax 0253 27864 | Hotel |

North Promenade Blackpool Lancashire FY1 5JQ   Map 6 A1

A modern conference hotel with massive conference and banqueting
facilities. In the main holiday season families are well catered for, with
baby-sitting, baby-listening and a large supervised crèche/playroom
(9am-9pm). Indoor equipment keep the children amused when they
are not taking part in competitions, swimming galas and discos.
Children's tea is served at 5.30pm (with a once-weekly barbecue
alternative) and there is an excellent menu with out-of-this-world
choices like solar soup, orbital omelette and transformer trifle.
Youngsters can also join their parents for small portions in the
restaurant, poolside snack bar or carvery. The best family rooms have
an alcove with fold-down bunk beds, plus scope for a cot. There's
a separate games room and bedrooms are equipped with video
machines. A large swimming pool and Springs night club are among
the leisure amenities. Metropole Hotels. **Rooms 274.** *Indoor swimming
pool, sauna, solarium.* Access, Amex, Diners, Visa.

Blackpool   **West Coast Rock Café**

Tel 0253 751283	Café
5/7 Abingdon Street Blackpool Lancashire FY1 2DG	Map 6 A1

As you might infer from its title, this is an American-style restaurant.
No need to elaborate on the menu; unless you are one of the three
people in Great Britain who has not yet tried a diner, you'll get what
you came for and plenty of it. There is a fish fingery menu for
toddlers and smaller, but half-price portions from the main menu will
tempt the pre-teens. Those of us unimpressed by Americana might
well ponder the gated play area filled with toys, and the childish
appeal of clutter, big-screen TV and an appropriate soundtrack behind
it all. The aerobics studio above can be used for nappy changing and
breast-feeding. Two high-chairs. Adult menu selection: garlic
mushrooms £2.75 Che Guevara's Revolutionary Chilli Burger £4.25.
Children's menu selection: sausages, spaghetti shapes, chips etc 75p per
item. *Open noon-2am Mon-Sat; noon-12 Sun. Access, Visa.*

Blakeney   **Blakeney Hotel**   64%   £108

Tel 0263 740797 Fax 0263 740795	Hotel
The Quay Blakeney nr Holt Norfolk NR25 7NE	Map 10 C1

A family-owned hotel, run in traditional style, on the quayside
overlooking the National Trust harbour. Public rooms include a first-
floor sun lounge which enjoys to the full the fine views across the salt
marshes towards Blakeney Point. Many front-facing bedrooms share
the view; there are several mini-suites, a four-poster room and
a ground-floor room suitable for wheelchairs. Some rooms
in an annexe have private patios. As well as the particularly warm
swimming pool, there is an attractive enclosed garden. The hotel offers
a friendly welcome to well-behaved children. High-chairs and
children's menu are available in the restaurant. *Rooms 60. Garden,
indoor swimming pool, keep-fit equipment, spa bath, sauna, snooker.
Access, Amex, Diners, Visa.*

Bolham   **Knightshayes Court**

Tel 0884 259416	Restaurant
Bolham nr Tiverton Devon	Map 13 D2

Amid re-pointed stone walls and polished brick floors, horse brasses
and plumes are ready reminders of these former stables' past use. From
morning coffee through daily hot lunches to Devon cream teas,
waitress service to red-stained wood tables and chairs assures an even
flow of fare. Homity pie is one choice on the Gardeners lunch (£4.95)
which comes with home-made cake and English cider. Beef hot pot,
vegetable goulash and a simple Sunday roast are typical summertime
lunches (£4.50). Full marks for their use of local suppliers of Devon
produce (listed on the menu) and for a strict no-smoking policy.
Admissions to the adjacent National Trust gardens and house are extra,
but there's no charge for access to the grounds and café. No smoking.
Seats 108. Open 10.30-5.30. Closed 1 Nov-end Mar. Access, Visa.

Bolton   **Tiggis**

Tel 0204 397320	Restaurant
63 Bradshawgate Bolton Lancashire BL1 1QD	Map 6 B2

Large airy Italian restaurant in the centre of Bolton with ceiling fans,
marble floor and table tops, hanging baskets filled with plants and

Italian music in the background. On being seated, a plate of crudités immediately appears with a mild tomato dip. The large menu is divided into Antipasti (di pesce £3.70), pasta (spaghetti alla matriciana £4.60 – bacon, tomato, onion and chili), pizzas (capricciosa £4.60), meat (pollo boscaiola £8.90) and fish, plus a 'vegetarian corner' (penne casalinga – macaroni with mushrooms, cream and a touch of tomato £4.60). In addition, daily special main courses are priced £8-10. The children's menu includes corn on the cob (70p), pizza margherita (£1.60), lasagne al forno (£1.60) and ice cream. If it's a birthday, a complimentary birthday cake is presented in a gold box while lights are dimmed. Three high-chairs, a booster seat, small plates and straws are all provided, and children leave Tiggis clutching a balloon, probably 'well happy'. **Seats** 100. **Open** 12-2, 6-11 (*Thu, Fri Sat to 11.30, Sun to 10.30*). **Closed** *L Sun, all Mon, Dec 25 & 26.* *Access, Diners, Visa.*

Also at:

Blackburn 71-73 King William Street Blackburn Lancashire Tel 0254 53135.

Preston 38-42 Guildhall Street Preston Lancashire Tel 0772 887766.

St Anne's Empress Buildings 21-23 Wood Street St Anne's Lancashire Tel 0253 711481.

Borrowdale	**Stakis Keswick Lodore Swiss Hotel** **71%**	£160*
Tel 076 87 77285 Fax 076 87 77343		Hotel
Borrowdale Keswick Cumbria CA12 5UX		Map 4 C3

Holiday hotel set in 40 acres by Derwentwater; good family facilities and convenient for Keswick ferry (3 miles) and town (3 miles). Picture windows afford splendid views from day rooms and the best, front-facing bedrooms. Several splendid family rooms, cots provided; resident nanny in summer; baby-sitting and listening arranged. Children charged £14.50 (0-1), £30.50 (1-6), £43 (6-16) for dinner, bed and breakfast; under-6s eat in the nursery. *Half-board terms only. No dogs. Stakis Hotels. **Rooms** 70. *Garden, tennis, indoor & outdoor swimming pools, gymnasium, squash, sauna, solarium, beauty salon, hairdressing, games room, nursery (8am-6pm), crèche, lock-up garage.* *Access, Amex, Diners, Visa.*

Bournemouth	**Beales Coffee Shop**	
Tel 0202 552022		Coffee Shop
36 Old Christchurch Road Bournemouth Dorset		Map 14 C4

The coffee shop in Beales Department Store can be found on the fourth floor. The choice is extensive and even the bread and pastries are baked on the premises. Choose from cottage pie, baked potato filled with cheese and ham or curry all £3.15. Sweet choices include caramel cream 90p, profiteroles £1.75 or cream tea £1.85. **Seats** 125. **Open** 9-4.45. **Closed** *Sun, Bank Holidays. Access, Amex, Visa.*

Bournemouth	**Chez Fred**	
Tel 0202 761023		Fish'n'Chips
10 Seamoor Road Westbourne Bournemouth Dorset		Map 14 C4

Fish and chips 'par excellence' chez Fred – a clever name and a classy product fostered by Fred Capel since 1989. A lunch special of cod, chips, peas and beverages (£3.60) is unbeatable in the area; daily shopping provides, alternatively, skate wings (£5.50) at competitive prices. Treacle sponge and custard (£1.95) and variously sauced New Forest ice creams (£1.65) turn 'mere' fish and chips into a family meal. Bright lights, lively music and friendly staff mark Fred's out from the milieu: look for Westbourne off the Wessex Way (A35) west of town towards Poole. **Seats** *48.* **Open** *11.30-1.45 & 5-9.45.* **Closed** *Sun, 25 & 26 Dec. No credit cards.*

Bournemouth	Henry's	£20
Tel 0202 297887		Restaurant
6 Lansdowne Road Bournemouth Dorset BH1 1SD		Map 14 C4

Coffee and cakes (perhaps ginger and honey sponge 90p) start the day at this relaxed vegetarian and vegan restaurant and basement wine bar, the latter selling organic wines, natural beers and lighter dishes. Lunch begins at 11.30 with starters such as houmus with pitta bread (£1.75) or pan-fried Cheddar wedges with grainy mustard sauce (£1.95), main courses (more choice and more elaborate in the evenings, booking advisable) such as cheesy vegetable hot pot (£2.75), hearty Somerset pie (£3.25) or just a salad (from £2) or open sandwich (£1.65), and some 10 or so desserts (£1.85). Children's portions. Non-smoking area. Within walking distance of the beach; no changing facilities. Two high-chairs. **Seats** *50.* **Open** *9-2 & 5.30-11.* **Closed** *Sun (except Summer). No credit cards.*

Bournemouth	Royal Bath Hotel	73%	£140
Tel 0202 555555 Fax 0202 554158			Hotel
Bath Road Bournemouth Dorset BH1 2EW			Map 14 C4

A heated kidney-shaped indoor swimming pool is the central feature of the splendid Leisure Pavilion, an up-to-date attraction of the Victorian Royal Bath (now over 150 years old). The hotel stands in a three-acre garden, with clifftop views out to sea. Space and elegance are keynotes, both in the bars and lounges and in the good-sized bedrooms, many of which face the sea. Rooms have very smart built-in furniture in mahogany or cream finish and modern bathrooms with brass fittings plus good toiletries; children up to 14 stay free in their parents' room. Supervised crèche daily in high season. No dogs. Dining is opulent and expensive in the grand style with a long à la carte full of French classical chestnuts executed with varying degrees of success. Parents win on facilities, but children are not left totally unconsidered. De Vere Hotels. **Rooms** *131. Garden, indoor swimming pool, sauna, solarium, spa bath, steam room, gymnasium, beauty salon, hairdressing, putting, croquet, snooker, coffee shop (10.30am-8.15pm), garage. Access, Amex, Diners, Visa.*

Bournemouth	Superfish	
Tel 0202 426158		Fish'n'Chips
186 Seabourne Road Southbourne Bournemouth Dorset		Map 14 C4

Part of a growing chain of above-average fish and chip restaurants. Set lunch (£3.35) includes shell-on prawns as an appetiser, small cod and chips, French bread, pickles and sauces from the trolley and a pot of tea. The weekly special offers an alternative for the evening – lemon sole £4.95. **Seats** *64.* **Open** *11.30-2 & 5-10.30 (to 11 Thurs-Sat), Sun Jul & Aug.* **Closed** *25 & 26 Dec. No credit cards.*

Bournemouth	**Swallow Highcliff Hotel**	**70%**	**£115**
Tel 0202 557702 Fax 0202 292734			Hotel
St Michael's Road West Cliff Bournemouth Dorset BH2 5DU			Map 14 C4

An imposing Victorian hotel with splendid cliff-top location giving
many of the rooms fine sea views. A funicular lift carries guests from
hotel to promenade. Good-sized bedrooms in the main house have
dark period-style furniture, those in the converted coastguard cottages
smart lightwood furniture. Eleven family rooms with cots, baby-
sitting and baby-listening available; supervised crèche in summer
(May-Oct from 10am-6pm – check before booking). Numerous public
rooms include a terrace bar, lounge for non-smokers and Magnums
night club. Cots, baby baths and potties are all supplied and there's
a fun pack for rainy days. Fenced-in children's play area includes
swings, slides and sandpit; the climbing frame is set on hard ground.
Children under 14 sharing parents' room free of charge. Easy walking
distance to the town-centre shops, Pleasure Gardens and pier. The lack
of indoor swimming pool, however, makes this more of a summer
rather than winter destination for families. **Rooms** *157. Garden, outdoor
swimming pool, sauna, solarium, all-weather tennis, putting, games room,
snooker, night club. Access, Amex, Diners, Visa.*

Bovey Tracey	**Devon Guild of Craftsmen, Granary Café**	
Tel 0626 832223		Café
Riverside Mill Bovey Tracey Newton Abbot Devon TQ13 9AF		Map 13 D3

Evidence of the Devon Guild of Craftsmen's output abounds
throughout the Granary, housed in a restored mill perched on the
river Bovey. Watercolours for sale alongside hand-thrown pottery and
colourful cookbooks add tone to the bright, airy service counter and
dining area. Healthy salads from houmus to mustardy potatoes
accompany a wide range of potted meals from steak pie to spinach and
ricotta lasagne (£3.45), reheated while you wait. Home baking ranges
from poppyseed cake to rich lemon slices (95p); speciality teas and
coffee are sold by the mugful; cider and apple juice are organic
(as is all the meat used), and wines include Bovey Tracey's own
Whitstone (£1.40 glass). Large summer courtyard. Children's
portions. No smoking. **Seats** *40.* **Open** *10-5 (lunch 12-2.30).*
Closed *25 & 26 Dec, 1 Jan. Access, Visa.*

Bradford-on-Avon	**Woolley Grange**	**75%**	**£89**
Tel 02216 4705 Fax 02216 4059			Hotel
Woolley Green Bradford-on-Avon Wiltshire BA15 1TX			Map 14 B3

A splendid Jacobean building set in lovely grounds, Woolley Grange
is a friendly, relaxed and civilised country house hotel catering well
for families, especially those including small children. Owners Nigel
and Heather Chapman take excellent care of their guests, a policy
which results in many repeat bookings. A variety of specially
commissioned paintings and floral displays is found throughout,
reinforcing the homely, traditional atmosphere. The panelled drawing
room has a log fire, period furniture and comfortable seating, and
there's also a small sitting room and a delightful conservatory with
a flagstone floor and rattan furniture. The bedrooms are individually
decorated in country style, with period beds, stripped pine, polished
floors, flowers and pictures; many of the rooms have gas coal fires and

all have nice little touches like home-made biscuits, fruit and mineral water. Bathrooms (some with shower/WC only) have Victorian fittings. Nigel and Heather have five children of their own and in creating the Woolley Bears Den, they have brought to life everyone's fantasies of the perfect nursery. Nanny is on duty from 10am-6pm and children's meals, based on healthy home-cooked fare are served in the 'Den'. Breakfast is a family affair and parents will appreciate the luxury of eating proper food in a dining room where there could well be a child at every table, not just at their own. ... *and Baby Comes Too* Family Hotel of the Year last year. **Rooms** *20. Garden, outdoor swimming pool, tennis, croquet, snooker, conference facilities. Access, Amex, Diners, Visa.*

Restaurant   £85

Twin dining rooms are light and inviting with humorous paintings adorning the soft-coloured walls. Chef Colin White's fixed-price menus offer a good choice, perhaps covering turbot ceviche, Cumbrian air-dried ham and melon, grilled scallops with leeks and ham, roast free-range chicken with lemon risotto and sherry vinegar sauce, and salmis of pigeon with red wine sauce and liver paté crouton. Many of the vegetables come from the hotel's own walled garden. Honest, welcoming and friendly, with food to match. Decent, all-round wine list. Simpler food is offered on a Terrace menu. **Seats** *52. Parties 30. Private Room. L 12-2.30 (Sat & Sun to 3) D 7-10. Set L (£16 Sun) £24.50 Set D £26.*

Brampton   Tarn End   £50

| Tel 069 77 2340 | Restaurant |

Talkin Tarn Brampton nr Carlisle Cumbria CA8 1LS   Map 4 C2

There are grand views of Talkin Tarn from the tiny lounge and dining room of this old red sandstone inn-cum-restaurant, two miles south-east of Brampton on the B6413. The firmly French à la carte menu changes quarterly but has weekly seasonal and vegetarian supplements. Light lunches are served in the bar. One high chair is provided, but junior diners are not expected in the dining room after 7.30pm. **Seats** *30. Parties 15. Private Room. D only 7.30-8.45 (light lunches 12-2). Closed Feb, D Sun in winter (except residents). Access, Amex, Visa, Diners.*

Rooms   £62

TVs and teamakers provide essential comforts in six otherwise fairly basic bedrooms; bathrooms are tiled and neatly kept. No dogs.

Branscombe   Bulstone Hotel

| Tel 0297 80446 | Hotel |

Higher Bulstone Branscombe nr Seaton Devon EX12 3BL   Map 13 E2

At The Bulstone you will find everything you might need on a family holiday. Twelve bedrooms (six en suite) have been designed with children in mind and are equipped with cots or extra beds, extra bedding in case of accidents, changing mats, tea-making facilities, baby-listening and nappy buckets, if required. Downstairs there is a playroom with toys and games plus an enclosed outdoor play area with swings, a climbing frame and a sand pit. The laundry room has coin-operated washing machine, tumble dryer and there is a microwave, sink, refrigerator and bottle sterilizer in the guest utility room. Children take tea together at 4.45pm – lasagne, roast pork, beans on toast (set price £3.50, under 2s free if parents are dining, similarly under 5s except during high season). Parents dine later, by candlelight. **Seats** 28. **Food** *No lunches. 7.45-8.30.* **Closed** *Mid Nov-mid Feb. No credit cards.*

Brent Knoll   Goat House
| Tel 0278 760995 | Café |

Bristol Road Brent Knoll Somerset TA9 4HJ   Map 13 E1

Don't be put off by the transport caff exterior, inside is bright and airy with fast, friendly service and a warm welcome for families. There's room enough to wheel the buggy up to the table if you don't manage to bag one of the two high-chairs. Your kids will be fascinated by their kids – around a dozen goats and their offspring live accross the courtyard and are used to the attentions of visitors. Goat's milk products are offered alongside sandwiches, cakes, pastries and pizzas. Get there before noon and there are good solid breakfasts to be had. No special changing facilities. Two no-smoking areas. Tables and seating outside in summer. **Open** *8-7* **Closed** *Dec 25 & 26, Jan 1 & 2. Access, Visa.*

Brentwood   Pizza Express
| Tel 0277 233569 | Pizzeria |

5 High Street Brentwood Essex   Map 11 B4

A small, friendly branch of the chain. This one offers candlelit dining and a range of Italian liqueurs and wines to go with the usual well-made and tasty range of pizzas (around £5). **Seats** *54.* **Open** *11.30am-midnight.* **Closed** *25 & 26 Dec. Access, Amex, Diners, Visa.*

Bretforton   Fleece Inn
| Tel 0386 831173 | Pub |

The Cross Bretforton nr Evesham Hereford & Worcester WR11 5JE   Map 14 C1

National Trust-owned timewarp of a pub with 19th-century and older atmosphere and a museum-like array of beautiful things, many of them extremely valuable and rare – note especially the priceless collection of Stuart pewter. Still, they say, run on the lines the pre-1977 owner, the redoubtable Miss Taplin, insisted upon: no crisps or nuts allowed, though they do offer a rather unadventurous chips-with-everything type menu. Weekends and holidays are particularly busy times when even the huge garden is full to overflowing; children will love the adventure playground and playhouse. *Free house.* **Beer** *Burton Bridge, Hook Norton Best, Jolly Roger Shipwrecked, Uley Pigs Ear.* **Cider** *Weston. Garden, outdoor eating, children's play area. Family room. No credit cards.*

Bridgnorth   Bambers
| Tel 0746 767364 | Restaurant |

65 St Mary's Street Bridgnorth Shropshire WV16 4DR   Map 6 B4

Sybil and Brian Tyler welcome families with children of all ages to their charming restaurant in the heart of the market town of Bridgnorth. The warm and intimate atmosphere makes this an excellent restaurant in which to relax. The French-influenced cooking relies heavily on alcohol and cream sauces but for a lighter touch there is an excellent selection of vegetarian dishes. Welcome

at lunch and dinner, children can have small portions, there is one
high-chair and toys to keep the little ones happy after filling their
tumblies. No space for nappy-changing but you can feed a baby
discreetly at your table as long as no other customers object.
Open *12-2 &* 7-10. **Closed** *all Mon &* Sun evening, Jan 1. Access, Amex,
Diners, Visa.

Bridgnorth   Down Inn

Tel 0746 35624	Pub

Ludlow Road Bridgnorth Shropshire WV16 6HA   Map 6 B4

This is an atmospheric pub where food is taken fairly seriously
by licensees Paul and Beverley Millington. Previously known for 250
years as the Unicorn, the pub is on the B4364, some two and a half
miles from Bridgnorth on the Ludlow road. The food retains
a traditional feel: the ploughman's (£2.75) is available with up to
thirty British cheeses. There are plenty of steaks, and a traditional
Sunday lunch is served throughout the bar and restaurant. Both menus
have a seasonal bias, so that pheasant, venison and guinea fowl come
into their own in autumn as the Down's celebrated fresh fish and
garden produce become more scarce. Nonetheless a late summer
specials board spoils for choice: home-potted shrimps (£2.95), baked
scallops with herbs and garlic (£4.50), sauté of chicken livers with
lemon and pomegranate juice (£3.30), pepper-crusted monkfish with
red pepper relish (£8.30), trout (£6.85) and fresh salmon (£8.50)
represented in various guises. Equally traditional, the bar menu lists
shish kebab (£3.10), casserole of wild boar with Calvados and cream
(£8.30) and Brixham crab salad (£8.50). Children's portions of any
of these can be provided should young palates have risen beyond the
(very fairly priced) fishfingers, baked beans and toasties. "Choccy rum
pots", treacle and nut tart, apple Bakewell or fresh fruit vacherin
(£2.50) weigh in at the end alongside cafetière or espresso coffee and
half a dozen teas, while light opera and classical overtures play softly
in the background. One high-chair and baby's bottle wil be heated;
nursing mums will find a chair in the ladies and plenty of room for
changing. **Bar Food and Restaurant Meals** *12-2, 7-9.30 (except Sun).*
Children's menu (£1.60 per dish). Free House. **Beer** *Constantly*
changing – five at any one time, plus guest beers. Patio, outdoor eating.
Family room. Access, Visa.

Bridport   George Hotel

Tel 0308 23187	Pub

4 South Street Bridport Dorset DT6 3NQ   Map 13 F2

The recently redecorated George has an eccentric quirkiness that
is appealing and creates an informal, beguiling atmosphere. Children
are welcome and a separate room, nicknamed 'Whipsnade',
is specifically available for families. The residents' bathroom upstairs
can be used for nappy changing. Fresh home-cooked food, particularly
the variety of pies, is popular and the landlord is always happy
to divide any dish to satisfy a child. The bar opens at 8.30pm for coffee
and croissants. Adult menu selection: smoked mackerel paté and toast
(£2.75), ratatouille (£3.50), ham, chicken and mushroom pie (£5),
fresh plaice and vegetables (£7). Chocolate mousse and bread and
butter pudding (both £1.75) are enjoyable desserts. **Bar Food** *12-2.30,*
also Fri, Sat and every day during school holidays 6.30-9.
Access, Visa.

Brightling   Jack Fuller's

Tel 0424 82212	Restaurant
Brightling East Sussex TN32 5HD	**Map 11 B6**

A mile from Brightling on the Robertsbridge road, a former pub has been turned into a fine country restaurant by Roger and Shirl Berman. Oak beams, exposed stone walls and a huge inglenook give character to the place, and red check tablecloths lend an air of informality. The menu majors on main courses and puddings; the former, served in serious portions, could include gammon and onion pudding, beef stew and dumplings, chicken and mushroom pie, or prawn and halibut pie pastry atop (all £4.95) with a wide choice of side dishes – bubble and squelch, poached mushrooms or Stilton cauliflower (all £1.10). The traditional theme extends to the puddings – vegetarian Spotted Dick, sticky treacle tart, mother's bread pudding (all £2.25). The same menu applies in the evening when prices increase slightly. Extensive patio area in the garden overlooking rolling countryside for alfresco eating. No-smoking area. *Seats 100. Open 12-3 & 7-11. Closed D Sun, all Mon (except Bank Holidays), Tue & Wed (Mar-Oct). Access, Amex, Diners, Visa.*

Brighton   Al Duomo & Al Forno

Tel 0273 26741	Restaurant
7 Pavilion Buildings Brighton East Sussex	**Map 11 B6**

It's the genuine, wood-burning pizza ovens that give this pair of pizzeria/trattorias an edge over the competition. Al Duomo (the larger of the two, plus better changing facilities), with bright yellow awning and rustic interior is next door to the Brighton Pavilion and Al Forno just 50 yards away with tables spilling out of a conservatory area into a small square. Near-identical menus cover the full range of standard Italian dishes along with the pizzas (from £3.80) – prosciutto con melone (£3.95), linguine vongole (£4.50), fritto misto (£6.75), saltimboca romana (£7.50). Pizzas available in children's sizes. The 60-seat **Al Forno** is at 36 East Street. Tel 0273 24905. *Seats 120. Open 12-2.30 & 6-11.30 (Sat 12-11.30). Al Forno 12-2.30 & 6-11 (Fri-Sun 12-11). Closed 25 Dec. Access, Amex, Diners, Visa.*

Brighton   Browns

Tel 0273 23501	Restaurant
3-4 Duke Street Brighton East Sussex	**Map 11 B6**

A popular and ultra-busy brasserie near the Lanes offering good value traditional food throughout the day, including breakfast. Meat and fish dishes provide the main bulk of the menu with good old favourites like country chicken pie (£6.85), steak, mushroom and Guinness pie (£6.95) and Scotch sirloin steak (£9.95). This, together with the pizza and spaghetti dishes, hot sandwiches, salads and a wide range of generous puddings, provide for just about every taste. Vegetarian options are available on the pizza and spaghetti dishes, together with other dishes such as fresh vegetable bake (£5.95) and vegetables in herb sauce (£6.85). A good selection of wine and some 15 cocktails to choose from. Family oriented and children-friendly. Branches in Oxford, Cambridge and now Bristol. *Seats 140. Open 11am-11.30pm (Sun and Bank Holidays from noon). Closed 24 & 25 Dec. Access, Amex, Visa.*

Brighton   China Garden

Tel 0273 251241	Restaurant

88-91 Preston Street Brighton East Sussex   **Map 11 B6**

A roomy restaurant serving mainly Peking specialities offering
a flavourful and varied menu – particularly in the fish department.
Braised mussels in black bean sauce (£4.50), king prawns with garlic
and spring onions (£1.95 each) and delicately seasoned minced meats,
prawns and vegetables served with lettuce (£7) are some of the dishes
on offer, together with a juicy array of sizzling dishes on an iron
griddle. Dim sum are available until 4. A karaoke room and pianist
in the evening makes for a good night out. Children are welcome (but
no under 9s after 8pm). *Seats 130. Open 12-11pm. Closed 25 &
26 Dec. Access, Amex, Visa.*

Brighton   Cripes

Tel 0273 27878	Creperie

7 Victoria Road Brighton East Sussex   **Map 11 B6**

This is a small creperie on Victoria Road going towards Seven Dials.
Owner Joy Leader offers crepes (from £2.50) and wholemeal
buckwheat galettes (from £4.50) with a variety of fillings: chicken
livers, spinach and sour cream; smoked salmon, asparagus, cheese and
cream; aubergine, Cheddar, pesto sauce and Parmesan; or on the sweet
side, bananas in rum with whipped cream, black cherries and ice
cream, rum and chocolate (from £2.50). Morning visitors may like
to try the scrambled eggs, bacon and mushrooms in a crepe or even
the champagne breakfast (£4.95). A choice of French farmhouse ciders
is the traditional accompaniment. *Seats 50. Open 10.30-2.30 & 6-11.30
(Sun to 11). Closed 25 Dec. Access, Amex, Visa.*

Brighton   Dig in the Ribs

Tel 0273 325275	Restaurant

47 Preston Street East Sussex BN1 2HP   **Map 11 B6**

Just off the main shopping street, down a street packed with
restaurants, Dig in the Ribs is a breath of fresh air, except on Sundays
when one might be forgiven for thinking that one had walked into
a Mexican crèche! Owner Tony Baker has a young family himself and
understands the requirements needed to cater for youngsters. On three
floors, the restaurant is clean, airy, informal, noisy and family-friendly
with seven high-chairs provided and requests for bottle or food
heating happily accommodated. The Mexican fare is mainly
vegetarian and the variety of food on offer is excellent. A new
children's menu (£2.85) includes a six-page colouring book/menu
from which junior diners can choose a main course, drink and sweet;
plastic mugs are also provided. Most children will enjoy the hustle and
bustle here, the ceiling fans, and the originality of the food. Parents
will enjoy the laid-back attitude and need never feel awkward about
making any special requests for their children. There is a nappy-
changer in the Ladies. *Seats 110. Open 12-11.30 (to 10.30 Sun) Closed
Dec 25 & 26 and Jan 1. Access, Visa*

Brighton   The Dove Hotel

Tel 0273 779222	Hotel

18 Regency Square Brighton East Sussex BN1 2FG   Map 11 B6

On arriving you can expect to be greeted like long lost friends and
presented with a welcome drink. Owner Mr Kalinke is happy
to do almost anything to keep his junior house guests happy – from the
provision of a toy box to a guided tour of the hotel. The hospitality
for families is almost second to none: even at breakfast a new selection
of toys can be provided for early risers who have already reached the
boredom threshold. The atmosphere is informal and low key and in
such a small place you feel as if you are in a private home (firedoors
notwithstanding). Bedrooms are comfortable and bright with a well-
chosen mix of antique furniture and modern fabrics; travel cots and
small beds are provided. Baby-listening and baby-sitting are on offer,
the latter by prior arrangement. Early high teas (either in the dining
room or in your room), nappies, potties, baby bottles...Mr Kalinke
is only too happy to oblige. Sea World, on the sea front by Palace Pier,
is a short walk away. **Rooms** *10. £50-£78 double room; under-2s free,
2-7 £7, 11-16 £10. Closed 1 week Christmas. Access, Amex, Diners,
Visa.*

Brighton   Ed's Easy Diner

Tel 0273 771955	Diner

16 Prince Albert Street The Lanes Brighton East Sussex   Map 11 B6

The Brighton branch of this popular American-style diner is larger
than its London counterparts with a wide circular bar (normally
horseshoe in shape at other branches) in the middle of which the
friendly staff cook and entertain at the same time. The Original burger
£3.65, hot dog with sauerkraut £2.95, toasted cheese sandwich
£3.45, fries £1 and milkshake £2.10. Children are always welcome
and even have their own 3oz burger 'Fast Eddy' (£2.25). 'Bottomless'
cups of coffee are also served. **Seats** *36.* **Open** *High Season
11am-midnight (Sat 11am-1am); Low Season noon-6 (Fri to midnight,
Sat 11am-1am, Sun 11-10.30). No credit cards.*

Brighton   Food for Friends

Tel 0273 202310	Restaurant

17-18 Prince Albert Street Brighton East Sussex   Map 11 B6

An informal, cosy establishment furnished with simple pine furniture
and potted plants offering an all-vegetarian menu in warm and
hospitable surroundings. Tasty hot dishes to cheer and warm the belly
on a cold winter's day are the masala dosa bake with coconut and
coriander dahl and fresh mango chutney (£2.55) and buckwheat and
cheese strudel with white wine and caraway sauce (£2.80). Other
dishes range from wholemeal broccoli and poppyseed quiche, exquisite
mushroom and lentil roast, to kidney bean and courgette goulash and
Turkish falafel. Excellent organic bread selection including croissants
and pain au chocolat. Lots of dips and salads. Children particularly
welcome. Non-smoking area. **Seats** *50.* **Open** *12-4 & 5.30-10.*
Closed *25 & 26 Dec. Access, Amex, Diners, Visa.*

Brighton   Old Ship Hotel   65%   £105
Tel 0273 29001   Fax 0273 820718   Hotel
King's Road Brighton East Sussex BN1 1NR   Map 11 B6

There's a long tradition of hospitality at this privately-owned seafront
hotel, which caters admirably for private and business visitors.
Children are well looked after, and two (up to the age of 16) can stay
free in their parents' room; a supervised crèche operates from 4-11pm
on Fridays and Saturdays. The panelled Tettersell's Bar is a popular
place for a drink, and guests are invited to look at the extensive wine
cellar. Many of the double-glazed bedrooms have seaviews. Regular
dinner dance on Saturday nights. *Rooms 152. Access, Amex, Diners,
Visa.*

Brighton   Pie in the Sky
Tel 0273 624233   Restaurant
87 St James's Street Brighton East Sussex BN2 1TP   Map 11 B6

Pie in the Sky is now more than just a pizza and pasta restaurant. With
its canopied fascia, tiled walls and floors and contrasting darkwood
furniture, the look and Italian menu have gone upmarket. However,
they are keen to maintain their family market and so two high-chairs,
children's portions and lollies are provided. *Seats 50. Open
11am-11.30pm Closed 25 Dec. Access, Amex, Diners, Visa.*

Brighton   Pizza Express
Tel 0273 23205   Pizzeria
22 Prince Albert Street The Lanes Brighton East Sussex Map 11 B6

One of the popular Pizza Express chain of restaurants offering freshly-
prepared, thin crispy pizzas cooked in an open-to-view oven. This
branch has two entrances – one in Prince Albert Street and the other
in the famous Lanes. The black and white decor is brightened with
potted plants and the dining area is divided into two by the cooking
area in the middle. *Seats 89. Open 12-12. Closed 25 & 26 Dec. Access,
Amex, Visa.*

Brighton (Hove)   St Catherine's Lodge Hotel
Tel 0273 778181   Hotel
Kingsway Hove East Sussex BN3 2RZ   Map 11 B6

St Catherine's Lodge is a warm and cosy Victorian hotel on the
seafront in Hove (a mile from central Brighton) and has been run
by owner James Houlton since 1965. The beaches in Hove are quieter
and the pace of life a little slower than in hectic Brighton. The
emphasis here is on courteous personal service tailored to suit
individual needs. Some family suites have two bunk beds
in an adjoining room while others can accommodate extra beds or cots
(provided); nappies and bottles are available on request. The baby-
listening service is unusual and vigilantly manned; baby-sitting should
be arranged in advance. Children are welcome in the restaurant but
may also have high tea in the Dutch Room where families will find
high-chairs and favourite family dishes. A pool table and table tennis
are in the basement games room and there is a playground and
modern leisure complex (complete with indoor swimming pool
suitable for toddlers) on the promenade just opposite the hotel.
*Rooms 50. £65 double room; under-5s free; longer stays at reduced rates.
Access, Amex, Diners, Visa.*

Bristol   Arnolfini Café Bar

Tel 0272 279330	Café

Narrow Quay Prince Street Bristol Avon   Map 13 F1

Adjacent to the Arnolfini Gallery in a thriving complex created out
of dockside warehouses, this roomy, airy café bar is an ideal stop-off
for a light lunch or afternoon tea. The blackboard menu changes daily
to offer such dishes as salmon fish cakes with crab sauce (£3.95),
rabbit pie cooked in cider and tarragon (£4.20), layered pancake with
fresh tomato and pepper sauce (£3.95) and home-made puddings –
banana pudding, chocolate pecan pie and chocolate St. Emilion (all
£1.95). There's a wide choice of teas and if it's sunny, the benches out
on the dockside provide a very pleasant place to sit and sip. *Seats 50.*
Open 12-10 (Sat & Sun to 3pm) & 5-10 (Sat & Sun only).
Closed 10 days Christmas. No credit cards.

Bristol   Aztec Hotel   74%   £100

Tel 0454 301090 Fax 0454 201593	Hotel

Aztec West Business Park Almondsbury Bristol Avon BS12 4TS   Map 13 F1

A smart, professionally run purpose-built, modern hotel in the Shire
Inns group of hotels, owned by brewers Daniel Thwaites. It provides
a good balance of facilities between mid-week conferences and
weekend family breaks. All bedrooms are of 'Executive' standard
with coffee tables, writing desk and fax point; children under 14 are
accommodated free in their parents' rooms. Syndicate rooms convert
to family use at weekends with wall-mounted let-down beds. Day
rooms are more than adequate, with lounges on two levels in the
central 'lodge' and a smart snooker room. The hotel also has a fine
leisure club and its own Black Sheep pub. Light meals and snacks are
served in Danby's Bar; more formal dining in Quarter Jacks
restaurant. Regional specialities at breakfast include Somerset venison
sausages and Alderley trout served with scrambled eggs. In a modern
business park near junction 16 of the M5 (south of the M4/M5
interchange). *Rooms 88. Garden, indoor swimming pool, gymnasium,
squash, sauna, solarium, steam room, children's playground. Access, Amex,
Diners, Visa.*

Bristol   Browns Restaurant and Bar

Tel 0272 304777	Brasserie

38 Queen's Road Bristol Avon BS8 1RE   Map 13 F1

Housed in the former University Refectory building at the top of Park
Street. This fourth in the chain of American-style brasseries (also
in Oxford, Cambridge and Brighton) has been an instant hit with
both students and city types. A busy bar and 200 seats still leave room
for a central grand piano and ubiquitous aspidistras, amongst which
all-day diners choose from pasta, burgers, chargrilled chicken and
puddings from pecan to chocolate mousse cake. Start the day with
an English breakfast (£4.75) or drop by for cucumber sandwiches and
scones at teatime (from £3.05). At night very much a see-and-be-seen
scene with fancy shaken cocktails, house wines from Louis St Croix
and ketchup from Heinz. *Seats 200. Open 11am-11.30pm (Sun & Bank
Holidays from noon). Closed 25 Dec. Access, Amex, Diners, Visa.*

Bristol   Café Première

Tel 0272 734892	Restaurant
59 Apsley Road Clifton Bristol Avon BS8 2SW	**Map 13 F1**

Mr and Mrs Narimani, the Iranian owners of the appropriately named
Café Première really have created a first-class café. Natural wood, pale
colours and large plants make up a chic, co-ordinated and stylish
interior. The menu is appetising and varied, the dishes are made with
the best ingredients and cooked with flair and confidence. A breakfast
menu that is second to none is served all day, and with selections from
all over the world. The staff are as kind and caring and good-
humoured as the owners. On top of all this, wonder of wonders,
children are not only welcome, they are adored. A dozen beakers,
a collection of plastic crockery, non-slip baby feeding bowls, child
safety cutlery and padded high-chairs are all provided. In the loo is a
changing mat and a supply of nappies. There's even a little area for
alfresco eating. Café Première has got it all just right. *Seats 42.*
Open 8-6 (Sun 9-5). Closed Dec 25, 26, Jan 1. Access, Visa.

Bristol   51 Park Street

Tel 0272 268016	Restaurant
51 Park Street Bristol Avon BS1 5NT	**Map 13 F1**

Summon the energy to climb up the half-a-dozen steps up to the front
door as you won't be disappointed – 30s' decor, a delightful ambience,
relaxed but efficient staff and excellent food. There are no half-
portions except for the pasta dishes but it is possible to have an extra
plate and share a meal. Two high-chairs are supplied and prams can
be stored in the entrance area. Adult offerings include deep-fried
onions (£1.95), lentil paté (£2.95), filo parcel with spinach and feta
(£2.95), sandwiches (tuna melt £4.75 with fries), grilled supreme
of chicken (£7.85), swordfish niçoise (£7.95) and banana cream pie
(£1.95). *Seats 80. Open 12-11 (Sun to 10). Closed Dec 25, 26 & Jan 1.
Access, Amex, Diners, Visa.*

Bristol   Guild Restaurant

Tel 0272 291874	Restaurant
68 Park Street Bristol Avon	**Map 13 F1**

Part of an elegant Georgian shop specialising in crafts and modern
furnishings, this restaurant with a covered conservatory offers home-
made soups, quiches (£3.50), salads, puddings and cakes as the
mainstay. Adventurous specials include cashew nut paté (£3.35), wild
mushroom and chicken liver terrine (£3.90), baked rabbit in mustard
sauce (£4.95), farmhouse sausages with baked potato (£3.75), leek
bake in Stilton sauce (£4) and apricot and almond fool (£2.25)
or trifle with framboise liqueur (£2.45). The 'spécialité de la maison'
is chocolate cake (£1.65) baked by their resident chocolatier.
Children's portions available. No smoking. *Seats 70. Open 10-4.30.
Closed Sun, Bank Holidays. No credit cards.*

Bristol   Pizza Express

Tel 0272 260300	Pizzeria
32 Berkeley Square Bristol Avon	**Map 13 F1**

Upmarket pizza house with a Mediterranean feel just off the upper end
of Park Street. Smoked glass and cool tiled floors. Pizzas prepared

in full view and bright cheerful staff mark this out from the
competition. Prices generally around £5. *Seats 70.*
Open 11.30am-midnight. Access, Visa.

Bristol   Rainbow Café

Tel 0272 738937	Café
10 Water Street Clifton Bristol Avon	Map 13 F1

This arts-orientated café remains a popular lunchtime favourite with
both meat-eaters and vegetarians since the middle of the day brings the
greatest choice: green pea and mint soup (£1.30), chicken with lamb
and fresh coriander (£3.50), mushroom and barley casserole (£4.95),
carrot and cashew nut paté (£3.60), quiches (£1.80 – smoked
haddock or spinach and bacon). Good fresh salads accompany main
courses. You may like to finish with blackberry and apple pie or pear
and ginger crumble (both £1.85). Outside lunch hours, the good
baking extends to fruit or cheese scones (60p), cakes and slices. Home-
made ice cream is always available (coconut and cardamon £1.85).
No-smoking area. *Seats 38. Open 10-5.30 (full meals 12-2.30).*
Closed Sun. No credit cards.

Bristol   Redwood Lodge   64%   £85

Tel 0275 393901 Fax 0275 392104	Hotel
Beggar Bush Lane Failand Bristol Avon BS8 3TG	Map 13 F1

Barely ten minutes from the city centre (via Clifton Bridge), off the
A370, Redwood bristles with conference facilities (for up to 175
delegates), and boasts Bristol's largest leisure club. Individual residents
may lose out on quiet corners, bedroom space and room service,
which is sporadic at best. Weekenders with families fare better,
as there's plenty to do: an all-day coffee shop, 175-seat cinema,
trampolining, and regular crèche facilities are available (10am-1pm).
Country Club Hotels. *Rooms 112. Garden, keep-fit equipment, sauna,
solarium, beauty salon, squash, badminton, tennis, snooker, indoor,
outdoor & children's swimming pools, cinema, coffee shop
(9.30am-10.30pm), children's playroom & playground.
Access, Amex, Diners, Visa.*

Bristol   Rowan Tree

Tel 0272 290112	Café
The Triangle Clifton Bristol Avon BS8 1EH	Map 13 F1

The Rowan Tree has a gift shop, book shop, library and this peaceful
vegetarian restaurant located in a bustling commercial area and
offering organic fare. Even children who put chicken and chips at the
top of their list of favourite foods have been known to clamour for the
generous granary sandwiches, soups (gluten-free and low salt), organic
jacket potatoes with cheese (£1.85) and onion squares. Beverages
include tempting teas, including one to ease tension. There is only one
clip-on high-chair but buggies can be taken inside on all but the
busiest days. The toilets are large enough to change nappies (mat
available). Adult menu selection: red lentil and vegetable (£1.50),
mixed pepper quiche (£1.60), onion bahji (80p) and kiwi and banana
trifle (85p) or vegan and sugar free hot Eccles cake (75p). No smoking
area. *Seats 50. Open 9-5.30. Closed Sun, Bank Hols, Dec 25, 26 &
Jan 1. Access, Visa.*

Bristol	**Swallow Royal Hotel**	77%	£110

Tel 0272 255100 Fax 0272 251515	Hotel

College Green Bristol Avon BS1 5TE	Map 13 F1

Swallow's multi-million development, faced in Bath stone, newly
dominates approaches to College Green and Bristol Cathedral. Equally
impressive, on arrival, is the Spanish marble hall flanked by country
house elegance in the Drawing room and Club Bar, and a basement
Leisure Club of Roman bath design. Secure covered parking is a bonus.
Generous space and stylish individual decor establish bedrooms high
in the comfort category; marble bathrooms are well-lit. Staff are
smart, attentive and motivated; company policy, it appears,
is responsible for some lapses in service (no evening turn-down for
instance) which such investment deserves. **Rooms** *242. Indoor
swimming pool, sauna, solarium, spa bath, beauty salon, hairdressing, keep-
fit equipment. Access, Amex, Diners, Visa.*

Palm Court Restaurant   £65

The grand Palm Court extends through three floors lined in Bath
stone with curved balustrades and topped by stained glass skylights.
Menus follow the grand format while the service is formal yet
unfussy. A fixed-price "Concept of the Kitchen" may run through
glazed asparagus with salmon tartare, poached oyster, rosemary-infused
lamb and summer pudding, supplemented by seasonal à la carte.
Seats *60. Parties 8. D only 7-10. Closed Sun & Mon. Set D £21.*

Terrace Restaurant   £50

A stylish, relaxed setting overlooking Cathedral Square. Moderately
priced table d'hote and lighter meals from cod and mash to goat's
cheese ravioli. **Seats** *150. Parties 20. Private Room. L 12.30-2.30
D 6.30-10.30. Set L £14 Set D £18.*

Bristol	**Watershed**	

Tel 0272 21435	Café

1 Cannons Road Cannons Marsh Bristol Avon BF1 5TX	Map 13 F1

Once a transit shed for the ships that fuelled Bristol's industry, the
Watershed Café-Bar now shares the premises with two galleries and
two arthouse cinemas. The decor is open plan and minimalist with
views of the water traffic giving children plenty to watch. The young
staff are helpful, tolerant and relaxed about babbling babies. The
atmosphere is great, there's loads of activity and the food is good.
To avoid the stairs up to the café you can take a lift (if you don't mind
being delivered to the bar store room). Open all day, the café serves
coffees, teas, pastries, croissants as well as hot dishes. Adult menu
selection: home-made carrot and lentil soup (£1.70), homity pie
(£3.50), beef stifado (£4 – tomato sauce with babyshallots), grilled
or stuffed mackerel (£3.85). Vegetarian choices are always available.
Children can have smaller portions of all hot food. Two no-smoking
areas. **Seats** *100.* **Open** *10.30-9 (Sun 11-7, hot food to 4).*
Closed *21-31 Dec. Access, Amex, Diners, Visa.*

Broadway	**Collin House Hotel**	

Tel 0386 858354	Hotel

Collin Lane Broadway Hereford & Worcester	Map 14 C1

A Cotswold-stone house about a mile north-west of Broadway
signposted off the A44 Evesham road (turn right at Collin Lane).

Lunch is served in the 17th-century bar and lounge (blazing log fires
in winter) or in the pleasant gardens if the weather's fine. Judith and
John Mills and their friendly staff offer a warm welcome and plenty
of advice on what to see and do in the neighbourhood. At lunchtime,
the snack menu might have macaroni cheese with crispy bacon
(£4.90), mussels in cider, celery and thyme (£4.95), beef and venison
pie with vegetables (£6) or wild rabbit casserole (£5.95), whilst
on the three-course set menu (£14.50) the choice might be Parmesan
cheese soufflé with watercress sauce, followed by chicken in grape and
vermouth sauce and date sponge with butterscotch sauce. On Sundays,
the four-course lunch (£14.50) starts with a basket of crudités with
dips and breads. Children's portions. *Seats 36. Open 12-1.30.*
Closed 1 week Christmas. Access, Visa.

Broadway	Dormy House	69%	£110
Tel 0386 852711 Fax 0386 858636			Hotel
Willersey Hill Broadway Hereford & Worcester WR12 7LF			Map 14 C1

Just off the A44, on an escarpment above Broadway and with views
over the local golf course and the Vale of Evesham, Dormy House
is an extended 17th-century farmhouse. Beams, exposed stonework
and tiled floors set the tone in the main house, whose two homely
lounges have fine bay windows. Converted outbuildings house
cottagey, comfortable bedrooms, many also with timbered ceilings;
two rooms have four-posters. Delegates at the purpose-built conference
centre seem to appreciate the rustic, Cotswold-stone bar where less
formal lunch and dinner menus are available (as well as afternoon tea).
Families welcome; baby-sitting by arrangement; children's supper
menu. *Rooms 49. Garden, table tennis. Access, Amex, Diners, Visa.*

Restaurant   £88

A conservatory overlooks the garden and surrounding countryside,
giving a brighter alternative to the more formal, dimly-lit dining
room, where John Sanderson produces à la carte, table d'hote,
vegetarian and gourmet menus that all display a modern leaning
in both presentation and content. Trio of salmon (smoked, tartare and
gravad lax), Cornish crabmeat with diced gherkin and sweet red
pepper coulis, medallion of beef fillet with stir-fried vegetables and
a sauce of soy, honey and sherry, gratin of red fruits with a red berry
and Cointreau sorbet in a brandy snap basket are all typical of the
style. Good French cheeses from Pierre Androuet served with walnut
and raisin bread. Rather too many notes accompany the wines on an
unexceptional list. *Seats 80. Parties 40. Private Room. L 12.30-2 (Sun
to 2.30) D 7.30-9.30 (Fri & Sat from 7, Sun to 9). Closed L Sat, 3 days
Xmas. Set L £14 Set D £25.50.*

Broadway	Goblets Wine Bar	
Tel 0386 852255		Wine bar
High Street Broadway Hereford & Worcester		Map 14 C1

Part of the world-renowned Lygon Arms Hotel, the cosy and
atmospheric Goblets Wine Bar has a beamed interior with leaded
mullion windows and an ancient inglenook fireplace. The seasonal
lunch and supper menu may offer avocado with prawns and sweet
pepper sauce (£3.50), potted smoked haddock with marinated
cucumber (£3), salmon, cod and barley pie (£5.20), country casserole
of chicken, leeks and honey (£4.80). Light meals and daily specials are
written up on the blackboard: omelettes (from £3.50), filled jacket

potatoes (£3.50) and casserole of the day. Home-made puddings are
£4.50 with the exception of sticky toffee pudding at £3.75. *Seats 65.*
Open 12-2 & 7-9.30. Closed 2 weeks early Jan.

Bromley   MacArthurs

Tel 081-460 4678	Restaurant
10 East Street Bromley Kent	**Map 11 B5**

Their own succulent, home-made burgers are at the heart of the menu
at this American-style burger restaurant with a baseball theme. The
basic half-pounder, which comes with dill pickle and fries for £4.25,
can be customised with various fillings at 60p a time. *Seats 60.*
*Open 10am-11pm (Sun 11am-10.30pm). Closed 25 Dec. Access, Amex,
Diners, Visa.*

Bromley   Pizza Express

Tel 081-464 2708	Pizzeria
15 Widmore Road Bromley Kent	**Map 11 B6**

Opposite The Glades Shopping Centre, this popular restaurant
in a well-run chain serves crisp, thin pizzas (£3.15-£5.40) with fresh
ingredients used for the toppings. Classical or opera music plays over
the loudspeakers at lunchtime whilst blues or jazz dominate in the
evenings. No-smoking area. *Seats 124. Open 11.30am-midnight.
Closed 25 & 26 Dec. Access, Amex, Visa.*

Burley   Burley Manor   61%   £78

Tel 0425 403522 Fax 0425 403227	Hotel
Burley nr Ringwood Hampshire BH24 4BS	**Map 14 C4**

A Victorian manor house surrounded by 54 ares of parkland in the
heart of the New Forest. Period decor includes stone fireplaces,
a creaky staircase with carved balustrade and unusual commode side-
tables. Bedrooms are simply decorated amd have smart, tiled
bathrooms; converted stable-block rooms are the largest and have the
best views, plus steps leading directly down onto the lawns. Riding
stables in the grounds offer rides in the New Forest for both novices
and experts. Cots, extra beds, baby-sitting/listening (given advance
notice), high-chairs and high tea (6.30pm) are all provided. Children
up to 14 accommodated free in their parents' room. Dogs are
as welcome as children. *Rooms 30. Garden, outdoor swimming pool,
hairdressing, putting, croquet, coarse fishing. Access, Amex, Diners, Visa.*

Burley   Manor Farm Tea Rooms

Tel 0425 402218	Tea Room
Ringwood Road Burley New Forest Hampshire BH24 4AB	**Map 14 C4**

Opposite the entrance to Burley Manor Hotel. Peter and Kathy Hunt
run this archetypal English tea shop, with thatched roof, black beams,
wheelback chairs and an open fireplace where a log fire burns
in winter and a display of flowers brightens in summer. Light snacks
are served until 1.45pm – perhaps a Cornish pastie (£1.05), bacon and
mushroom muffin (£1.65) or a piece of fruit cake (80p). The lunch
menu, served from midday to 1.45, might offer home-cooked ham,
chips and peas (£3.25) or a mushroom omelette (£2.95). Only set
afternoon teas are served after lunch but the choice of nine different
versions caters for all tastes (£2.30-£3.95). Families are usually seated

at the rear, where there is more room. High-chairs, baby food, bottles and children's portions are all provided. No-smoking area. **Seats** *84.* **Open** *10-5 (Mon from 2).* **Closed** *25, 26 & 31 Dec. No credit cards.*

Burnley	**Butterfingers**		
Tel 0282 458788			Café
10 St James Row Burnley Lancashire BH11 1DR			Map 6 B1

A tiny café with just six small round pine tables with stools. No high-chairs are provided but on a quiet day you could bring in a buggy. You order at the serving hatch and are served at the table. Butterfingers offers a wide range of sandwiches, toasties, filled jacket potatoes, salads, sweets, supplemented by blackboard specials, cakes and pastries, all very fresh and wholesome. The only loo is far too small for baby changing. A single table is reserved for non-smokers. **Open** *9-4 (Tues until 2).* **Closed** *Sun, Bank Hols. No credit cards.*

Bury St Edmunds	**Angel Hotel**	**69%**	£120
Tel 0284 753926 Fax 0284 750092			Hotel
Angel Hill Bury St Edmunds Suffolk IP33 1LT			Map 10 C2

In continuous use as a hotel since 1452, the vine-clad Angel is to this day in private hands, priding itself on a high level of customer care and service. The lounge exudes quiet comfort, with deep-cushioned sofas facing the log fire; below, the 11th-century vaults make a striking setting for one of the two restaurants. Pride of place among the individually furnished and decorated bedrooms goes to the Charles Dickens room, where four-poster and antique furniture are sympathetically added to by today's expected accoutrements. Bathrooms, indeed, are entirely modern with good over-tub showers and plentiful toiletries; most also have bidets. Cots, baby-sitting/listening, high-chairs and children's portions make this a well-appointed family hotel. Secure covered garage. **Rooms** *40. Access, Amex, Diners, Visa.*

Bury St Edmunds	**Butterfly Hotel**	**62%**	£67
Tel 0284 760884 Fax 0284 755476			Hotel
Symonds Road Bury St Edmunds Suffolk IP32 7BW			Map 10 C2

Take the Bury East exit from the A45 to the Butterfly, a modern low-riser with modest accommodation. Delegate and private dining rooms for up to 40. Under-12s free in parents' room. No dogs. **Rooms** *66. Access, Amex, Diners, Visa.*

Bury St Edmunds	**Porters Tea Rooms**	
Tel 0284 706198		Tea Room
5 Whiting Street Bury St Edmunds Suffolk IP33 1NX		Map 10 C2

Porters is a small, rather old-fashioned tea room just off the bustling high street. Treat the children to a traditional tea with sandwiches, sausage rolls, toasted tea cakes with jam, followed by an enormous slice of home-made cake. The tables are well-spaced enough to make pushchair access easy and the owner is quick to produce children's books for restless children; no high-chairs. There is a small room/office which can be used for changing or breastfeeding and small portions are no problem for the kitchen whose tinkling bell is heard summoning the waitresses to collect customer's food. Lunchtimes are busy so come early or at tea time. **Seats** *96.* **Open** *9.30-5.* **Closed** *Sun, most Bank Hols, 1 week Xmas. No credit cards.*

Buxton   Nathaniel's

Tel 0298 78388	Restaurant
35 High Street Buxton Derbyshire	Map 6 C2

Situated at the top of the hill in what could be called 'old' Buxton, on entering Nathaniel's one is welcomed by an open coal fire in the small reception/bar area. The restaurant (divided into two rooms) takes up the ground floor of Andy and Yvonne Coates' home. The rear room, leading to the kitchen, has a Mediterranean feel with bare bricks, hanging plants, check tablecloths while the front room is painted pink. Three menus feature – à la carte, 'Bistro' (evenings only) and lunchtime. The latter two change daily and are less expensive than the former: curried mushrooms (£2.35), cheese beignets with Cumberland sauce (£2.95), roast rib of beef with Yorkshire pudding (£8.10), pork chop au poivre (£6.10), tandoori chicken with rice and salad (£5.45), bread and butter pudding or chilled vanilla soufflé (both £1.95). Coffee is served with cream. The traditional 3-course Sunday lunch (£8.95) is copious with a varied choice. Half portions and high-chairs are available for children; telephone before visiting with a child and one of the larger tables will be set aside for you. The Coates are happy for one of their private rooms to be used for nappy changing or breast-feeding. Not very ideal for a very active toddler, perhaps but friendly and flexible. *Seats 35. Open 12-2.30 & 7-10.30. Closed D Sun, all Mon. Access, Amex, Diners, Visa.*

Cadeby   Cadeby Inn

Tel 0709 864009	Pub
Main Street Cadeby nr Doncaster South Yorkshire DN5 7SW	Map 7 D2

Stone-built ex-farmhouse pub with a cricket-mad main lounge, comfortable with one or two old pieces and a good open fire. Another little room, to the front, is usually quieter, and there's a separate darts room/public bar. No music. 184 whiskies. *Free House. Beer Sam Smith, Tetley, John Smiths. Garden. Children's play area. Family room.*

Camberley   Frimley Hall   68%   £111

Tel 0276 28321 Fax 0276 691253	Hotel
Portsmouth Road Camberley Surrey GU15 2BG	Map 15 E3

A short distance from J3 of the M3, a turn-of-the-century Victorian manor house surrounded by splendid grounds that are floodlit at night. Magnificent stained-glass windows overlook an impressive carved wooden staircase – Victorian style that is carried through to the traditionally furnished bedrooms in the main house, two of which have four-poster beds. However, most of the bedrooms are located in a modern extension and are smaller, but equally appealing; 16 are designated non-smoking. Families are well catered for, particularly at weekends when rates are reduced. Forte Heritage. *Rooms 67. Garden. Access, Amex, Diners, Visa.*

Camberley   Pizza Express

Tel 0276 21846	Pizzeria
52 Park Street Camberley Surrey	Map 15 E3

One of many popular pizza restaurants in this well-run chain. Crisp bases and mainly fresh ingredients for the toppings, plus a 'pizza of the month' – typically prawns, tabasco and parsley on a mozzarella and tomato base. *Seats 94. Open 11.30am-midnight. Closed 25 & 26 Dec. Access, Amex, Visa.*

Cambridge	**Browns**	**£30**
Tel 0223 461655 Fax 0233 460426		**Restaurant**
23 Trumpington Street Cambridge Cambridgeshire CB2 1QA		**Map 15 F1**

Opposite the Fitzwilliam Museum, this is one of a small chain of Browns (the others are in Brighton, Bristol and Oxford). The all-day menu spans hot sandwiches, spaghetti, salads, savoury pies, burgers, ribs, steaks, daily fish specials and puddings. Separate children's menu should cause little stress to health-conscious parents: wholemeal club sandwich with chicken, lettuce, bacon, tomato and mayonnaise, cheese and fruit salad, jacket potatoes or chips with main dishes. Reasonable prices, charming staff, prompt service, high-chairs, an excellent changing/nursing room and a convenient location – thus very, very popular, so arrive early; if you don't, then expect to queue at busy times. *Seats 240. Parties 40. Private Room. Meals 11am-11.30pm (Sun & Bank Holidays 12-11.30pm). Access, Amex, Diners, Visa.*

Cambridge	**Cambridgeshire Moat House**	**63%**	**£78**
Tel 0954 780555 Fax 0954 780010			**Hotel**
Bar Hill Cambridge Cambridgeshire CB3 8EU			**Map 15 F1**

The grounds of this well-designed modern hotel on the A604 include an 18-hole golf course (available to guests at a 50% reduction on green fees). There's also a leisure centre and numerous conference suites. Several bedrooms are suitable for family use, and baby-listening and baby-sitting can be organised in advance. Children have their own paddling pool. Special mid-week family rates. Snacks in the Gallery bar and lounge; 5.50-6.30pm children's meal time in the dining room at weekends; high-chairs provided; carvery at Sunday lunch. *Rooms 100. Garden, indoor swimming pool, spa bath, solarium, steam room, keep-fit equipment, squash, tennis, pool table, dinner dance (Sat). Closed 25 & 26 Dec. Access, Amex, Diners, Visa.*

Cambridge	**Hobbs Pavilion Restaurant**	
Tel 0223 67480		**Creperie**
Hobbs Pavilion Park Terrace Cambridge Cambridgeshire CB1 1JH		**Map 15 F1**

Tucked behind the University Arms and bordering the cricket squares of Parker's Piece, Stephen and Susan Hill welcome children to their creperie at lunchtime only and a note on the menu asks that you prevent the child in your care from 'dominating the restaurant's atmosphere'. The 'Menu Enfant' (£3.50) – bacon sandwich, ice cream with chocolate flake and orange drink – has been created for the younger visitors but a shared pancake is another option. Food will also be blended if required. The pancakes are generously filled with imaginative mixtures (Hobbs special steak £6.75, cheese and garlic mushroom £3.50) and their home-made white chocolate ice cream is a particularly popular filling (£2.75). Cappuccino £1. There are no changing facilities and parking is very difficult. No-smoking area. Classical or melodic music plays throughout the day. *Seats 50. Open 12-2 & 7-9.45. Closed Sun, Mon, all Bank Hols, mid Aug-mid Sept, Christmas period.*

Cambridge — Kings Pantry

Tel 0223 321551	Restaurant
9a Kings Parade Cambridge Cambridgeshire CB2 1SJ	**Map 15 F1**

A very "nook and cranny" vegetarian restaurant located down a little alley opposite King's College chapel. The staff are very helpful so don't struggle down the stairs with a pushchair unaided, give a shout and someone will come and help you. Run by mothers with small children, visiting youngsters are understandably well catered for and looked after. High-chairs, bibs, baby cups and nappies are available. Space can be found for nappy changing and for nursing. Imaginative vegetarian dishes are on offer: split pea, mint and cauliflower cream soup (£1.95), spinach lasagne (£5.50), gado gado (£5.50), jacket potatoes with a variety of fillings (£4.75) and home-baked carrot cake with cream cheese topping (£1.85). Children's half portions. No smoking. *Seats* 52. *Open* 8-5.30 & 6.30-9.30 (*Sun & Mon* 8-5.30). *Closed* Sun & Mon evening, Dec 25 & 26, Jan 1. Access, Visa.

Cambridge — Pizza Express

Tel 0223 324033	Pizzeria
7 Jesus Lane Cambridge Cambridgeshire	**Map 15 F1**

Many past Pitt Club members (whose premises are on the upper floors) who became MPs or Prime Ministers now look down on diners from oak-panelled walls in one of the dining-rooms here. The other room has the familiar Pizza Express decor style of white-tiled floor, marble-topped tables and large mirrors on the walls. Crisp, thin pizzas are topped with fresh ingredients (£3.15-£5.30). *Seats* 165. *Open* 11.30-midnight. *Closed* 25 Dec. Access, Amex, Visa.

Camelford — Lanteglos Country House Hotel

	£100*
Tel 0840 213551	Hotel
Camelford Cornwall PL32 9RF	**Map 12 C3**

Lanteglos is set in 15 acres of gardens and woodland and on entering the estate you are immediately made aware of the presence of children, by road signs warning of children at play. In all there are 66 self-catering villas and lodges (sleeping 5) as well as 17 rooms in the 19th-century hotel. Along with 100 cots, they can provide baby baths, potties, safety gates and nappy buckets and a sophisticated baby-listening device. It is an absolute paradise for children, with secret play areas in the woods, four playgrounds, an adventure playground and a games room. The outside pool is well heated and the shallow children's pool has a central island with a fountain. Bedrooms are tastefully furnished, spacious and comfortable. Children's teatime is a carefree affair when children can choose dishes like roast chicken and gravy or Cornish pastie, as well as the usual beefburger and spaghetti Bolognese. Don't be late finishing dinner or you'll miss the children's entertainment which starts at 6 o'clock. The minimum stay is two nights and with so much to do this is probably just as well. *Half-board terms only. *Rooms* 17, 66 villas. *Closed* Dec-March. Under-5s free (except in August). Access, Visa.

Canterbury   Ebury Hotel   58%   £60

Tel 0227 768433 Fax 0227 459187	Hotel
65 New Dover Road Canterbury Kent CT1 3DX	Map 11 C5

Family-owned and run hotel in two Victorian houses, standing just
back from the road, with a large garden and a small indoor swimming
pool. Simply appointed bedrooms; four self-catering flats. Baby-
listening and baby-sitting are available for the four family rooms.
No children's menu, but small portions from an uncomplicated menu
will be comfortingly familiar to most children. Two high-chairs.
Rooms 15. *Garden, indoor swimming pool. Closed 24 Dec-14 Jan. Access,
Amex, Visa.*

Canterbury   Falstaff Hotel   £80

Tel 0227 462138 Fax 0227 463525	Inn
8 St Dunstan's Street Canterbury Kent CT2 8AF	Map 11 C5

A centuries-old coaching inn whose day rooms get character from
original beams, leaded windows and polished oak tables. Bedrooms are
neat and pretty and the majority use solid modern furniture that suits
the feel of the place perfectly. Children under 16 are accommodated
free – with a full traditional English breakfast – when sharing with
an adult. At other meals, they have their own menu of simple
favourites as well as small portions from the main menu. Bedrooms
have many useful extras including tea/coffee facilities and a TV video
channel showing family films. Baby-listening and baby-sitting services
are available. Within easy walking distance of the town centre, at the
end of the high street, near the Westgate Tower. No dogs. Lansbury
Hotels. **Rooms 25.** *Access, Amex, Diners, Visa.*

Carey   Cottage of Content

Tel 0432 840242	Pub
Carey Hereford & Worcester HR2 6NG	Map 14 B1

Signposted from Hoarwithy, this aptly named, idyllic little 15th-
century cottage pub is located by a stream far enough off the beaten
track to be a haven of peace at lunchtimes despite its fame and
precipitous garden. A warren of tiny oak-beamed rooms, with open
fires and ancient settles. Recommended for its bed and breakfast,
in three delightful bedrooms brimming with creaky character.
Modern comforts include simple carpeted bathrooms, tea-makers and
television. *Free House.* **Beer** *Bass, Hook Norton, Worthington. Garden.
Family room.* **Accommodation** *4 bedrooms, 3 en suite, £45. Children
welcome overnight. Check-in by arrangement. Access, Amex, Visa.*

Carlisle   The Grapevine

Tel 0228 46617	Restaurant
22 Fisher Street Carlisle Cumbria	Map 4 C2

Hanging baskets of greenery and pictures by local artists decorate this
friendly, counter-service restaurant in the YMCA building. A varied,
all-day menu ranges from hot dishes like sweet and sour chicken
(£2.75); lasagne and pitta bread; and vegetable soup (65p)
to cranberry, turkey and ham pie (£1.75), nut roast and vegetarian
pizza (both £1.50). There's a splendid choice of some 18 salads
to accompany and for the sweet-toothed there are various gateaux

(£1.25) a moist, buttered teabread (80p) and scrumptious coconut and cherry slice with chocolate. Two evenings a month there's a bookable, eat-as-much-as-you-like, hot and cold buffet at £7.75. Upstairs, under the same ownership, is a fully fledged crèche/nursery where they will look after the little ones while you eat. *Seats 70.* **Open** *8.30-4.30 (Mon 10-2).* **Closed** *Sun, 25 & 26 Dec, 1 Jan. No credit cards.*

Carlisle   Hudson's Coffee Shop

Tel 0228 47733	Coffee Shop
Treasury Court Fisher Street Carlisle Cumbria CA3 8RF	Map 4 C2

Steve Hudson has recently extended his coffee shop upstairs. With its William Morris wallpaper, bentwood and wicker chairs, plus views across an attractive courtyard and mini garden centre, the coffee shop is a pleasant place to stop for breakfast, snack lunch or tea. Vegetarian (£2.95) or traditional (£4.05) breakfasts are served all day. Snacks include toasted sandwiches (from £1.30), breaded plaice or battered cod, scampi (£4.55), vegetarian beanburger (£3.75) or lasagne (£4.25) and griddled steak (£7.95). Home baking brings shortbreads, tea breads, spicy carrot cake, cheesecake and scones (from 65p). There's a children's menu, high-chairs, mother and baby room, and 'emergency' toys. The waitress service extends to the courtyard outside on fine days. The Ladies is thoughtfully equipped with a changing bench and a bin for nappies and a courtyard provides space for playing. No smoking. *Seats 90.* **Open** *9-5.* **Closed** *Sun, Bank Holidays (except Fri).* Access, Visa.

Carlyon Bay   Carlyon Bay Hotel   68%   £132

Tel 0726 812304 Fax 0726 814938	Hotel
Sea Road Carlyon nr St Austell Cornwall PL25 3RD	Map 12 B3

Set in 250 acres of sub-tropical gardens and grounds, the hotel enjoys superb views over the bay. It was built in 1930, and, while still admirably fulfilling its role of family holiday hotel, it also offers extensive conference/function facilities. Large-windowed lounges, furnished in traditional style, make the most of the splendid setting, as do most of the light, attractive bedrooms. Families are particularly well catered for, with baby-sitting and baby-listening arranged. Under-2s stay free in their parents' room during low season (£3 per day in high season); 2-8s are charged 25%, 9-13s 50% of adult rates. Summer entertainment for children ranges from bouncy castle, fancy dress party magic show during high tea and competitions arranged by a resident entertainer. For the under-5s a childminder can be arranged (at extra cost). Parents can also use the in-house launderette facility on the lower ground floor. A children's menu contains a treasure chest of smuggled goodies (let the baby try the purée of fresh vegetables) and is available each day in the restaurant from 5.30-6.30pm. Outside, an adventure paddock incorporates swings, slides, tree house (and even a pets' corner in summer) within a safe, contained, easily-supervised wooded area. Parents can enjoy the excellent leisure facilities; the restaurant's offerings are not so exciting and gentlemen need a jacket and tie after 7pm. Brend Hotels.
Rooms 73. Garden, croquet, 18-hole golf course, 9-hole approach golf course, tennis, helipad, indoor & outdoor swimming pools, spa bath, sauna, solarium, snooker, children's playground, dinner dance (monthly). Access, Amex, Diners, Visa.

Castle Hedingham — Colne Valley Railway Restaurant

Tel 0787 62254	Restaurant
Yeldham Road Castle Hedingham nr Halstead Essex CO9 3DZ	Map 10 C3

Apart from providing excellent, freshly cooked, imaginative food, speedy service and a genuine welcome, what more does the Colne Valley Railway Restaurant do for you? Plenty. There are engines to inspect, railway sleepers to jump about on and steam engine rides on Sundays. Not only that but the setting of the restaurant in an old railway carriage is a novelty that children really appreciate. Birthday parties with a steam theme can be arranged in one of three carriages available and an engine-shaped cake plus an entertainer can be ordered. No smoking. *Open 10-5 & 7-10. Closed call ahead for seasonal closures. Access, Amex, Visa.*

Castleton — Moorlands Hotel

Tel 0287 660206	Hotel
Castleton Whitby North Yorkshire YO21 2DB	Map 5 E3

The provision of good facilities for families is a priority with the owners of this small hotel near Whitby. Not only do they provide two high-chairs, a baby bath, a stock of nappies and a children's menu, but parents are greeted on arrival with a reviving pot of tea. Six of the bedrooms are suitable for family use, the best being a large first-floor room with fitted units, cot, two easy chairs and an immaculate bathroom (with potty). Tots are welcome in dining room or bar, with children's portions of dishes or from their own menu, burgers with waffles or beans, fish fingers or sausages. A separate breast-feeding/changing area caters for non-residents. 0-3s free, 4-5s 50% reduction on adult tariff (call for seasonal details). *Rooms 10. Closed Dec-mid Mar.*

Chagford — Mill End — 63% — £83

Tel 0647 432282 Fax 0647 433106	Hotel
Sandy Park Chagford Devon TQ13 8JN	Map 13 D2

The old flour mill, whose wheel still turns in the courtyard, has been a hotel for about 60 years. It stands in the beautiful valley of the river Teign, on whose banks the hotel has fishing rights. Shooting is another popular pastime, while for quiet relaxation the chintzy sitting rooms have the appeal of a well-loved private house. Bedrooms are furnished with a mixture of traditional, antique and modern pieces. Children sharing their parents' room are accommodated free of charge; good facilities for young families include cots, baby baths, potties, nappies and high-chairs. The hotel is on the A382 (don't turn off towards Chagford). *Rooms 17. Garden, fishing, shooting. Closed 10 days mid-Dec. Access, Amex, Diners, Visa.*

Chale — Clarendon Hotel & Wight Mouse Inn

Tel 0983 730431	Pub
Chale Isle of Wight PO38 2HA	Map 15 D4

The Clarendon continues along its merry course, a haven for families. A family suite offers grand comfort and style at only a little more than the regular room price. More than half of the bedrooms are suitable for families and bunk-beds and cots can easily be moved in. Extras

include baby-baths, potties and nappies; there are no phones to wake
beautiful dreamers and baby-listening is done with a plug-in electrical
system, although baby-sitters are always on hand if required. The
Wight Mouse Inn offers plenty of choice for children on its bar menu
as well as offering a 'chips with everything' children's menu. For rainy
days there is a well-equipped games room. *Open* *12 noon-10, (Sun
12-2.30 & 7-9.30). *Closed* *Dec 24-26. *Accommodation* *Under-1s £2,
1-2s £4, 3-5s 50% reduction on adult rates. *Rooms* *15.*

Challock   Halfway House

Tel 0233 740258	Pub

The Crossroads Challock nr Ashford Kent TN25 4BB   Map 11 C5

A large fenced garden, well-stocked with play equipment, is upstaged
by a loudly braying donkey in pet's corner; all of these attractions
leave parents free to enjoy their lunch on the patio or in the new
conservatory extension while the little darlings frolic in view. There
are three high-chairs, a (limited) children's menu, and storage space for
pushchairs. Children may have small portions from the adult menu
or bring their own bottles and food which will be heated. Standard
pub food in easy-going surroundings. Nappy-changing surface in the
ladies. *Open* *12-2 & 7-9.30 *Closed* *for food Sun eve, Dec 25 & 26.
Access, Visa.*

Charlbury   Bell Hotel   £75

Tel 0608 810278 Fax 0608 811447	Inn

Church Street Charlbury Oxfordshire OX7 3PP   Map 16 B2

Once a coaching inn, the Bell stands in the centre of town on the
banks of the Evenlode. The flagstoned bar and restaurant are popular
with locals so ask for a room that is not directly above these if you
or your baby are light sleepers. Bedrooms offer adequate
accommodation and any could take a cot – one is large enough for
an extra bed. Facilities for children are limited but little ones are fussed
over and owner David Jackson is cheerily reassuring about the
reliability of the baby-listening service. Children can request anything
breakfasty for tea at around 6pm but are discouraged from the
restaurant after dark. Small functions are catered for and fishing,
gliding and hot-air ballooning are among the activities which the
hotel can organise. Children up to 16 stay free in parents' room.
Rooms *14. Garden. Access, Amex, Visa, Diners*

Charmouth   Fernhill Hotel   £45

Tel 0297 60492	Hotel

Charmouth Dorset DT6 6BX   Map 13 E2

Whether you stay in the hotel itself, or one of the self-catering
bungalows (not really bungalows but blocks of rooms), Fernhill
is suitable for family holidays. Although the accommodation
is extremely modest, the hotel's fourteen acres have excellent facilities
for children – its own heated swimming pool, paddling pool, games
room, crazy golf and an outdoor play area. There is even a laundrette
for when you are forced to remember what you came to get away
from. The bungalows (bring your own linen and towels) have
a double bedroom, separate twin-bunk room, galley kitchen,
bathroom and child-listening service; TVs can be hired although there
is a television room in the hotel, as well as a lively bar. *Rooms* *52
(35 bungalows, 17 hotel). *Closed* *End October-March. Access, Visa.*

Chawton   Cassandra's Cup

Tel 0420 83144	Tea Room
The Hollies Winchester Road Chawton nr Alton Hampshire GU34 1SB	Map 15 D3

Directly opposite Jane Austen's house in a pretty Hampshire village, Cassandra's Cup is a small, bright tea shop with a few outside tables. The menu covers a range of fruit tarts and teacakes (from 70p), gateaux and scones, hot snacks on toast, jacket potatoes and breakfast (bacon, egg and toast £3.10 served till noon). Parents will appreciate the spotless loo. On warm days tables are set outside and there is an adjacent public playground to keep children amused. *Seats 60.*
Open 10.30-5.30. *Closed* *Telephone for winter hours. No credit cards.*

Cheam   Superfish

Tel 081-643 6906	Fish'n'Chips
64 The Broadway Cheam Surrey	Map 15 E3

Part of a Surrey-based chain of above-average fish and chip restaurants. See Morden entry for more details. *Seats 22. Open 11.30-2 (Sat to 2.30), 5-10.30 (Thu-Sat to 11). Closed Sun, 25 & 26 Dec, 1 Jan. Access, Visa.*

Cheddar   Wishing Well Tea Rooms

Tel 0934 742142	Tea Room
The Cliffs Cheddar Somerset BS27 3QA	Map 13 F1

A long-running family enterprise which offers original choices in its range of afternoon teas. Plain tea £1.75 with bread and butter, cake and tea, cream tea £2.25 (with fresh fruit salad and cream £2.35) and in season a strawberry tea served with clotted cream, scones, cake and tea. Savoury snacks include omelettes, toasted snacks and freshly made sandwiches. On Sunday the Lewis family serve a roast lunch (£5.25 for three courses). Unlicensed. Tucked under the towering cliffs of the Cheddar Gorge, it's very busy in the tourist season. Two high-chairs; buggies need to be left outside; changing shelf in one of the loos. *Seats 64. Open 10-6. Closed all Dec/Jan, Mon-Fri Oct/Nov & Feb/Mar. Access, Visa.*

Chelmsford   Pizza Express

Tel 0245 491466	Pizzeria
219 Moulsham Street Chelmsford Essex	Map 11 B4

Opposite the Bingo Hall, on two floors: ground floor is the main restaurant while upstairs sees live jazz on Tuesday evenings (£3 entrance fee). Familiar decor of white-tiled floor and marble-topped tables plus prints of old masters on the walls. Crisp, thin pizzas with fresh topping ingredients (£3.15-£5.30). *Seats 120.*
Open 11.30-midnight. Closed 25 & 26 Dec. Access, Amex, Visa.

Chelmsford   Saracens Head Hotel
Chambers Restaurant

Tel 0245 262368	Restaurant
3-5 High Street Chelmsford Essex CM1 1BE	Map 11 B4

Chambers Restaurant is one of the few places in central Chelmsford where families can have a good healthy meal – not fast food – in pleasant surroundings. High-chairs are instantly produced and staff are

quite happy to purée something like roast chicken with vegetables
for a baby. Older children have their own menu which includes
chicken nuggets and pizzas (from £2.50). They are equally welcome
to have a small portion from the main menu. The loo is not far away
and a hotel room on the first floor is available for nursing/nappy
changing. No-smoking area. *Seats 60. Open 7-2.30 & 6.30-10, Sat &
Sun 8-2.30 Closed D Sun, 26 Dec, 1 Jan. Access, Amex, Diners, Visa.*

Cheltenham   The Retreat

Tel 0242 235436	Wine bar
10 Suffolk Parade Cheltenham Gloucestershire	Map 14 C1

Michael and Lella Day have been running this friendly and informal
wine bar for ten years. Food is served at lunchtimes only and varies
daily: home-made chicken liver paté (£2.95), herrings in mild
mustard sauce (£4.50), salmon en croute with leek and cheese stuffing
(£4.95), grilled sardines (£4.50), hot smoked chicken sandwich
on granary bread (£2.95), broccoli and cheese quiche (£3.25), with
treacle tart or bread-and-butter pudding and various cheesecakes (all
£2) to finish. Children's portions are available. Alfresco eating
is popular in the enclosed courtyard. *Seats 60. Open 12-2.15.
Closed Sun, Bank Holidays (except Sats). Access, Amex, Diners, Visa.*

Chester   Francs

Tel 0244 317952	Brasserie
14 Cuppin Street Chester Cheshire CH1 2BN	Map 6 A2

Chester's busiest, noisy, bustling and chaotic brasserie serves traditional
French provincial fare. Bare floors, wood tables, timber beams, ceiling
fans and French rock music playing over the loudspeakers set the
scene. The à la carte menu changes every six months and the 'plats
du jour' every day (served from noon to 7pm with salad and plenty
of bread) – excellent cassoulet (£7.85), boudin blanc (£5.75), moules
Bretagne (£3.20), saupiquet (£5.35), crepe au poulet ((£6.95), boeuf
bourguignon. Desserts are just as French with names such as tartelette
marnissimo (red fruits – £3.50), Perigourdine folle (£3.50), tendresse
(£2.50 – egg custard) and Le Napoleon (£3.50 – vanilla génoise cake
filled with light blackcurrant mousse). Sundays are family days when
part of the first floor is given over to a play area for children (four-
course set menu £7.85) and under-10s eat free – reservations
recommended. *Seats 100. Open 12-11. Access, Amex, Visa.*

Chester-le-Street   Whitehills

Tel 091 388 2786	Pub
Chester-le-Street Waldridge Co Durham DH2 3AB	Map 5 E2

A perfect place for children to let off steam, with a climbing set and
slide in the car park; an inside playroom has a similar but smaller
climbing set and a child-sized toilet. Television screens in the pub
allow parents to watch their children snatch, push, get walloped and
head off crying. Children have their own menu from which they can
choose chip-based meals (sausage beans and chips with ice cream
£1.75) which they eat in a conservatory-style family room. Babies are
catered for with three high-chairs and the heating of their own bottles
and food. *Bar Food 12-2 & 7-9.15 (not Sun eves). Access, Amex,
Diners, Visa.*

Chestfield **Chestfield Barn**

Tel 0227 793086	Restaurant
Chestfield nr Whitstable Kent CT5 3LU	**Map 11 C5**

A converted 14th-century barn houses a free house and family
restaurant. The unflustered attentiveness of the staff is more typical
of the modern well-drilled chain establishment, but the late medieval
building is charmingly cussed. Thankfully, the low beam has been
padded for the tall, and there is storage for prams when it gets too
busy to lug them up the awkward stairs to the restaurant. Burgers and
chicken nuggets sum up the children's menu, but small portions of the
meat'n'seafood adult fare are also on offer. High-chairs and booster
seats provided, as are crayons and colouring sheets. A landscaped water
garden is safe for children under supervision. *Open 12-2.30
(Sun to 3) & 6-10 (Sun from 7)*. *Closed Dec 25, 26. Access, Visa.*

Chichester **Clinchs Coffee Shop**

Tel 0243 789915	Coffee Shop
4 Guildhall Street off North Street West Sussex PO19 1NJ	**Map 11 A6**

Bright, airy and lively, this predominantly vegetarian restaurant makes
eating out with children a breeze. Clinchs is always very busy and
there are several eating areas, including a sunny conservatory with
patio and a self-service area where parents can select tot-size portions
of quiches, bakes, pizzas and other savoury dishes, followed
by wholesome desserts like lemon meringue pie or walnut cake.
A high-chair is available and there is plenty of room for prams
or pushchairs. The loos, although clean and well supplied, are too
small to permit nappy changing. Increased no-smoking area this year.
*Seats 82. Open 8.15-5.30, 6-9.30 Closed all Sun & Mon, 25 Dec.
Access, Visa.*

Chichester **Pizza Express**

Tel 0243 779265	Pizzeria
27 South Street Chichester West Sussex	**Map 11 A6**

One of the many popular pizza restaurants in a well-run chain. This
branch is very spacious with prints on the walls and is located about
10 minutes from the railway station. Crisp, thin pizzas (£3.15-£5.40)
with fresh ingredients for the toppings. No-smoking area. *Seats 90.
Open 11.30am-midnight. Closed 25 & 26 Dec. Access, Amex, Visa.*

Chichester **Shepherds Tea Rooms**

Tel 0243 774761	Tea Room
35 Little London Chichester West Sussex	**Map 11 A6**

In a period house just off the main shopping street, Richard and
Yvonne Spence set up their lace-clothed tea room to provide a 'haven
of peace and tranquillity' some ten years ago. Today you may have
to queue at busy times to enjoy the home-made cakes – cherry and
coconut (£1), chocolate mousse cake (£1.95) – sandwiches (from
£2.65) and savoury snacks like filled jacket potatoes (from £3.65) and
various 'rarebits' (a speciality of the house) including Hawaiian (with
pineapple), Stilton (£4.30), buck (with poached egg), Shepherds (with
Brie and tomato) as well as the traditional Welsh rarebit (£3.95).
There are also teacakes, croissants, muffins and crumpets to accompany

the fine selection of loose-leaf teas that include gunpowder (a green tea), Lapsang Souchong, fruit teas and their own special English Breakfast Tea blend – a mixture of Assam, Ceylon and African. *Seats 50. Open 9.15-5 (Sat from 8). Closed Sun, Bank Holidays. No credit cards.*

Chipping Camden   Kings Arms Hotel, Saddle Room

Tel 0386 840256	Hotel Bar
The Square Chipping Camden Gloucestershire GL55 6AW	Map 14 C1

The panelled Saddle Room is the bar at this 16th-century Cotswold-stone hotel in the market square. If the weather is fine, take your lunch out into the walled garden. The choice may include home-made soup (£1.75), sardines fried with garlic and prawns (from £3), Cumberland sausage in red wine sauce (£5) and chicken tikka (£5.25) as well as jacket potatoes and sandwiches, with banoffi pie or chocolate lover's delight (both £1.75) to follow. A roast is served on Sundays (£6.50). *Seats 30. Open 12-3 & 6-9.30. Access, Visa.*

Cirencester   Brewery Arts Coffee House

Tel 0285 654791	Coffee Shop
Brewery Court Cirencester Gloucestershire	Map 14 C2

Pictures adorn the Cotswold stone exposed walls of this attractive coffee shop specialising in wholefood and vegetarian food. Staff serve the food at the counter where cold dishes prevail in summer and hot meals are available in winter. The choice could be savoury pastry slices (£2.60), home-baked ham with salad (£3), watercress soup (£1.40), spinach, mushroom and rice in Stilton sauce (£3), and hazelnut and celery en croute (£2.60). The resident confectioner bakes over 100 different kinds of cakes for their 'cake-away' service, many of which are available for tea: lemon and mace cake, coffee streusel or sticky fig and almond cake (all 75p). Good choice of tea. No smoking. *Seats 53. Open 10-5. Closed Sun, 25 & 26 Dec, 1 Jan. No credit cards.*

Clare   The Peppermill

Tel 0787 278148	Restaurant
1 Well Lane Market Square Clare Suffolk CO10 8NH	Map 10 C3

Local produce gets careful treatment at this cottage-style restaurant with origins in the 15th century. Sandwiches (from £1.50) and omelettes (£2.50) are popular lunchtime snacks, with fish pie (£4.50), nut roast or a steak for something more substantial. Cheesecake (£1.80) and bread pudding figure among the sweets. Children's portions available plus crayons and books. The ladies' loo upstairs has nappy-changing and nursing facilities. No smoking. *Seats 20. Open 12-2 (& 7-9 Thur-Sat). Closed Mon, around 26 Dec & 1 Jan. Access, Visa.*

Clavering   Cricketers

Tel 0799 550442	Pub
Clavering nr Saffron Walden Essex CB11 4QT	Map 10 B3

200 yards from the cricket green, this recently refurbished pub offers well-prepared home-made food with a menu that changes every 2-3 months. Tuesdays are seafood evenings and a roast beef carvery (£6.50) is available on Wednesday and Sunday evenings (plus

lunchtimes throughout winter). The restaurant has seating for 70, the bar for 120 and 75 can eat outside. The restaurant offers a 3-course meal with choice of 10 starters and main courses for £18. Paula, the resident pastry chef, cooks 12 wonderful desserts daily. *Bar Food 12-2, 7-10. Restaurant Meals 12-2 Sunday only, 7-10 (except Sun and Mon), Vegetarian dishes. Children's menu (£2.25 per dish). Free House. Beer Flowers IPA, Wethered Bitter, Boddingtons. Garden, outdoor eating. Access, Visa.*

Clawton	Court Barn	61%	£70
Tel 040 927 219			Hotel
Clawton Holsworthy Devon EX22 6PS			Map 12 C2

Five acres of garden surround a delightful 1853 manor house three miles south of Holsworthy (follow the A388). Day rooms like the lounge and tiny bar are easy places in which to relax; the patio is also a lovely place to take a traditional tea in good weather. Three bedrooms are suitable for family use, and children up to 14 stay free in parents' room. Cots, high-chairs and baby-listening are available. Bar snacks throughout the day in the old dining room and bar lunches from 12 to 2. 5 to 12-year-olds are served their own supper menu between 5 and 6pm and older children eating with their parents at 8 pm are charged 50%. No smoking. *Rooms 8. Garden, pitch & putt, putting, badminton. Closed 1 wk Jan. Access, Amex, Diners, Visa.*

Clearwell	Wyndham Arms	
Tel 05948 33666 Fax 05948 36450		Pub
Clearwell nr Coleford Gloucestershire GL16 8JT		Map 14 B2

You will find tranquillity, old-fashioned hospitality and good food at this charming inn, dating from the 1340s. A modern annexe houses 17 well-equipped bedrooms; family facilities are first class and there is plenty of room in the family suites for cots and extra beds. If you fancy a nocturnal stroll in the Royal Forest of Dean, baby-listening can be arranged. Friendly staff and high standards of housekeeping. In the restaurant, each child is given a toy to play with so that parents can peruse the menu uninterrupted (well, that's the idea). High-chairs are provided. *Free House. Beer Flowers Best Bitter, Bass. Garden. Accommodation 17 bedrooms, all en suite, £55 (single £30). Children welcome overnight, additional beds, cots available. Access, Amex, Diners, Visa.*

Cleveleys	Bay Tree	
Tel 0253 865604		Restaurant
44 Victoria Road West Cleveleys nr Blackpool Lancashire		Map 6 A1

You will find this pleasant wholefood and vegetarian restaurant above a health food shop. The menu is imaginative – to start you could choose from soup or paté (£1.50) and main courses could be curried lentil pie, courgette and tomato bake or vegetable goulash (all at £3.60). Desserts might include plum crumble, strawberry almond roulade and gooseberry frangipane. For Sunday lunch there is a special menu £5.50-£6.50 for 3 courses. Children's portions. No smoking throughout. *Seats 36. Open 10-3 & (Fri/Sat) 7-9. Closed All Mon except Bank Holidays, D Tue-Sun, 25 & 26 Dec, 1 Jan. No credit cards.*

Coggeshall   White Hart   69%   £82

Tel 0376 561654   Fax 0376 561789   Hotel

Market End Coggeshall Essex CO6 1NH   Map 10 C3

A centuries-old inn that still retains all its character with flagstone
floors, low beams, inglenook fireplace and no fewer than two resident
ghosts. Careful renovation and refurbishment in recent years has added
style and comfort to the atmospheric surroundings. Individually
decorated bedrooms, 12 in a new extension, offer little extras like fresh
fruit and mineral water; two family rooms have a cot each. Room
service is limited to continental breakfast. Children are welcome and
baby-sitting/listening can be arranged in advance. *Rooms 18. Garden,
Access, Amex, Diners, Visa.*

Restaurant   £60

A long, low and narrow dining room with sturdy beams and cheerful
staff. An Italian menu ranges from risotto milanese and spaghetti
carbonara to escalope of veal cooked in Marsala wine. Sunday brunch
is popular. *Seats 70. L 12-2 D 7-10. Closed D Sun.*

Colchester   Butterfly Hotel   61%   £67

Tel 0206 230900   Fax 0206 231095   Hotel

Old Ipswich Road Ardleigh Colchester Essex CO7 7QY   Map 10 C3

Colchester's newest hotel is part of a small chain offering practical
accommodation (there is separate work space in all the bedrooms).
No dogs. Located on the A12/A120 near the Business Parks. Handy
stop-over. *Rooms 50. Access, Amex, Diners, Visa.*

Collier Street   Butcher's Mere

Tel 0892 730495   Tea Room

Collier Street nr Marden Kent TN12 9RR   Map 11 B5

Stay cosy in Louise Holme's popular beamed tea room or take the sun
in the mature garden, which sports its own duck pond (no fence
so watch the little ones) complete with wisteria-clad wicket bridge.
Louise excels in home baking and jam-making. The light scones, fruit
cake, lemon curd sponge, meringues, chocolate cake, coffee and walnut
cake, and apricot log are some of the most popular choices to have
with freshly ground coffee or cup of tea. Diabetic cream teas (£3) and
fat-free sponges are also available. £1.25 minimum charge.
Unlicensed. No smoking. Delightful for families in summer when the
garden can be based, but cramped inside when the weather's not
so good. *Seats 32. Open 10-7 (winter to 6, Thu from 3). Closed 1 week
Christmas. No credit cards.*

Congresbury   White Hart

Tel 0934 833303   Pub

Wrington Road Congresbury Avon BS19 5AR   Map 13 F1

Off the A370, follow signs to Wrington/Redhill and you will find the
White Hart. Mr and Mrs Beck have carried on the tradition
of welcoming families to the White Hart by retaining the spacious
family room where the vaulted glass roof lets in light and a box
of toys keeps children happy. If you visit on a sunny day, so much the
better; there is a big safely enclosed, grassy garden with bench

tables, a slide, swings, a climbing frame, a trampoline, Wendy House and rabbits. Children have their own menu (£1.95 per dish). *Bar Food 12-2 & 6-9.30. Access, Visa.*

Cooden	**Cooden Resort Hotel**	**60%**	**£75**
Tel 042 43 2281 Fax 042 43 6142			Hotel
Cooden Sea Road Bexhill-on-Sea East Sussex TN39 4TT			Map 11 C6

Right on the beach, with views across Pevensey Bay, this 30s' hotel caters well for both leisure and business guests. There are facilities for up to 200 conference delegates, a health and leisure club, a modern lounge, a cocktail bar and a tavern serving real ale. One of the bedrooms has been adapted for disabled guests; 12 are suitable for family use, with cots and baby-sitting available. The jolly jester menu for junior diners offers typical favourites like Neptune's platter (fish fingers) and royal porker (sausage, beans and chips). *Rooms 41. Garden, keep-fit equipment, indoor & outdoor swimming pools, spa bath, sauna, solarium, beautician, hairdressing, squash. Access, Amex, Diners, Visa.*

Corfe Castle	**Corfe Castle Restaurant & Tea Rooms**	
Tel 0929 481332		Tea Room
Corfe Castle Dorset		Map 14 C4

The tea room is suitably old and beamed, with lattice windows and floral drapes. At the back is a garden with views up to the brooding ruins of the castle. Breakfast with toast or croissants starts the day, then at lunchtime come sandwiches, salads (from £4), jacket potatoes and a hot dish of the day. Afternoon tea presents huge home-baked scones, clotted cream and jam (£2.65) or a slice of home-made cake – perhaps coffee walnut sponge or rich sticky fruit cake – with bread and butter (£2.35). Sunday roast £4.75 with a vegetarian alternative. Everything is spot on – a proper job – and they're happy to cater for young children. No smoking. *Seats 50. Open 10.30-5.30 (Nov-Mar 11-4). Access, Amex, Diners, Visa.*

Corse Lawn	**Simply Corse Lawn**	
Tel 0452 780771		Hotel Bistro
Corse Lawn House Hotel Corse Lawn nr Tewkesbury Gloucestershire		Map 14 B1

Baba Hine's cooking is as impressive as the splendid Queen Anne house (on the B4211). Baba and husband Denis have recently opened Simply Corse Lawn, their new bistro-style section where good food is produced at affordable prices (all dishes under £10) in a more casual and less formal atmosphere than in the restaurant. Starters or light snacks might be soupe au pistou (£2.95), fish cakes with seafood sauce (£4.95), home-made sausages with vegetables (£5.95), open ravioli of lamb's kidneys with mustard sauce (£5.50); main courses range from French onion tart (£3.95) to mixed vegetable risotto with saffron and garlic (£6.50), bourride of mixed seafood with prawns and mussels (£7.50) or shank of lamb provençale (£7.50). Desserts are a must – hot butterscotch sponge pudding (£2.95), chocolate indulgence (£3.95) or iced nougat (£3.95). Children's portions on request. There's outdoor seating around the pond. *Seats 35. Open 12-2 & 7-10. Access, Amex, Diners, Visa.*

Crathorne   Crathorne Hall   72%   £105

| Tel 0642 700398   Fax 0642 700814 | Hotel |

Crathorne nr Yarm Cleveland TS15 0AR   Map 5 E3

At the end of a long driveway, among 15 acres of beautiful
countryside between the Yorkshire Dales and the North Yorkshire
Moors, the imposing hall was one of the last major houses built in the
Edwardian era. Now fully restored to its former glory by Richard
Branson's Voyager Hotels. Great care has been taken with
refurbishment to retain the house's inherent character. The sumptuous
drawing room is a good example of this work, with large oil paintings
of the Kings George hanging either side of a fine fireplace and
abundant comfortable seating. Similar style and taste is shown in the
bedrooms and bathrooms, where choice furnishings and rich fabrics
contribute to the elegant decor and luxurious feel. Improvements are
continuing with further rooms planned. Themed weekends are
popular, involving fishing, murder/mystery events, birdwatching and
wine appreciation; last Easter, for example, families were offered
an egg hunt in the grounds, special meal times, baby-sitting and
listening services plus a dinner dance for the parents once the
youngsters were in bed. Children under 5 stay and eat free if sharing
their parents' room. *Rooms 37. Garden. Access, Amex, Diners, Visa.*

Crawley   Fortune Villa

| Tel 0293 520432 | Restaurant |

98 High Street West Sussex RH10 1BZ   Map 11 B6

Crawley boasts very little on the entertainment front but does serve
Gatwick Airport so a recommendation here could be useful after too
many hours in a crowded plane. There is no children's menu but
Chinese food is ideal for sharing so portion size is not a problem. The
sizzling Peking duck is good and is the perfect teaching aid for the
'don't touch – it's hot' lesson. Sesame prawn toasts are popular with
children as are mild dishes like lemon chicken or soft noodles with
crunchy beansprouts. Two high-chairs. *Open 12-2.30 & 10.45 (Sun
10.30). Closed L Sun, 25 & 26 Dec. Access, Visa.*

Croydon   Pizza Express

| Tel 081-680 0123 | Pizzeria |

3 South End Croydon Surrey   Map 11 B5

Another popular pizza outlet in this well-run chain. Crisp, thin
pizzas and fresh ingredients used for the toppings. *Seats 100.
Open 11.30am-midnight. Closed 25 & 26 Dec. Access, Amex, Visa.*

Cuckfield   Murray's   £55

| Tel 0444 455826 | Restaurant |

Broad Street Cuckfield West Sussex RH17 5LJ   Map 11 B6

Several cottagey rooms provide a cosy setting for enjoying Sue
Murray's skilled and imaginative cooking. Influences from Europe and
beyond appear in dishes on a spring dinner menu: bagna cauda,
haddock timbale, chicken in Marsala, honey-glazed pork with ginger,
spring onions and sticky sugar-and-rice-wine sauce served with egg
thread noodles. Short wine list with many bottles under £15.
*Seats 30. Private Room. L 12-1.30 D 7.15-9.30. Closed L Sat, all Sun,
Bank Holidays, 2 weeks Feb, 2 weeks Sep. Access, Visa.*

Dartington   **Cranks Health Food Restaurant**

Tel 0803 862388	Café
Shinners Bridge Dartington nr Totnes Devon	**Map 13 D3**

Recently bought out by its own managers, Cranks continues its former success with a high throughput of visitors to the ever-popular Cider Press Centre. Service is courteous and efficient at the self-help counter, and seating ample if closely spaced at varnished pine tables. Mexican bean broth (£1.70), vegetarian crumble and Boston bean bake (£3.25) are the stuff of lunchtime, amply supplemented by mixed and green salads (£1.30). Baking weighs in with pizza slices and homity pie (£1.90) and a wealth of such sweets as Bakewell slice (£1.65) and lemon cheesecake (£1.90). Especially handy parking and disabled access. Take-away service also. Licensed 12-3 with meals only. No smoking. No dogs. *Seats* 70. *Open* 10-5. *Closed* Sun in winter, 25 26 Dec & 1 Jan. No credit cards.

Dartmouth   **Stoke Lodge**   **60%**   £67

Tel 0803 770523	Hotel
Stoke Fleming Dartmouth Devon TQ6 0RA	**Map 13 D3**

Family-run, and with family holidays very much in mind, the hotel overlooks the village and the sea. The sun terrace is a popular spot when the weather's kind, and inside are homely, unpretentious lounges and neat bedrooms. Under-2s accommodated free (cots available), 2-5s 25%, 5-14 50% of adult rate. 6pm children's supper (order before noon); high-chairs provided. *Rooms* 24. *Garden, indoor & outdoor swimming pools, tennis, putting, keep-fit equipment, giant chess. Access, Visa.*

Dedham   **Dedham Centre Vegetarian Restaurant**

Tel 0206 322677	Restaurant
Arts & Crafts Centre High Street Dedham Essex	**Map 10 C3**

The three-storey, former United Reform church in the delightful village of Dedham has been remodelled (but has retained the organ) to house the Arts and Crafts Centre – various open-plan shops selling clothes, jewellery, paintings, pottery plus a toy museum on the first floor – and a vegetarian self-service restaurant on the ground floor. Home-made food suitable for vegans includes vegetable soup with wholemeal bread (£1.85), mushroom and cashew roast (£4.45), cheese pancake with filling of the day, stuffed jacket potatoes (from £2.45), and toasted cheese or egg sandwich. A daily special (£4.75) may be a vegetable cottage pie or leek and mushroom pastie, and daily-changing puddings feature fresh lemon tart or apricot and almond tart (both £2.25). A set tea (£2.95) is served all day. Unlicensed. Service is brisk and children are well looked after with beakers, high-chairs and small portions on offer. There are no changing facilities and the one loo is very small. No-smoking area. *Seats* 54. *Open* 10-5 (Sat & Sun to 5.30). *Closed* Mon (Jan-Mar only), 25 & 26 Dec. No credit cards.

Dent   **The Hop Bine Restaurant**

Tel 05875 400	Restaurant
Dent Crafts Centre Helmside Dent Cumbria LA10 5SY	**Map 5 D4**

Part of Dent Crafts Centre and housed in a converted Dales barn with splendid views across Dent Dale, the Hop Bine restaurant is also a gallery. Pictures line the walls and crafts are displayed in a room with rustic tables and stone-flagged floors. Fourteen 'international platters' are available all day (£2.95-£3.25) – Greek: salad, houmus, tsatsiki, olives and feta cheese. Cheese-eaters may like to sample the local varieties (£3.25). Lunch is a three-course set menu (£7.25 coffee included) which might include home-made soup, Mexican chicken pie, and three-fruit crumble. Evening meals are available by prior arrangement only (four-course menu £12.95). There's a set afternoon tea (£4.25) with a choice of ten loose-leaf teas and several home-baked cakes (Porter ale cake, lemon whisky buns, coffee kisses, date bars). Outdoor eating in the yard (next to playground). Children's portions. No smoking. *Seats* 40. *Open* 9.30-5.30. *Closed weekdays Jan-Feb. Access, Visa.*

Derby   International Hotel   62%   £60
| Tel 0332 369321   Fax 0332 294430 | Hotel |
| Burton Road Derby Derbyshire DE3 6AD | Map 6 C3 |

On the A5250 south-west of the city centre, the privately-owned International concentrates very much on conference and exhibition business. Of the numerous meeting rooms, the largest comfortably seats up to 50 theatre-style. Bedrooms offer many extras and the suites boast spa baths. Greatly reduced rates at weekends. *Rooms* 62. *Dinner dance (weekly). Access, Amex, Diners, Visa.*

Devizes   Wiltshire Kitchen
| Tel 0380 724840 | Restaurant |
| 11 St John's Street Devizes Wiltshire | Map 14 C3 |

Behind a corner shop just off the market square lies a very special eating place. Ann Blunden has been running her popular restaurant for eight years and now also specialises in outside catering. Customers help themselves and can sit downstairs, on ground level or outside at a table on the pavement. The day begins with breakfast (full £3.50) and cappuccino with croissant or fresh roll. The menu for lunch changes every day and could include potato and coriander soup (£1.20), seafood roulade (£4.10), roast lamb with garlic herb crust (£4.30), chicken in orange marmalade sauce, spaghetti bolognese or one of the basics, filled jacket potatoes (from £2.95), slice of quiche (Stilton and leek or calabrese, £2.95 with salad). Leave a space for the home-made puddings (£1.95 with custard or cream) – coffee meringues, fruit crumble, French lemon tart, ginger apple cake. At teatime, choose one of the many teas available, with a scone if desired. No smoking. *Seats* 48. *Open* 8.30-5 (*summer to* 5.30). *Closed Sun, 24 Dec-2 Jan. No credit cards.*

Didsbury   Est Est Est
| Tel 061-445 8209 | Restaurant |
| 756 Wilmslow Road Manchester Greater Manchester | Map 6 B2 |

A large and friendly Italian restaurant decorated in light, white trattoria style and divided across a centre curve giving a raised stage effect to the rear seating section. The menu has 16 starters (deep-fried mushrooms and mozzarella cheese balls £3.35), and 16 pastas that can be eaten as starters or main courses (penne tossed with tomato, peperoni and chili £2.45/£4.55), 12 pizzas (£4.35-£5.45) and 15 secondi piatti (scampi in a mild curry sauce £9.95). Tables with

parasols on the pavement in summer. *Seats 200. Open 12-2.30 &*
6-11.30 (Sun 12-10.30). Closed 25 & 26 Dec. Access, Amex, Diners.

Diss   Weavers Wine Bar and Eating House

Tel 0379 642411	Restaurant
Market Hill Diss Norfolk	Map 10 C2

This charming restaurant is housed in what was a chapel for the Guild
of Weavers nearly 500 years ago. Some original beams remain and
small alcoves with banquettes are popular for quieter moments. The
lunchtime menu is depends on what's in season: soup is the only starter
(£1.25 – apple and parsnip, ham and cauliflower with crispy bacon)
although guests can choose others off the evening menu, followed
by poached breast of pigeon with redcurrant, juniper and sloe gin
sauce (£4.45), wing of skate with prawns and capers, braised oxtail
with red wine, garlic and herbs, seafood tagliatelle (£4.95) or fresh
Cromer crab salad. Home-made puddings (£1.95) are brown bread
ice cream in brandy snap basket, cornflake and apple crunch with
custard or rich chocolate truffle cake. Slightly more elaborate evening
à la carte menu averages about £17.50 a head before drinks. Children's
portions. No smoking during mealtimes. *Seats 80. Open (bar food)*
12-2 & 7-9.30. Closed L Sat, all Sun, Bank Holidays, 6 days Christmas,
last week Aug. Access, Diners, Visa.

Dorking   Pizza Express

Tel 0306 888236	Pizzeria
235 High Street Dorking Surrey	Map 15 E3

Housed in what was once a coach works at the beginning of the
century and its leisurely atmosphere encourages families. The usual
selection fo a dozen or so thin pizzas with fresh ingredients for
toppings. Live jazz evenings. *Seats 110. Open 11am-midnight.*
Closed 25 & 26 Dec. Access, Amex, Visa.

Dorstone   Pandy Inn

Tel 0981 550273	Pub
Dorstone Golden Valley Hereford & Worcester HR3 6AN	Map 9 D5

Located off the B4348, the Pandy was the oldest inn in Herefordshire,
built in 1185 by Richard De Brito, a Norman knight, to house his
workers while building Dorstone Church as atonement for his part
in the murder of Thomas Becket. Vegetarians are particularly well
catered for on the daily changing menu, with a variety of dishes
to choose from including spinach and mushroom lasagne (£4.95) and
vegetable moussaka (£4.75). There's a 'From the Sea & River' menu
as well as 'Light Bites & Starters'. 'Puddings & Treats' includes a choice
of seven desserts (all £1.95). The large garden has swings and plenty
of space in which to run around. *Bar Food 12-2, 7-9.45. Children's*
menu (£1.95 per dish). Children allowed to eat in bar. Free house. Beer
Bass, Charles Wells Eagle, Hook Norton. Garden, outdoor eating, children's
play area. Family room. No credit cards.

Dovedale   Izaak Walton Hotel   59%   £90

Tel 033 529 555 Fax 033 529 539	Hotel
Dovedale Nr Ashbourne Derbyshire DE6 2AY	Map 6 C3

A splendidly located hilltop hotel on the Duke of Rutland's estates; its
17th-century farmhouse building affords rolling views of Thorpe
Cloud and Dovedale in the Peak District Park. Leather chesterfield

sofas and open fires add comfort and warmth to the public rooms;
bedrooms are more noteworthy for the vistas without than the space
within. Five good-sized bedrooms are suitable for families and there
are plenty of cots and Z-beds available (up to two under-16s stay free
in their parents' room). Baby-listening is provided by means of a two-
way radio, with parents carrying receivers themselves. High tea
is served in the Buttery from 5.30-6pm; children may also dine in the
restaurant with their parents or at tables in the safe garden in summer;
high-chairs are provided. The new children's menu reflects the interest
shown by guests in healthier eating options for their families.
A children's fun pack is promised on arrival. **Rooms 34.** *Dinner dance
(Sat), helipad. Access, Amex, Diners, Visa.*

Downton   White Horse Inn

Tel 0725 20408	Pub
The Borough Downton Wiltshire SP5 3LY	**Map 14 C3**

A giant-size boot with slide attachments dominates the play area and
is one of the more up-to-date additions to the original 16th-century
coaching inn. A family dining room is housed in what was once
stables. The printed children's menu is just a starting point; they are
open to suggestions and where possible will prepare small portions
of adult dishes. Most of the food is home-made and you can expect
fo find pubby dishes like steak and kidney pie made with Dorchester
bitter or Taunton pie (pork, chicken and ham with Stilton and dry
cider). **Open** *12-2 & 7-9.30 (Sun 9). No food Dec 25 & 26, Sun eves
Xmas-Easter. Access, Visa.*

Dulverton   Tarr Farm

Tel 064385 383	Tea Room
Tarr Steps Dulverton Somerset TA22 9PY	**Map 13 D2**

The old English garden is the best place to sit when the weather
is kind, watching the river rushing around the famous steps below.
Otherwise snuggle up inside this cosy Exmoor farmhouse and enjoy
the cream teas. Lunch might include soup, ploughman's platter, pasties,
quiche, lasagne or macaroni with salad. Apple crumble for pud.
Open *11-5.30.* **Closed** *end Oct-end Mar.*

Dunwich   Ship Inn

Tel 072873 219	Pub
St James Street Dunwich Suffolk IP17 3DT	**Map 10 D2**

Well-loved old smugglers' inn overlooking the salt marshes and sea.
The delightfully unspoilt public bar offers nautical bric-a-brac,
a wood-burning stove in a huge brick fireplace, flagged floors and
simple wooden furnishings. There's also a plain carpeted dining room.
A fine Victorian staircase leads to simple, homely bedrooms, light and
clean with pretty fabrics and period touches, but no televisions. Good
simple food in generous portions, too: the restaurant menu applies
throughout the pub in the evenings; bar meals menu lunchtime only.
Families can eat in the breakfast room/conservatory; one high-chair
is provided. There is a huge garden where children can run free. **Bar
Food & Restaurant Meals** *12-2, 7.30-9.15. Children's portions.* **Beer**
Adnams, Greene King. Garden, outdoor eating. Family room.
Accommodation *3 bedrooms, 1 en suite, £48. Children welcome overnight,
additional beds (£12), cots supplied. Check-in by arrangement.
No credit cards.*

Easingwold   Truffles

Tel 0347 22342	Café

Snowdon House Spring Street Easingwold Yorkshire YO6 3BN   Map 7 D1

Truffles is in the middle of Easingwold's delightful, cobbled market
place. Children are warmly welcomed and have their own menu; one
high-chair is provided, along with beakers, plastic cups, plates and
small knives and forks. The food comes into its own in the sweets,
cakes and desserts section; good hot chocolate and whipped cream,
honey and cinnamon milk and excellent Taylors coffee. *Open 10-4.30
(to 9 in winter), Sun 12-4, Mon 12-2, Tues (winter) 10-4. No credit cards.*

East Horsley   Thatchers Resort Hotel   63%   £95

Tel 048 65 4291 Fax 048 65 4222	Hotel

Epsom Road East Horsley Surrey KT24 6TB   Map 15 E3

Mock-Tudor building in three acres of grounds. Modern decor in the
bedrooms; two four-poster rooms; several family rooms (children
up to 14 stay free in parents' room; cots available). Plans for 1993
include more bedrooms, an additional conference room (holding
up to 120) and a health and leisure club. *Rooms 59. Garden, outdoor
swimming pool, baby-sitting, baby-listening, helipad. Access, Amex, Diners,
Visa.*

East Molesey   Superfish

Tel 081-979 2432	Fish'n'Chips

90 Walton Road East Molesey   Map 15 E2

Part of a Surrey-based chain of above-average fish and chip restaurants.
See Morden entry for more details. *Seats 30. Open 11.30-2 (Sat
to 2.30), 5-10.30 (Thu-Sat to 11). Closed Sun, 25 & 26 Dec, 1 Jan.
Access, Visa.*

East Sutton   Shant Hotel

Tel 0622 842235	Pub

East Sutton nr Maidstone Kent ME17 3DT   Map 11 C5

An attractive old-world pub on a quiet country lane with a safe
garden. Bedrooms are spacious and all have en-suite bathrooms. There
are two cots (under-2s free in their parents' room) and a Z-bed will
be brought into your room (£5 charge) for older children. The
extensive bar menu changes frequently and is supplemented
by a blackboard list of daily specials. All food is cooked on the
premises and proves to be an enjoyable change from the usual pub
grub. Children can have small portions and will be given small cutlery
with which to eat. Staff are very understanding and take the sting out
of any tantrums by calmly assuring you that they've been there too.
*Open 12-2 & 6.30-10 (Sun 7-10). Closed Dec 25 &
26. Accommodation 16 rooms £55, 5 family rooms. Access, Amex, Visa.*

Eastbourne   Grand Hotel   75%   £150

Tel 0323 412345 Fax 0323 412233	Hotel

King Edward's Parade Eastbourne East Sussex BN21 4EQ   Map 11 B6

Sound management and smart, committed staff try hard to keep
up the grand image and reputation for good service at a whitewashed,
seafront establishment that dates back to Victorian times. Marble
pillars, crystal chandeliers, vast corridors and high-domed day rooms

evoke a more leisurely, bygone age of spacious and gracious hotels.
Some of the sea-facing bedrooms have balconies and are huge, with
bright furniture and up-to-date fabrics, but not all are as smart
or as generous in size. 24hr room service, comprehensive leisure and
exercise facilities, themed weekend breaks and children's hostesses keep
the Grand apace with its more modern competitors. Families are well
catered for. **Rooms** *164. Garden, indoor & outdoor swimming pools, spa
bath, sauna, solarium, beauty & hairdressing salons, keep-fit equipment,
snooker, play room (summer). Access, Amex, Diners, Visa.*

Mirabelle Restaurant   £67

Chef Keith Mitchell produces imaginative menus executed with flair
and served by polished and professional staff in elegant surroundings.
Fixed-price lunch (2- or 3-course) and dinner (4-course, priced
by choice of main course) menus offer a small choice of dishes like
crab bisque, a ragout of sole and mussels with carrots and coriander,
a daily roast served from a silver trolley, smoked haddock, salmon and
crab cakes with a tomato and chive compote, or English lamb chump
chop topped with a leek and onion soubise and a rosemary jus.
In addition, an à la carte offers classic dishes with modern touches.
Longish list of wines includes half a dozen English wines and a choice
of 16 brandies by the glass. **Seats** *50. Parties 50. Private
Room. L 12.30-2.30 D 7-10.30. Closed Sun & Mon, Bank Holidays,
2 weeks Jan, 2 weeks Aug. Set L from £13 Set D from £19.50.*

Easton   Clarke's   £50

Tel 0603 880241	Restaurant
Dereham Road Easton Norwich Norfolk NR9 5AH	Map 10 C1

Adrian and Rachael Clarke run a cheerful little restaurant on the A47,
six miles out of Norwich. A la carte and set menus provide plenty
of good eating, from seafood pancake or lamb's sweetbreads with
a cream and French mustard sauce to grilled brill with lemon and
parsley butter, breast of duck with blackcurrant sauce and veal
escalopes cooked in a cognac, cream, mushroom and tarragon sauce.
The Clarkes have two children of their own and therefore welcome
families, particularly on Sundays when children are just as happy to eat
the roast lunch as a burger (£1.50) or fish fingers from their own
menu. Buggies can be easily stored and there's a rarely used back
dining-room where mothers may like to retreat to nurse or change
their baby. **Seats 50.** *Parties 50. Private Room. L 12-2 D 7-9.30.
Closed D Sun, all Mon, 1 Jan. Set meals from £13.50. Access, Amex,
Visa.*

Easton Grey   Easton Grey Garden Restaurant

Tel 0666 840345	Restaurant
Easton Grey nr Malmesbury Wiltshire SN16 OPQ	Map 14 B2

A relaxed atmosphere and excellent service are attractions of this
pastel-shaded restaurant. Should your children not wish to be relaxed,
then they will enjoy running around the pleasant manor house
grounds surrounding the restaurant (although supervision is needed for
playing by the river at the bottom of the garden). There are no special
facilities for children except for two high-chairs and the heating
of bottles and baby food. Small portions of all dishes are available –
cottage pie, lasagne and a regular fish dish are typical. No-smoking
area. **Seats** *60.* **Open** *10.30-5.30.* **Closed** *Sun & 10 days Christmas.
Access, Visa.*

Edburton   **Tottington Manor Hotel**

Tel 0903 815757	Pub

Edburton nr Henfield West Sussex BN5 9LJ   Map 11 B6

A Grade II listed 17th-century inn-cum-hotel in its own grounds at the
foot of the South Downs, with lovely views. The bar is simple and
properly pubby, with country furniture and an open fire hogged
by an assortment of animals. Good bar food can be eaten either in the
bar or outside in the garden overlooking the Downs; prices are a little
higher in the grander restaurant, whose £15, 3-course menu includes
half a bottle of wine. Breast of French duckling with honey and fig
sauce, roast South Down lamb and a wide variety of fresh fish are
some of the main courses; several vegetarian dishes are always
available. Bedrooms are pretty, with soothing colours and good sturdy
furniture, and en-suite bathrooms have proper guest toiletries. The
residents' lounge is also rather fine. *Bar Food 12-2, 7-9.15. Restaurant
Meals 7-9.15 (except Sun). Children's portions. Free House. Beer
Adnams, Bateman 4X, Fullers. Garden, outdoor eating. Accommodation
6 bedrooms, all en suite, £60. Children welcome overnight, additional beds
(£12), cot supplied. Pub closed on Sundays from January to end March.
Access, Amex, Diners, Visa.*

Elsted Marsh   **Elsted Inn**

Tel 0730 813662	Pub

Elsted Marsh Midhurst West Sussex GU29 0JT   Map 11 A6

It would be very easy to drive past this unprepossessing Victorian
roadside pub, but that would be to miss out on some good food and
a warm welcome. It was built to serve the railway in the steam age,
when there was a station here, but was later left stranded by Dr
Beeching's 'axe' in the 1950s. This explains the old railway
photographs that adorn the thankfully unmodernised and
unpretentious bars, in what is very much a local community pub, free
of background music and electronic games but with plenty
of traditional pub pastimes like shove ha'penny, darts, cards, dominoes
and even conversation. There are two small bars with lots of wood
in evidence, original shutters and open fires. A small dining room,
candle-lit in the evening, boast an old pine dresser and colourful cloths
on a few dining tables surrounded by a motley collection of old chairs.
Tweazle Jones and her partner Barry Horton have between them
a varied catering background, resulting in a globetrotting menu –
always home-made and based on good local produce – with the likes
of osso buco from Italy, coq au vin from France or Mexican tacos.
England is also well represented though, with dishes like braised oxtail,
mutton with caper sauce and sandwiches closely resembling door
steps; vegetarians are well served, too, with lentil bakes and vegetable
roulades. Children can have half portions at half price, and there's a car
tyre hanging from a plum tree in the shady garden to keep them
amused, plus pétanque for the adults; no high-chairs. Dogs are
welcome or at least tolerated by the house hounds, Truffle and Sam,
and an area of the garden is fenced off to keep dogs and children apart.
*Bar Food 12-2.30, 7-10 (9.30 Sun). Beer Adnams, Ballards, Batemans,
Mitchells. Family room. Outdoor play area, garden, outdoor eating, summer
barbecue. Access, Visa.*

Elton   Loch Fyne Oyster Bar

Tel 0832 280298	Restaurant
The Old Dairy Elton nr Peterborough Cambridgeshire PE8 6SG	Map 7 E4

The Old Dairy is a stone building standing on its own in a car park
opposite a walled garden, 100 yards from the A605 bypass to Oundle.
The wood-panelled interior (Scots pine and larch from Argyll),
natural slate floor in walkways and aquamarine carpet give
a Scandinavian feel to this predominantly fish (some game) restaurant
which has a retail outlet next door. A pair of kippers served with
sautéed potatoes (£4.95) or Finnan haddock with a poached egg
(£3.95) are breakfast choices. A good supply of white fish from the
East coast provides the basis of several dishes of the day – grilled Dover
sole (£8.95), seafood marinière (£9.50), monkfish in white wine sauce
(£7.95). Shellfish include a platter of cold langoustines on seaweed
(£12.95), and of course the Loch Fyne oysters (3/£2, 6/£3.90,
12/£7.80). A recent addition to the menu is wild oysters from the
Hebrides (3 for £4.95). Mull Cheddar, Dunsyre Blue and Inverlochy
goat's cheese are a good alternative to a pudding, unless of course you
cannot resist trifle, sticky toffee pudding, apple crumble or banoffi pie
(all £2.85). Tea with cake and shortbread is available in the
afternoons. A ramp at the entrance makes access easy for prams and
wheelchairs and there's a toilet for the disabled. Courtyard for outdoor
eating. *Seats 85. Open 9-9 (Fri & Sat to 10). Closed 25 & 26 Dec,
1 Jan. Access, Amex, Visa.*

Ely   Old Fire Engine house

Tel 0353 662582	Restaurant
St Mary's Street Ely Cambridgeshire	Map 10 B2

Good, well-seasoned home-baked food in a traditional and attractive
18th-century house-cum-art gallery. It's open every day with a daily
changing menu according to what's in season. Dishes include a wide
range of starters such as tomato, onion, Stilton or lovage soup (from
£2); mitoon of pork (£3) and smoked salmon paté (£4.80). More
substantial fare weighs in with dishes such as pigeon with bacon and
black olives casseroled in red wine, jugged hare, pork chops in Suffolk
cider, hot game pie, traditional roasts (lamb, beef, pork) and numerous
fish dishes such as lemon sole with prawn sauce and fresh vegetables
(all £10.80). The more expensive options at £12 tend to be the game
dishes such as wild duck with orange Cointreau sauce or pheasant
(roast or casseroled). There are puddings to match which include
home-made yoghurt with honey and almonds, home-made fruit pies
(£2.40), or bread-and- butter (£2.90) and coffee meringue or syllabub
(£3.10). There are also a number of home-made ice-cream options
(£3.65). Try the afternoon full cream tea, with scones, jam and a slice
of cake – all freshly home-baked (£3.55). Good selection of British
cheeses and a choice of some 100 wines. No smoking in main eating
area. Tables in the garden for summer. *Seats 34. Open 10.30-5.30 &
7.30-9). Closed D Sun, Bank Holidays & 1 week Christmas. Access, Visa.*

Epsom   Pizza Express

Tel 0372 729618	Pizzeria
8 South Street Epsom Surrey	Map 15 E3

One of many popular pizza restaurants in a well-run chain. Crisp, thin
pizzas and fresh ingredients used for the toppings. *Seats 90.
Open 11.30-11.30. Closed 25 & 26 Dec. Access, Visa.*

Evesham	Evesham Hotel	62%	£90

Tel 0386 765566   Fax 0386 765443 — Hotel

Cooper's Lane Evesham Hereford & Worcester WR11 6DA — Map 14 C1

The first and enduring impression of the Jenkinson family's modernised Tudor mansion set in 2½ acres (dominated by a large old cedar of Lebanon) is of fun, friendliness and a truly relaxed atmosphere. That feeling starts in the foyer, continues in the chintzy bar and is still strong in the bedrooms which are provided with all sorts of extras, from games and cards to teddy bears and rubber ducks. The whole caboodle is mildly eccentric and very friendly towards families – even the key fobs are teddy bears. "Well-behaved children are as welcome as well-behaved grown-ups and fully catered for"; cots and high-chair are available. Children under 12 are charged £1 (for B&B) for each year of their age when sharing the parent's room. Wordy menus with deliberate spelling mistakes and corny jokes include a junior à la carte offering "small steak – probably beef or yak or warthog" and "shoe pastry buns" plus a breakfast menu that includes "Heinz baked beans (not the cheap grotty ones!)". *Rooms 40. Garden, indoor swimming pool, croquet. Closed 25 & 26 Dec. Access, Amex, Diners, Visa.*

Ewell	Superfish		

Tel 081-393 3674 — Fish'n'Chips

9 Castle Parade By-Pass Road Ewell Surrey — Map 15 E3

Part of a Surrey-based chain of above-average fish and chip restaurants. See Morden entry for more details. *Seats 36. Open 11.30-2 (Sat to 2.30), 5-10.30 (Thu-Sat to 11). Closed Sun, 25 & 26 Dec, 1 Jan. Access, Visa.*

Eyam	Eyam Tea Rooms		

Tel 0433 631274 — Tea Room

The Square Eyam Derbyshire — Map 6 C2

Situated in a village square in the heart of the Peak District National Park, the Tea Rooms are family-run and everything is freshly baked in their own ovens. Snacks include soup (£1.50), sandwiches (from £1.75), salads (from £4.25) served with relishes and jacket potatoes (from £3). Their famous speciality Eyam Cream Tea (£2.50) has two scones fresh from the oven, cream and jam and a pot of tea. A more unusual option is the Fruitcake Tea (£3) – fruitcake, served with Wensleydale cheese, fresh fruit and whole Chinese walnuts plus tea. There's no children's menu but half portions are always available. Two highchairs are provided and nappy changing is feasible in the ladies loo. No smoking. *Seats 52. Open 10.30-5. Closed Mon (except Bank Holiday Mons), Nov-March. No credit cards.*

Fairford	Hyperion House	63%	£70

Tel 0285 712349   Fax 0285 713126 — Hotel

London Street Fairford Gloucestershire GL7 4AH — Map 14 C2

A comfortable, Cotswold-stone establishment right on the A417 Cirencester to Burford road. The hotel takes its name from the 1933 Derby winner, and the bar and restaurant have a racing theme. Bedrooms, all doubles, twin or triples, include Executive rooms offering the most space. Children up to 12 stay free in parents' room – one cot and one high-chair, so reserve them in advance. Handy stopover, but not a long-stay family hotel. *Rooms* 27. *Garden. Access, Amex, Diners, Visa.*

Falmouth	**Falmouth Hotel**	**63%**	**£130**
Tel 0326 312671 Fax 0326 319533			Hotel
Castle Beach Falmouth Cornwall TR11 4NZ			Map 12 B4

Solid and imposing Victorian seaside hotel in French chateau style. Gardens are neat and trim and the day rooms, including a conservatory, are light and peaceful. Half the bedrooms have commanding views of the sea (other rooms overlook the river), and three executive bedrooms have balconies and whirlpool baths. There are also self-catering cottages and apartments, and facilities for large-scale conferences and banquets. The latest attraction is a smart new leisure centre. Families with young children are admirably catered for. Children under 6 are accommodated and fed (cooked breakfast and high tea, the latter served in bedrooms from 5.30-6.30pm) free if sharing with their parents on a full-board basis; those aged between 7 and 15 are charged for meals as taken (if sharing with parents); children in their own rooms are given a 25% discount on the room tariff. *Rooms 72. Garden, putting, indoor & outdoor swimming pools, spa bath, sauna, solarium, beauty salon, hairdressing, snooker. Access, Amex, Diners, Visa.*

Falmouth	**St Michael's Hotel**	**65%**	**£82**
Tel 0326 312707 Fax 0326 211772			Hotel
Gyllingvase Beach Seafront Falmouth Cornwall TR11 4NB			Map 12 B4

Within yards of the beach, St Michael's is a holiday resort hotel and conference centre with a self-contained leisure complex – Club St Michael's. It's well set up for family holidays, including 15 family-size bedrooms, baby-sitting (prior arrangement required) and baby-listening, a children's menu, high-chairs, high teas (from fresh soups to pizza, scampi to fruit jelly and Cornish ice creams, served 5.30-6.30pm) and a children's activity organiser during school holidays. No charge for up to two children under 5 sharing their parents' room; additional children and those between the ages of 6 and 15 are charged £18 per day (for meals taken). Safe, outside play area includes a climbing frame, see-saw and swing. *Rooms 66. Garden, indoor swimming pool, children's splash pool, keep-fit equipment, spa bath, sauna, water sports. Access, Amex, Diners, Visa.*

Fareham	**Solent Hotel**	**75%**	**£101**
Tel 0489 880000 Fax 0489 880007			Hotel
Solent Business Park Whiteley Fareham Hampshire PO15 7AJ			Map 15 D4

A most unexpected location for a get-away-from-it-all weekend; suitably cosy in winter, airy in summer. Adjacent to junction 9 of M27 (10 miles from both Portsmouth and Southampton), this modern, gabled hotel successfully balances wood and brick in its design as happily as it satisfies the contrasting needs of business and leisure guests. A good leisure club has a private membership and access from within the hotel; it keeps the hotel turning over at weekends when businessmen are thin on the ground; thus, although somewhat remote, the Solent Hotel is a relaxing place for families who are on their way to the Channel ferries or who want a quiet weekend away (good-value break rates are offered). All of the bedrooms are of executive standard, in traditional style, with both working and relaxing space and comprehensive comforts from bathrobes to mini-bars. Families should ask for a suite at weekends; children up to 15 are accommodated free in their parents' room and wooden cots are provided. Just one high-chair in the restaurant is available, which can be inconvenient at breakfast. Committed young staff and expert management show good direction throughout. A pub in the grounds offers informal eating and a place for parents to unwind while taking up the hotel's baby-listening facility (or baby-sitting at reasonable rates by advance arrangement). High tea served in the bar area while Dad can enjoy a good pint of Thwaite's! One room in the elegant dining area overlooks grass and woodlands beyond, in which older children will happily spend an hour or two playing hide and seek before plunging into the leisure centre's fine pool. Shire Inns. **Rooms** 90. *Indoor swimming pool, whirlpool bath, children's splash pool, sauna, steam room, solarium, keep-fit equipment, squash, snooker. Access, Amex, Diners, Visa.*

Felixstowe   Marlborough Hotel

Tel 0394 285621	Hotel
Sea Road Felixstowe Suffolk IPl6 8BJ	**Map 10 D3**

The small paragraph in the hotel's tariff concerning children is much like many hotel brochure's promises, which so often prove to be hollow. In this instance the promises are lived up to. Although the hotel has no special facilities for children, it is a relaxed and comfortable place for families. Situated on the seafront of a polite east coast resort town, the hotel has no garden, but the beach is close; the small fun-fair and nearby leisure centre are suitable for families, too. The kitchen will prepare small portions, cater for special dietary needs, including vegetarian, and reheat baby food. Thirty rooms and two family suites share two cots and four Z-beds. Baby-sitting/baby-listening available. No smoking. **Rooms** 47, £57 (*under-11s free*). *Access, Amex, Diners, Visa.*

Feock   Trelissick Garden Restaurant

Tel 0872 863486	Restaurant
Feock nr Truro Cornwall	**Map 12 B3**

The restaurant is a converted barn overlooking the River Fal on a superb National Trust estate with a beautiful garden and parkland. Just three miles south of Truro on the A39, the Trelissick Garden is open for light snacks, lunch and afternoon tea. Salads (beans with tomato and onions) or a daily hot special (West Country fruity lamb £4.45, stuffed cabbage leaves with vegetables £3.35 or beef with horseradish and redcurrants) provide the lunchtime choice, preceded by morning coffee with biscuits and followed by scones, cakes (mixed fruit slice £1.15, carrot cake £1.05) or cream tea (£2.75). There's a three-course traditional Sunday lunch (£9.75). For an even lighter bite, The Courtyard Room, housed in a former farm building, is a self-service snack bar. Children's portions. No smoking. **Seats** 65. **Open** 10.30-4.30 (L 12-2.15). **Closed** 22 Dec-1 Mar. *Access, Amex, Visa.*

Finchingfield   Jemima's Tea Rooms

Tel 0371 810605	Tea Room
The Green Finchingfield Essex	**Map 10 B3**

Finchingfield is situated in North Essex and is probably the prettiest village in the county. The 900-year-old beamed cottage that houses

Jemima's looks over the picturesque village green alongside other thatched cottages. A blackboard supplements the very simple menu of sandwiches (from £1.25), scones and toasted tea cakes (from 85p) with ploughmans, soups and various locally-made ice creams. Cream tea £2.95. The scones and generously served cakes are all home-made. Eating outdoors in the courtyard in the summer. Unlicensed. No-smoking area. *Seats 80. Open 10.30-6 (Nov-Feb to 5). Closed Mon & Fri Nov-Feb, 25 Dec. No credit cards.*

Flitwick	Flitwick Manor	74%	£98
Tel 0525 712242 Fax 0525 712242			Hotel
Church Road Flitwick Bedfordshire MK45 1AE			Map 15 E1

A late 17th/early 18th-century house set in rolling parkland just a couple of minutes off the M1. The high-ceilinged music room (the main day room) sets the tone of the hotel with its combination of elegance, comfort and homely touches like a chess board set up ready for play and a mini hi-fi system. Characterful antique-furnished bedrooms offer all sorts of extras from ice and slices of lemon with the drinks tray to a tin of home-made biscuits; cots, books and board games are provided for junior visitors. Baby-sitting can be arranged and baby-listening is provided. Bathrooms vary from two with showers and WC only to one huge one with his'n'hers bathrobes. Good breakfasts. The extensive grounds include a tree house where children can safely play. As we went to press a new chef was being appointed. *Rooms 15. Garden, croquet, putting. Access, Amex, Diners, Visa.*

Fordwich	Fordwich Arms	
Tel 0227 710444		Pub
Fordwich nr Canterbury Kent CT2 0DB		Map 11 C5

Located next to the smallest, half-timbered medieval town hall in the country, the Fordwich Arms is a solid Tudor-style village pub, with a rather handsome but not intimidatingly smart interior – standard enough furnishings with a parquet floor, green hessian walls, open fireplaces and lovely arched windows. The menu is the same in the bar as in the restaurant, with dishes like smoked haddock mornay (£5.75), lamb chops in redcurrant sauce (£5.25) and chicken fusilli (£5.50). A safe, sunny garden is a pleasant spot for a summer lunch by the narrow river Stour. Railings enclose the area but there is open access from the car park, so do not let children wander off. Pushchairs are permitted in the family room for parents who arrive too late for the solitary high-chair. Children's portions are served and baby food will be warmed. Business people from Canterbury throng the pub on weekday lunchtimes; Saturdays are better for families. *Bar Food 12-2, 6.30-10 (not Sun eve). Beer Boddington's, Fremlins, Marston. Garden, outdoor seating. Family room. No credit cards.*

Framfield	Bay Trees Restaurant	
Tel 0825 890636		Restaurant
The Street Framfield East Sussex TN22 5NL		Map 11 B6

The 17th-century building used to be the village store and is now a friendly family-run restaurant with considerate, personal service. There is a lovely garden for al fresco eating and an open-air swimming pool which can be used by the restaurant customers. The food on the adult menu is good, much better than the nuggets and ice-cream

neighbourhood trat. Sauces and pastas can be combined to customers'
liking, though heartily recommended are dishes like gnocchi alla
bolognese, taglioni verdi gratinata and fettuccine all'Alfredo (all
£4.50). Grilled sardines (£2.50) and carpaccio (£4.95) are tasty
starters; tiramisu, lemon torte and crème caramel satisfying endings
(from £2.25). Each day sees an additional 'specials' list of starters and
main courses – perhaps fresh asparagus and veal milanese. **Seats 44.**
Open *12-2.30 & 6.30-10.30.* **Closed** *D Sun. Access, Visa.*

Gittisham	**Combe House**	**73%**	**£92**
Tel 0404 42756 Fax 0404 46004			Hotel
Gittisham nr Honiton Devon EX14 0AD			**Map 13 E2**

Thérèse and John Boswell came here in 1970, and both are very much
involved in the day-to-day running of their stately Elizabethan
mansion. The 3000-acre estate is predictably peaceful, and there are
views of the Blackmore Hills, but it's not remote, being less than two
miles from the A30. Public rooms have carved panelling in the
entrance hall, ancestral portraits in the panelled drawing room,
a charming pink sitting room, a cosy bar with pictures of John's horse-
racing activities (the hotel owns several racehorses trained nearby –
visits to the stables can be arranged), and everywhere architectural
features, antiques and personal touches by painter and sculptress
Thérèse (and her mother). Bedrooms vary in size and price, larger
rooms tending to have better views and more interesting furniture and
pictures. Two rooms have four-poster beds. The hotel owns fishing
rights on the River Otter, with a season running from April to the end
of September. High-chair and cot provided. **Rooms 15.** *Garden, croquet,
fishing. Access, Amex, Diners, Visa.*

Goudhurst	**Star & Eagle Inn**		**£40**
Tel 0580 211512			Inn
High Street Goudhurst Kent TN17 1AL			**Map 11 B5**

The bedrooms at this gabled 14th-century inn come in all shapes and
sizes, and one sports a restored four-poster bed. In the public areas
period appeal survives in exposed beams, open brick fireplaces and old
settles. High-chairs are provided in the restaurant, where cheek-by-
jowl tables preclude parked buggies. There is no children's menu but
there is always something to tempt a youngster and small portions are
served. A cot is available and an extra bed can be moved in at a small
charge. No dogs. Whitbread Hotels. **Rooms 11.** *Garden. Access, Amex,
Visa.*

Grasmere	**Wordsworth Hotel**	**72%**	**£116**
Tel 053 94 35592 Fax 053 94 35765			Hotel
Grasmere nr Ambleside Cumbria LA22 9SW			**Map 4 C3**

Centrally located in Grasmere village, the Wordsworth's two acres
of well-tended gardens and paddock nevertheless promise calm and
tranquillity. The conservatory bar and adjacent lounge have bold
floral fabrics, some cane seating and the best of the views. The more
active will enjoy the well-equipped leisure centre or the *Dove & Olive
Branch* pub. Individually decorated bedrooms vary widely in size and
aspect; the best are two suites with whirlpool baths and an antique-
furnished four-poster room. Many rooms are suitable for family use,
cots and extra beds are provided (charged), and baby-sitting and baby-
listening are available. Half-day crèche at the local school can

be arranged in advance. **Rooms** *37. Garden, indoor swimming pool, spa bath, sauna, solarium, keep-fit equipment, games room. Access, Amex, Diners, Visa.*

Prelude Restaurant   £74

There's a traditional feel to the dining room but many of the variations on Bernard Warne's menus have a modern ring. Jellied terrine of seasonal fowl and game, grilled monkfish and prawn sausage, millefeuille of rabbit with sweet pepper sauces, steak topped with Stilton mousse on toasted brioche, rosewater and passion fruit mousse with crystallised freesias. Junior diners are offered small portions or choose from their own menu between 5.30 and 6.30pm. **Seats** *60. Parties 100. Private Room. L 12.30-2 D 7-9 (Fri & Sat to 9.30). Set L £17.50 Set D £29.50.*

Grays   R Mumford & Son

Tel 0375 374153	Fish'n'Chips
Cromwell F oad Grays Essex	**Map 11 B5**

Long known for its fish and chips, and run by the same family for 80 years. Ingredients are bought daily from the market. Cod (£5.75, £4.50 at lunchtime), plaice, sole, skate and rock eel are the regular favourites, joined by specials such as halibut. Prawn salad is another popular order, and there's chicken and steak for meat-eaters. Children's menu. **Seats** *64.* **Open** *11.45-2 & 5.30-10 (later Fri/Sat).* **Closed** *Sun, Bank Holidays, 25 Dec-6 Jan. No credit cards.*

Great Bircham   Windmill Tea Room

Tel 048523 393	Tea Room
Great Bircham nr King's Lynn Norfolk	**Map 10 B1**

Gina Wagg and her husband bought a derelict windmill in 1975 and have carefully restored it as well as the bakery, which produces bread and rolls daily in the 200-year-old coalfired oven during the high season. Bicycles can be hired and there's a children's play area. After visiting the mill and bakery museum, Gina's set teas (£2 or £2.40) which include delicious light scones, rich fruit cake, ginger cake, shortbread and flapjacks, are very popular. At lunchtime, a few savoury snacks are available – such as rolls (65p), sandwiches (50p) or a ploughman's platter (£2.50). On fine days, the patio or small garden are open to customers. The mill, which dates from 1846, stands on the B1155 Bircham-Snettisham road. Unlicensed. No-smoking room. **Seats** *70.* **Open** *10-6.* **Closed** *end Sep-Easter, all Sat. No credit cards.*

Great Wishford   Royal Oak

Tel 0722 790229	Pub
Great Wishford nr Salisbury Wiltshire SP2 OPD	**Map 14 C3**

Friendly service and excellent food at reasonable prices are good reasons for pulling in at this attractive, rambling, ivy-covered pub, parts of which are 700 years old. Families are welcome in the eating area, which has plenty of pine tables and padded benches, and choose from a comprehensive menu or from the daily specials blackboard – Somerset pork, steaks, local trout and good salads. Children have their own menu of good-value favourites and can work off excess energy in the garden. Two high-chairs, beakers and cutlery are available and bottles and baby food can be heated. Well-behaved youngsters are rewarded with a lollipop. **Open** *Bar Food 12-2 & 7-10. Access, Amex, Visa.*

Great Yarmouth   Carlton Hotel   67%   £79

Tel 0493 855234   Fax 0493 852220   Hotel

Marine Parade Great Yarmouth Norfolk NR30 3JE   Map 10 D1

With its fine seafront location and recent complete refurbishment, the
Carlton is the flagship of East Anglia's Waveney Inns Group.
An impressive interior now houses good conference facilities. Bonuses
for individual guests include the all-day café-bar and a hair salon.
Bedrooms have bright colour schemes and smart tiled bathrooms. The
nine family rooms are well equipped and spacious. Baby-listening
is available and baby-sitting can be arranged. There are three high-
chairs in the dining-room which, apart from on Sundays, is only open
for dinner. Children are made welcome and small portions of the
main menu will be served. ***Rooms 90.*** *Access, Amex, Diners, Visa.*

Grimsby   Leon's

Tel 0472 356282   Fish'n'Chips

Riverside 1 Alexandra Road Grimsby South Humberside   Map 7 F2

A 'family fish restaurant' serving fish fresh from local boats. Favourites
on the short, simple menu include haddock £4.80, plaice and skate
both £5.20. All served with chips, roll and butter and tea or coffee.
Apple pie and custard or ice cream to finish. Children's portions.
Seats 80. Open *12 (Fri from 11.30)-2 & 5-9 (Sat 11.30am-9, Sun 12-8).*
Closed *Mon, 2 weeks Christmas, Bank Holidays. No credit cards.*

Halifax   Holdsworth House   69%   £87

Tel 0422 240024   Fax 0422 245174   Hotel

Holdsworth nr Halifax West Yorkshire HX2 9TG   Map 6 C1

Much period charm has been retained by the Pearson family at their
17th-century manor, although modern housing and an industrial estate
have encroached in recent years. The impressive oak-panelled
restaurant is the main feature (spreading out over three rooms) and
a bar-lounge provides much-needed additional space. The best
bedrooms are four split-level suites and the rest are both neat and
comfortable with colourful fabrics and mainly period furniture.
Bathrooms are a bit cramped. Two rooms specially adapted for
disabled guests. Baby-sitting available if requested in advance.
Rooms 40. *Garden. Closed Xmas/New Year. Access, Amex, Diners, Visa.*

Harome   Star Inn

Tel 0439 70397   Pub

Main Street Harome nr Helmsley North Yorkshire YO6 5JE   Map 5 E4

The Star is a little gem of a pub. Originally a 14th-century long house,
the single thatched building is picture-postcard pretty outside and
no less delightful within, with its low, beamed ceiling, high-backed
settles, 'Mousey' Thompson rustic furniture (somewhere on each piece
that he made he carved a small mouse), and, by the fireplace, a rack
of magazines to browse through and a box of Lego and other toys for
those customers not yet of reading age. That the cottage garden to the
rear is just a little unkempt serves only to enhance its charm. Add
a friendly landlord – Thomas Blackburn, good beer, classical music
in the background and good food, and one has what for many would
be the ideal pub. The menu has something to suit most appetites and
tastes from sandwiches (for which they are well-known), Stilton paté
(£2.95) and vegetarian crèpe (£2.95) to a plate of fresh poached

salmon with chives and cream (£4.95), jacket potatoes (from £2.95), croque monsieur (£4.95), savoury mince with Yorkshire pudding (£5.95), Gressingham duck in port, black cherry and cream sauce (£9.95) and home-made puddings (all at £2.50) like apple crumble and mincemeat and brandy tart, and a children's menu. At night there is also an especially attractive restaurant and above in the 'loft' a coffee lounge (also used by families at lunchtime) that comes complete with playing cards and board games to keep you amused over post-prandial drinks. *Bar Food* 12-2.30, 7-9. *Restaurant Meals* 7-9. *Children's menu/portions. Free House. Beer Tetley, Theakstons, Timothy Taylors. Garden, outdoor eating. Family room. Access, Visa.*

Harrogate	**Bettys**	
Tel 0423 502746		Tea Room
1 Parliament Street Harrogate North Yorkshire		Map 6 C1

Select one of the rare coffees or an unusual tea and enjoy the occasional morning café concert at this genteel tea room, the first of the Bettys chain (established 1919). The tea room is divided into two – the Verandah Café which overlooks the Stray (grassed area in the centre of town bedded with flowers) with an airy 1920s atmosphere and the Spindler Café which, with its marquetry pictures on the walls, alcoves and teapot display on the fire surround has a more cosy feel (closed in the evenings). The day begins with breakfast – warm Yorkshire oatcakes (£1.40), mushroom and bacon omelette (£4.80), rösti potatoes (£3.10) or simply two croissants or brioches with jam and butter (£1.65). Light lunches bring sandwiches (from £2.35), salads (corn-fed chicken £4.98), grills, omelettes, hot dishes such as haddock and prawns au gratin and the speciality of the house, rarebit made with Theakston's Yorkshire Ale served with apple or tomato chutney (£5.45). Bettys famous warm Yorkshire fat rascal (£1.90), buttered pikelets (98p) and banana and walnut loaf (£1.10) are some of the tea breads. On the evening menu, smoked Wensleydale cheese croquettes (£2.98) and seafood vol-au-vents are served as starters, and haddock and prawn croustades (£5.85) or mushroom and chestnut roulade with casserole red cabbage (£4.55) as a main course. Various ices (from £2.05), desserts (toffee and brandy snap fanfare) and cakes (from £1.78 – chocolate brandy roulade, Yorkshire curd tart) to follow. Pianist in the evenings. Children's menu. No-smoking area. *Seats 174. **Open** 9-9. **Closed** 25 & 26 Dec, 1 Jan. Access, Visa.*

Harrogate	**Imperial Hotel**	65%	£95
Tel 0423 565071 Fax 0423 500082			Hotel
Prospect Place Harrogate North Yorkshire HG1 1LA			Map 6 C1

In the heart of town, overlooking attractive gardens, just a few minutes walk from the railway station and the Harrogate Exhibition and Conference Centre. Day rooms have a slightly faded appearance from the throughput of conference visitors and bedrooms are uniform. A wood-panelled snooker room has an open fire, leather chesterfield sofas and a cosy cocktail bar. There are four cots and ten Z-beds available. Children stay free in parents' room. Six high-chairs are available in the restaurant where the children's menu (2-courses £3.50, 3-courses £4.50) offer such dishes as starship nuggets. On Sundays, entertainment is laid on in the form of videos. Discounted tickets for entry to National Trust properties and local cultural and leisure facilities are also available. Principal Hotels. *Rooms 85. Access, Amex, Diners, Visa.*

Harrogate   West Park Hotel   £50

| Tel 0423 524471 | Hotel |

19 West Park North Yorkshire HG1 1BL   Map 6 C1

John and Lesley Barton are continuing the West Park's tradition
of welcoming families. The relaxed and cheerful atmosphere together
with attentive staff and housekeeping make for a stress-free stay for
young families. There are two family suites and five large family
rooms plus baby-sitting by prior arrangement. Cots, baby baths,
nappies and potties are all provided. From 6pm children under 10 can
choose their dinner from the 'Tiny Tums' menu in the restaurant
where high-chairs and baby food are provided, and once the little ones
are asleep, you can creep downstairs to the traditional pub. Under-5s
free. *Rooms* 17. *Closed Dec 25. Access, Visa.*

Harrow   Pizza Express

| Tel 081-427 9195 | Pizzeria |

2 College Road Harrow Middlesex   Map 15 E2

The well-loved format of open-to-view oven, choice of fourteen pizzas
(as well as ham and eggs and salad niçoise) and high-chairs for
youngsters. Treat the children to chocolate fudge cake or an ice cream
bombe to finish. *Seats 64. Open 11.30am-midnight. Closed 25 &
26 Dec. Access, Amex, Visa.*

Harwich   The Ha'Penny Pier at Harwich   £50

| Tel 0255 241212 Fax 0255 322752 | Restaurant |

The Quay Harwich Essex CO12 3HH   Map 10 C3

Overlooking the harbour, the first-floor restaurant is just the place
to enjoy good, fresh seafood which comes both plain and fancy. The
choice is extensive – from crab terrine, oysters or coquilles St Jacques
mornay to fish pie and a filo pastry gateau of cod, salmon and prawns.
The *Ha'penny Pier* on the ground floor is a second, family-orientated
restaurant with views over the harbour, a modestly-priced, mainly fish
menu – ha'penny pie, fillet of cod mornay or simple fillet of haddock
or plaice (£4.75-£5.45). Sweets on offer are home-made lemon
cheesecake and brandy snaps (£2.75). Children's menu and one high-
chair; nursing mums can ask to use a vacant bedroom. *Seats 70.
Parties 30. L 12-2 D 6-9.30 (Sun to 9). Closed 25 & 26 Dec.
Set L £9 Set D £16. Access, Visa.*

Rooms   £68

Accommodation comprises six bedrooms of varying standards, all
with a nautical theme. All have en-suite bathrooms.

Hatton   Country Café

| Tel 0926 843350 | Café |

Hatton Country World Hatton nr Warwick Warwickshire CV35 8XA   Map 14 C1

Treat the whole family to a day at the craft centre, pick-your-own
farm, farm shop, rare breeds farm park, adventure playground and
garden centre, as well as the café. Baking takes place in full view and
the results are good – savoury items include quiches £1.20 and hot
specials such as cottage pie £2.80 or filled jacket potatoes £2.75, while
a changing selection of cakes such as coffee and walnut gateau,
pineapple and ginger, apple and banana and walnut cake (£1) should
please the sweet-toothed. No smoking. Beakers and high-chairs are

provided, changing facilities are not. *Seats 66. Open 10-5.30.
Closed* Dec 25-mid Jan. *No credit cards.*

Haywards Heath   Chukka's Café Bar

Tel 0444 416870	Café Bar
59 The Broadway Haywards Heath West Sussex RH16 3AJ	Map 11 B6

Themed around the 'hectic equestrian ballet' that is polo, a surprisingly
light and spacious basement café-bar and restaurant thanks to an
attractive rear conservatory overlooking a leafy patio. An eclectic
menu offers anything from an all-day English breakfast (£4.50)
to roasted poussin with a creamy mustard sauce (£6.95) via guacamole
with tortilla chips (£2.95) or tagliatelle marinara (£5.95). Home-
made desserts from a trolley could complete a meal or complement
a good cappuccino for afternoon tea. Friendly, efficient service.
*Seats 75. Open 10.30-10.30 (Mon to 3pm, Sat from 6pm).
Closed* D Mon, L Sat, all Sun, Bank Holidays. *Access, Amex, Diners,
Visa.*

Helmsley   Monets

Tel 0439 70618	Restaurant
19 Bridge Street Helmsley North Yorkshire FY8 5LU	Map 5 E4

John and Heather Dyson's homely restaurant with rooms, a large
private house just out of the town centre, is the perfect spot
(particularly the terrace in fine weather) for enjoyable daytime
snacking. Morning and afternoon teas with home-made fruit scones
(85p), toasted cinnamon bread (65p) and sandwiches (from £1.70) are
joined at lunch by more substantial dishes such as steak and oyster pie
(£6.99), poached salmon with herb butter (£6.75) and vegetable
lasagne (£4.50). Good puds. More serious fixed-price evening meals.
No high-chairs but children are welcome and there's a room provided
upstairs for mums who want to change their charges. *Seats 30.
Open* 10-5 *(Oct to Mar from 11) Closed* Mon, Bank Holidays.
Access, Visa.

Hemel Hempstead   The Gallery Restaurant

Tel 0442 232416	Restaurant
The Old Town Hall High Street Hemel Hempstead Hertfordshire HP1 3AE	Map 15 E2

A bistro-style restaurant on the first floor of a converted complex
housing an art gallery and theatre. An all-day menu embraces paté
with toast or pitta bread (£2.50), Danish open sandwiches (from
£2.95), filled jacket potatoes (from £2.60), various cakes and desserts,
perhaps pancakes with maple syrup and cream (£2), and a seasonal
blackboard dish of the day such as venison casserole (£7.95).
Particularly popular for pre-theatre dinners. *Seats 60.
Open* 10.30am-11pm *(Mon to 4.30pm) Closed* Sun. *Access, Visa.*

Hereford   Gaffers

Tel 0432 278226	Café
89 East Street Hereford Hereford & Worcester	Map 14 A1

A friendly, vegetarian co-operative where customers seem more like
friends who just happen to have dropped in. The kitchen is within
the restaurant so you can see the cooking going on and there's
a secondhand 60s clothes shop in one corner. Italian vegetable stew
(£2.95), watercress and cream cheese flan (£1.25), filled rolls (65p),

baked potatoes (£1.15), lovely cheesecake (£1.20), carrot cake and poppy seed cake (both 60p) typify the fare. Kids are welcomed with small portions, high chairs, comics and books to keep them amused. Smoking is only allowed before 12.30pm. *Seats 35. Open 10-4.30. Closed Sun, Bank Holidays. No credit cards.*

Hindon   Lamb at Hindon

Tel 0747 89573	Pub

High Street Hindon Wiltshire SP3 6DP   **Map 14 B3**

Wisteria clings to one corner of this mellow 17th-century coaching inn. At its height, 300 post horses were kept here to supply the great number of coaches going to and from London and the West Country. Prime Minister William Pitt was apparently most put out to find no fresh horses available when he stopped off here in 1786. But there have also been less reputable visitors. Silas White, a notorious smuggler said to be leader of the Wiltshire Moonrakers, used the Lamb as the centre of his nefarious activities. These days, things in Hindon are rather more peaceful and the Lamb limits itself to providing honest hospitality to modern travellers who bring their own horsepower in four-wheeled form. The bar is slightly disappointing, a less characterful room than the build-up suggests, although there is a splendid old stone inglenook fireplace, and the atmosphere is enhanced by an ever-changing collection of paintings by local artists both here and in the rather smarter restaurant, which features splendid dark green tartan curtains (and high-chairs). Picky junior eaters might prefer to share their parents' meals; extra plates will cheerfully be provided. The blackboard bar menu is sensibly not over-long, but still manages to offer a reasonable choice – rabbit and pigeon pie (£4.95), cod steak and prawn mayonnaise (£5.50) or puff pastry case with asparagus. The emphasis is fishy on Tuesdays and Fridays, when the fishmonger calls, and in winter there's also plenty of game, from the estate of the local landowner who bought the inn just a couple of years ago. In the restaurant, a 3-course table d'hote menu (£18.95) is available with such choices as roast guinea fowl in strawberry sauce, chicken breast with Stilton or fillet of beef with wild mushrooms. Overnight accommodation is also offered – standards are variable. *Bar Food 12-2, 7-10. Children's portions. Free House. Beer Wadworth 6X, Smiles, Stonehenge. Patio/terrace, outdoor eating. Accommodation 13 rooms, all en suite, £55. Children welcome overnight, additional beds (£12), cots supplied. Access, Amex, Diners, Visa.*

Hope   The Hopechest

Tel 0433 20072	Tea Room

8 Castleton Road Hope nr Sheffield Derbyshire   **Map 6 C2**

In the heart of the Hope Valley, this little tea room is part of a restored stable. "Everything is home-made and not just home-baked" – soup (£1.50), patés (£2.90), hams (£3.10), cakes (Bakewell tart, fruit cake, carrot cake – all 95p), biscuits (15p) and scones (65p). Set afternoon tea £3.20. Coffee is ground on the premises. Two highchairs are available and nappies can be changed in the Ladies loo. Not particularly ideal for very small children or large families (it's on the cramped side), but popular with local mothers and toddlers nevertheless. Small patio in walled garden for outdoor eating. Easy parking 50 yards away. Children's portions on request. No smoking. *Seats 20. Open 9-5. Closed Sun, Mon (except Aug & Dec), 25 Dec, 1 Jan. Access, Visa.*

Hope Cove   **Cottage Hotel**   56%   £80

| Tel 0548 561555 | Hotel |

Hope Cove nr Kingsbridge Devon TQ7 3HJ   Map 13 D3

John and Janet Ireland are the resident proprietors of this popular
family holiday hotel extended, originally, from just one small cottage.
It stands in a fine clifftop position in gardens close to the beach. The
main lounge is largely 30s in style, and the cocktail bar was built from
the timbers of a wrecked ship. The sun terrace is the place to be
in summer. Accommodation includes de luxe rooms with extra
accessories; just over half the rooms have en-suite facilities and some
have balconies. A few singles at the back miss out on the sea views.
Children up to 12 stay free in parents' room; cots and high-chairs
available; children's tea between 5.30 & 6pm – bibs and trainer cups
available. Small kiddies' playground and a games room for rainy days,
but the sandy beach and cliff walks should give them enough fresh air
to sleep soundly. **Rooms 35.** *Garden. Closed Jan. No credit cards.*

Horton-cum-Studley   **Studley Priory**   64%   £98

| Tel 0865 351203   Fax 0865 351613 | Hotel |

Horton-cum-Studley nr Oxford Oxfordshire OX9 1AZ   Map 16 C2

A striking Elizabethan building set in 13 acres of wooded grounds.
Impressive day rooms include a splendid hall panelled in pitch pine,
a lofty drawing room and a Victorian bar. Six bedrooms are in the
main house (antiques, some wood panelling, one with a four-poster),
while the majority are in the Jacobean wing reached through
a labyrinth of corridors. These rooms are smaller and more modern.
Small conferences are big business here, so you'll sometimes be sharing
the drawing room with the delegates. Although its a gracious and
imposing hotel, children are charmingly tolerated. One recent visitor
expressed her delight at her baby being allowed to crawl around the
bar! Owner Jeremy Parke has three children and is keen to embrace
the European ethic of dining out as a family, especially at Sunday
lunchtime, although children are banned from the restaurant after
dark. There is one family suite and another four rooms that are
suitable for families. There is one cot and one high-chair. Surrounded
by 13 acres of woodland there is plenty of space for little legs to run
wild and let off steam after the constraints of being on best behaviour
inside. **Rooms 19.** *Garden, tennis, clay-pigeon shooting. Access, Amex,
Diners, Visa.*

Hungerford   **The Tutti Pole**

| Tel 0488 682515 | Tea Room |

3 High Street Hungerford Berkshire   Map 14 C2

Located a few yards from the Kennet and Avon canal, The Tutti Pole
tea room is housed in a cottage dating back to 1634. The name 'Tutti'
derives from the 'Tithing' or 'Tutti' men who still to this day call each
year to collect a penny from all the Common right houses and a kiss
from the cottage occupants. The men carry a 'Tutti Pole' – a long pole
decorated with flowers and blue ribbon and topped with an orange.
For many years the poles were made in the house where the tea shop
now is. A full English breakfast (£3.80) is served until 11.30am (but
the chef can be persuaded to extend the deadline!). Light snacks are
available all day – a large assortment of sandwiches (£1.10-£1.45),
poached eggs on toast (£2.40), paté on toast (£2.40), salads (from
£4.15), Cajun prawns (£4). Canal walkers stop by in the afternoon

for the Tutti Pole Cream Tea (£3.05) – two home-made scones and jam ("with stones"), Guernsey cream and pot of tea, two crumpets with butter (85p) or perhaps a fresh cream gateau (£1.50). Home-made cakes and meringues are also on sale at the counter. Three-course traditional Sunday lunch £5.50. Children and babies are frequent visitors to The Tutti Pole; they do not have their own menu but the owners try to satisfy children's requests. There's ample storage for prams, high-chairs are provided, food will be blended, bottles can be heated, and nappies can be changed in the loo. No smoking area. *Seats 80.* **Open** *9-5.30 (Sat to 6, Sun 10-6).* **Closed** *25 Dec-1 Jan.* *No credit cards.*

Huntsham	Huntsham Court	68%	£99
Tel 039 86 365 Fax 039 86 456			Hotel
Huntsham Bampton nr Tiverton Devon EX16 7NA			Map 13 D2

A rather gaunt Victorian Gothic pile run in friendly, very casual style by owners Mogens and Andrea Bolwig. Eating is communal, there's an honour system in the bar, and you just wander into the kitchen if you need anything. There's great atmosphere in the day rooms (log fires, a panelled great hall, splendid pieces of furniture) and in the roomy bedrooms, named after composers, there are Victorian beds and baths and pre-war radios with an authentic crackle – not a teasmaid in sight! The hotel is dedicated to music, with the classical variety played *forte* in the evening. The day starts with an excellent buffet breakfast. Children are well catered for and accommodated free of charge if they share a family room – two cots are available; baby-sitting is available. The grassy garden has swings and a Wendy House. No dogs, however "good" or "small". An eccentric home away from home. **Rooms** *17. Garden, tennis, croquet, coarse fishing, shooting, bicycles, sauna, solarium, snooker. Access, Amex, Diners, Visa.*

Restaurant   £72

Five-course dinners (no choice, but variations possible in advance) are enjoyed in leisurely fashion at a convivial candle-lit table. Crisp local duck with a Périgord sauce is a favourite dish, so too fillet of brill sauce américaine, and for dessert, treacle tart. Guests are welcome to browse around the wine cellars where they'll find the New World and Spain particularly well represented; fair prices and some wine charged by the glass from bottles left open on the table. *Seats 30. Parties 30. Private Room. D only 8-10.30. Set D £28.*

Hythe	Hythe Imperial Hotel	71%	£117
Tel 0303 267441 Fax 0303 264610			Hotel
Princes Parade Hythe Kent CT21 6AE			Map 11 C5

A large, family-run hotel set right on the seafront and surrounded by 50 acres of grounds. An imposing, cream-painted exterior of Victorian splendour belies the more classical air within. The polished mahogany reception area is adorned with brown leather chesterfield sofas and leads through to comfortable bars and lounges. All bedrooms have views of the sea or gardens and are mostly of good size with a mixture of quality period furniture, although some have more ordinary darkwood pieces. Excellent, unusually pleasant staff and leisure facilities that include go-karting and a children's play area with Scalextric. Board games are also available from reception (a refundable deposit is required). The indoor swimming pool has a stepped shallow end. Families are particularly well catered for with baby-sitting, baby-listening and crèche facilities available. A child-minder is on call from 10am to 1pm on Saturdays in the new children's playroom where slides, toys, games and puzzles are provided. The Marston Minor Diner menu is served at children's tea time at 5.30. High-chairs, baby food, bottles, and children's portions are also available. Outdoor playground. No dogs. Marston Hotels. *Rooms 100. Garden, coffee shop (8.30am-10.30pm), indoor swimming pool, gymnasium, spa bath, sauna, solarium, steam room, beauty & hair salons, squash, tennis, games room, 9-hole golf course, putting, dinner dance (weekly), helipad. Access, Amex, Diners, Visa.*

Ickford   Waterperry Gardens Tea Shop

Tel 0844 339254	Café
Ickford Waterperry nr Wheatley Oxfordshire OX9 1JZ	Map 15 D2

Self-service tea shop in the horticultural centre. The counter holds a tempting show of baking, all made on the premises: scones with jam and cream (95p), cheesecake (£1.40), walnut pie (£1.40), Stilton flan (£2.20), French pastries (from £1.20), chicken, ham and turkey pie (£2.20 per slice). All the cakes are made with free-range eggs. Eat outside and admire the gardens in fine weather. One high-chair (fetch it yourself while juggling trays and buggies), lidded beakers, ramps for easy access, ample room to park buggies at tables and a big green space outside for children to run about on. There is no children's menu but with careful choosing you should be able to select a suitable meal for your child without having to rely on the obvious attraction of cakes and pastries. On a warm day the table in the outside ladies loo could be used for nappy-changing. No-smoking area. *Seats 80. Open 10-5.30. Closed 1 week Christmas. No credit cards.*

Ilkley   Bettys

Tel 0943 608029	Tea Room
32 The Grove Ilkley West Yorkshire	Map 6 C1

Rarebits made with Yorkshire ale served with apple or tomato chutney and bacon or ham are Bettys' speciality (£5.45-£6.15). Also popular is the Yorkshire cheese lunch with blue, white and smoked Wensleydale cheeses with apple chutney, celery, rolls and butter £5.20. Uniformed waitresses will guide you through the cake trolley featuring curd tarts, chocolate brandy roulade, vanilla heart and apple strudel from £1.10. Breakfast grill £4-£5. Part of a very successful and well-run chain with branches in Harrogate, Northallerton and York. *Seats 110. Open 9-6 (Fri-Sun to 6.30). Closed 25 & 26 Dec. Access, Visa.*

Ipswich   Marlborough Hotel   65%   £113

Tel 0473 257677 Fax 0473 226927	Hotel
73 Henley Road Ipswich Suffolk IP1 3SP	Map 10 C3

Peacefully located within walking distance of the town centre, the Marlborough is a privately owned hotel run with care and enthusiasm by manager David Brooks. The tasteful public areas and the comfortable bedrooms (the best have antique furniture) are equally well kept. 24hr room service. *Rooms 22. Garden, croquet. Access, Amex, Diners, Visa.*

Ipswich   The Orwell House Restaurant

Tel 0473 230254	Restaurant
4 Orwell Place Ipswich Suffolk	**Map 10 C3**

The food at this town-centre restaurant certainly justifies a visit: fresh fish, well-sauced meat dishes and a vegetarian selection that includes a delightfully moist nut cutlet. On the face of it, facilities for families are unremarkable: a single high-chair, a secluded space found for breast-feeding and changing nappies, and no burger&nugget&fish fingers. However, what distinguishes this from so many restaurants is the standard of service families can expect. In a perfect world, staff at every restaurant would greet the whole family, help settle the children, bring something for them immediately, discuss children's meals with their parents and offer to find something for them when they get bored. We can only hope that the restaurant can maintain this quality of welcome. **Seats** 50. **Open** 12-2, 7-10 Tues-Fri. **Closed** Sat L, all Sun & Mon, some Bank Holidays. Access, Diners, Visa.

Kendal   The Moon

Tel 0539 729254	Bistro
129 Highgate Kendal Cumbria	**Map 4 C3**

A small half-vegetarian bistro-style restaurant in the middle of Kendal opposite the Brewery Arts Centre. Formerly an old greengrocer's shop, it has a bar in the central area and linen tablecloth-clad tables laid out around it. The comfortable and cosy atmosphere is perfect for enjoying good food, much of it made from local produce: mushroom, onion and nut paté (£2.55), guacamole with taco chips (£2.55), chicken breast in parsnip, ginger and orange sauce (£7.55), spinach, mushroom and garlic lasagne with mozzarella cheese sauce (£6.35), fennel, rice and Gruyère pancakes with tomato and basil sauce (£6.35). The Moon hosts a pudding club once a month and consequently the adventurous choice of puddings (£2.55) is ever-changing: sticky toffee pudding, steamed puddings, chocolate, apricot and cointreau glory, unusual cheesecakes. Children's portions. No smoking. **Seats** 38. **Open** 6.30-10 (summer 6-10.30). **Closed** 25 & 26 Dec, 1 Jan.

Kendal   Posh Nosh   £35

Tel 0539 725135	Bistro
Yard 11 Stramongate Kendal Cumbria LA9 4BH	**Map 4 C3**

Sophisticated family restaurant with a dreadful name. Chef-patron Stephen Burrows,   provides carefully-priced daytime and nightime menus that range from home-made soups, speciality sandwiches, baked potatoes and Cumberland sausage with home-made chutney at lunchtime to pear and Parmesan risotto and sautéed scallops in lime, yoghurt and bacon sauce for dinner. Scones, cakes and teas at anytime Mon-Thurs. Feeding cups and a high-chair are provided. Beware – you have to go upstairs to order and pay for your food – not easy for a mum with a pushchair. **Seats** 52. Parties 38. Meals 9-6 (Fri & Sat 9-3 & 7-9). Closed D Mon-Thu, all Sun, Bank Holidays. Access, Diners, Visa.

Kendal   Waterside Wholefoods

Tel 0539 729743	Restaurant
Kent View Kendal Cumbria LA9 4DZ	Map 4 C3

Housed in an old converted mill with low ceilings and cottage plaster
walls, this wholefood restaurant shares the premises with its adjoining
shop. Owner Mrs Dean provides home-baked breads, cakes, puddings
and scones (date, sultana, cheese) to accompany lunchtime specials and
a large variety of teas (18 herbal). The daily-changing blackboard
menu may offer mulligatawny soup with herb bread roll (£1.60),
three-cheese paté (£2.60), broccoli and sweetcorn pie (£3.80), pasta
and vegetable bake (£3.80) as well as a choice of 10-15 salads (small
portion of each £2.60, large £3.60). Puddings feature rum and raisin
tart, fig and ginger cake, lemon and orange meringue pie, plum and
apple tart (from 98p). Tables with parasols are set up outside
in summer on the banks of the River Kent. Children are made most
welcome with a clip-on seat and beakers supplied. Unlicensed.
No smoking. *Seats 36.* **Open** *9-4.* **Closed** *Sun, 25 & 26 Dec, 1 Jan.*
No credit cards.

Keswick   Bryson's Tea Room

Tel 07687 72257	Tea Room
42 Main Street Keswick Cumbria	Map 4 C3

Above Bryson's bakery shop, with its tempting display, is their
immensely popular tea room. Hot snacks include Cumbrian ham and
eggs (£5.50), Borrowdale poached trout and Cumberland sausage, and
more simple dishes might be filled baked potatoes (from £2.55),
omelettes (from £3.95) and salads (£4.70). The output of the bakery
is strongly reflected at teatime when you can choose either the
Cumberland Farmhouse Afternoon Tea (£3.50) or the Lakeland
Cream Tea (£4.15) – served with scones, tea breads and cakes.
Children's portions. No smoking. *Seats 84.* **Open** *8.30-5.30.*
Closed *Sun, 25 & 26, 1 Jan. Access, Amex, Diners, Visa.*

Kingscote   Hunters Hall Inn

Tel 0453 860393	Pub
Kingscote Gloucestershire GL8 8XZ	Map 14 B2

Unusually spacious, comfortably genteel old 19th-century coaching
inn, licensed since the 15th century. High-ceilinged, connecting rooms
hold a pleasing variety of furniture, both squashy and elegant, exposed
stone walls, and open fires. An upstairs Gallery (that families can use)
takes more diners, and there's also a quite separate, low-ceilinged locals'
public bar. Bar food is buffet-servery style, with hot dishes listed on a
blackboard: from home-made soups (£2.20), seafood crumble (£5.50)
and steak and kidney pie (£4.95) a Sunday roast (£5.95). The
restaurant menu is more involved – from devilled chicken livers
to pigeon breast and apple and walnut pie. Recommended for family
expeditions; the family room upstairs offers high-chairs and toddler's
chairs. The landlord has a relaxed, informal style and a positive
approach towards children that is shared by his staff. The idyllic
setting includes a large landscaped garden with an imaginative
playground and swings. **Bar Food** *12-2 (Sun to 2.30), 7-9.45.*
Restaurant Meals *7.30-9.45 (Tues-Sat).* **Beer** *Bass, Hook Norton.*
Family room. Outdoor play area, garden, outdoor eating, summer barbecue.
Accommodation *12 bedrooms, all en suite, £54. Children welcome*
overnight, cots available. Access, Amex, Diners, Visa.

King's Lynn   Butterfly Hotel   62%   £67

| Tel 0553 771707   Fax 0553 768027 | Hotel |

Beveridge Way Hardwick Narrows King's Lynn Norfolk PE30 4NB   Map 10 B1

A modern, town-fringe hotel at the A10/A47 roundabout; part
of a small East Anglian group aiming at the middle of the market.
Under-16s stay free in parents' room. Z-beds, cots and high-chairs are
available. *Rooms 50.* Garden. *Access, Amex, Diners, Visa.*

Kingston   Pizza Express

| Tel 081-546 1447 | Pizzeria |

41 High Street Kingston Surrey   Map 15 E2

Situated by the river Thames in a listed building over 300 years old.
The atmosphere is cheerful and children are positively encouraged
with balloons and hats on offer. Consistently good, thin pizzas.
Seats 125. Open 12-12. Closed 25 & 26 Dec. Access, Amex, Visa.

Kington   Penrhos Court   £65

| Tel 0544 230720   Fax 0544 230754 | Restaurant |

Penrhos Kington Hereford & Worcester HR5 3LH   Map 14 A1

Martin Griffiths and Daphne Lambert's restaurant is in the beautifully
restored 13th-century Cruck Hall, complete with flagstone floors and
heavy beams – a characterful setting for occasional medieval banquets.
Daphne offers daily-changing menus with a short choice; perhaps
smoked breast of duck with orange salad or queen scallops grilled with
a herb crust to start, followed by beef in ale with mustard dumplings
or medallions of venison with Grand Veneur sauce. Simple, but well-
executed, desserts such as pear meringue, lemon tart and passion fruit
water-ice. 2- or 3-course Sunday lunches offer a small choice, but
always includes a traditional roast; under-5s eat free. Plenty of space
inside and out for children to let off steam, although toddlers need
ot be watched as there's an open pond in the courtyard. *Seats 50.
Parties 90. Private Room. L (Sun only) 12.30-3 D 7.30-9. Closed 25 &
26 Dec. Set L £10.50/£15.50. Access, Amex, Diners, Visa.*

Rooms   £110

Individually styled bedrooms, named after birds, show some fine taste.
The latest eight rooms are in converted Elizabethan barns and are
expected to come on line in spring '93; of a fair size, they use fine
lightwood and mahogany furniture, co-ordinated contemporary
fabrics and bright, clean decor. Bathrooms (some with shower/WC
only) have attractive fittings and quality toiletries. Limited hotel-style
public areas, but high bedrooms standards. Children
up to 5 accommodated free in parents' room. *Rooms 19.*

Knapp   Rising Sun

| Tel 0823 490436 | Pub |

Knapp North Curry Somerset TA3 6BG   Map 13 E2

Very much a dining pub, pretty, white-painted and cottagey, and
totally refurbished, though many original features remain in this "most
perfect example of a Somerset longhouse open to the public", dated
1480. On the edge of the Somerset Levels, it was originally a cider
house, it has retained some features including two inglenook fireplaces
which provide open log fires in winter. Fish from Brixham
predominates – the board can feature over 30 different dishes.

For non-fish eaters, ribeye steak (£7.50), garlic chicken (£8.50) and duck in orange sauce (£9.75) are also available. Vegetarians can choose from two or three dishes. Book a high-chair in advance, particularly at weekends. *Bar Food 12-2. **Restaurant Meals** 7-9.30. Children's portions. Free House. **Beer** Bass, Exmoor, Boddingtons. Patio, outdoor eating. Family room. Access, Visa.*

Knutsford   Cottons Hotel   65%   £112

Tel 0565 650333 Fax 0565 755351	Hotel

Manchester Road Knutsford Cheshire WA16 0SU   Map 6 B2

Five minutes from the M6 (junction 19), Cottons has a New Orleans French colonial theme. There's plenty of free parking and a well-designed leisure club. Two bars quench the weekday conference delegates' thirsts, and Sunday brunch comes with live jazz. A children's menu is served from 6.30-7.15pm in the Magnolia restaurant; at other times one has to make do with lounge or room service as there is no all-day, informal brasserie or café. Children up to 14 are accommodated free in their parents' room; cots and high-chairs are provided. Special weekend 'refresher' rates. Shire Inns. *Rooms 86. Indoor swimming pool, gymnasium, spa bath, sauna, solarium, tennis. Access, Amex, Diners, Visa.*

Knutsford   David's Place   £60

Tel 0565 633356	Restaurant

44 King Street Knutsford Cheshire WA16 6DT   Map 6 B2

In one of Knutsford's oldest shops, a family-run operation offering both simple, fresh produce like crab-stuffed mushrooms or goat's cheese and leek flan and more involved dishes such as fisherman's strudel, oxtail ragout with orange and an onion mash, baked ham with Gruyère and tomato purée, or breaded 'fingers' of leg of lamb with béarnaise sauce and pease pudding. Daily blackboard specials (including fresh fish dishes) supplement the carte. Menus change monthly. Varied wine list and sensibly priced house wines. No longer open for Sunday lunch (and there's also no longer a table d'hote), but Saturday lunch is a good time for a family meal. Two high-chairs are provided; children should ask for exactly what *they* want and it will be provided – perhaps chicken and chips, or a daily special of Cumberland sausages and mash (hold the garlic). *Seats 60. Parties 30. L 12-2 D 7-10 (Fri & Sat to 10.30). Closed all Sun, all Bank Holidays. Access, Amex, Diners, Visa.*

Knutsford   Est Est Est

Tel 0565 755487	Restaurant

81 King Street Knutsford Cheshire WA16 6DX   Map 6 B2

Light, bright and spacious, this is one of a small North-East chain of friendly Italian trattoria. The long menu includes all the traditional favourites from calamari fritti (£3.25), some 18 pasta dishes (from £1.95 as a starter or £3.75 as main course) – served with excellent, freshly grated Parmesan – and pizza (from £3.95), to pollo cacciatore (£8.05) and scaloppine al limone (£9.40). Lunchtimes and until 7.30 at night (except Saturday) there's a good value set menu at £9.95. No minimum charge for Just-a-Biters but you're expected to have a main-course dish at night. *Seats 180. **Open** 12-2.30 & 6-11 (Fri & Sat 11.30, Sun 12-11). Closed 25 & 26 Dec, 1 Jan. Access.*

Langdale   Langdale Hotel & Country Club   71%   £140

Tel 096 67 302 Fax 096 67 694	Hotel

Great Langdale nr Ambleside Cumbria LA22 9JD   Map 4 C3

An extensive hotel and timeshare complex in 35 acres of woodland overlooking Great Langdale Beck. Centrally, an open-plan bar-lounge and restaurant incorporate the old mill stream, while an adjacent pub bar features slate walls and a log fire. Accommodation comprises a number of satellite blocks, constructed in Lakeland stone, where there is plenty of room for families in the former self-catering chalets; cots, baby-sitting and listening plus high-chairs are all provided. Wet-weather provision includes fine leisure facilities, a supervised crèche, Lego table in the bar and coffee shop seating by the large pool. Children under 3 free of charge; under-14s with parents £15 per night including cooked breakfast. No dogs. *Rooms 65. Garden, croquet, gymnasium, indoor swimming pool, spa bath, sauna, solarium, beauty & hair salon, adventure trail, coffee shop (10am-10pm). Access, Amex, Diners, Visa.*

Lanhydrock   Lanhydrock House Restaurant

Tel 0208 74331	Restaurant

Lanhydrock nr Bodmin Cornwall   Map 12 B3

The former servants' hall of Lanhydrock House with its oak panelling and bell-boards is now the House Restaurant. Uniformed waitresses serve light lunches and teas. The daily hot special might be Elizabethan pork (£5.25) or steak and kidney with Guinness sauce. Other dishes include courgette and tomato flan, salads (locally smoked mackerel fillet, house-baked ham £5.25). Two puddings feature daily (£2.15 each), one hot (bread-and-butter pudding with fruit sauce) and one cold (fresh lemon tart). The cream tea (£2.75) and the copious Country House Tea (£3.95) are served later in the day with a choice of home-made cakes, scones and splits (Cornish speciality). The wine list extends to elderflower, strawberry and apple wines. Light lunches of jacket potatoes, small salads, soups and puddings are also served in the former housekeeper's and housemaids' sitting rooms in the servants' quarters. Across the courtyard, the Stable Bar serves snacks, drinks, and ice cream throughout the day. Three-course traditional lunch (£9.75) on Sundays. Children's portions. No smoking. *Seats 46. Open 12-2.15 & 3-5.30. Closed Christmas-end March. Access, Amex, Visa.*

Lavenham   Great House   £45

Tel 0787 247431	Restaurant

Market Place Lavenham Suffolk CO10 9QZ   Map 10 C3

The Great House is 15th-century with a Georgian facade, and stands just opposite Lavenham's historic Guildhall. Frenchman Régis Crépy provides excellent food served in cosy surroundings on rural French and English menus, applying a modern touch to the best local ingredients. Also lighter lunchtime menus. No smoking. *Seats 40. Parties 50. L 12-2.30 D 7-9.30 (Sat to 10.30). Closed D Sun, all Mon. Set L £10.90 Set D £14.95. Access, Amex, Diners, Visa.*

Rooms   £68

There are four charming bedrooms/suites. Thick beams, antique furniture and floral fabrics create the look of village England.

Leamington Spa   Piccolino's Pizzeria

Tel 0926 422988	Restaurant
5 Spencer Street Leamington Spa Warwickshire	Map 14 C1

A dependable alternative to the larger high street chains (there are
branches also in Warwick and Stratford – see entries). Piccolino's
is family-owned and family-friendly, too. Cooked-to-order pizzas
(*napolitana* £4.85; *quattro formaggi* £5.60) are notably good, pasta
alternatives (*ravioli di pomodoro* £4.95; *tagliatelle alla marinara* £5.85)
richly sauced, and there are steaks (*pizzaiola* £9.75) for those wishing
to splash out more. Functional decor suggests their heart lies in the
kitchen; the location, close to the main Post Office, is rather less than
fashionable. **Seats 100. Open** *12-2.30 & 5.30-11 (Fri to 11.30, Sun
to 10.30, Sat 12-11.30).* **Closed** *25 & 26 Dec. Access, Visa.*

Leamington Spa   Regency Fare

Tel 0926 425570	Restaurant
86 Regent Street Leamington Spa Warwickshire CV32 4NS	Map 14 C1

Small portions are available for 75% of the adult charge and aside from
warming food or bottles, the staff will liquidise vegetables and cream
potatoes for babies. Typical dishes are casseroles (£6.50), roast of the
day (£7.50) and crumble or fruit pie (£1.40). The restaurant is small
so push-chairs are stored/crammed in the tiny hallway. Friendly and
welcoming staff will instantly offer one of the two high-chairs and
drinks and then make a big effort to ensure that children feel at ease.
No special facilities for nappy changing but there's a mother and baby
room opposite in the Royal Priors shopping mall. **Seats 32.**
Open *9-5.30.* **Closed** *Sun & Bank Hols. Access, Amex, Visa.*

Leeds   Bibi's

Tel 0532 430905	Restaurant
16 Greek Street Leeds West Yorkshire LS1 5RU	Map 6 C1

Squeezed in between city-centre office blocks, there's a certain
incongruity to Bibis' classical Roman facade behind which
is an appealingly smart yet informal restaurant. The menu caters to all
occasions from a simple pizza or pasta dish (both around £4.50)
to a comprehensive range of skilfully prepared fish and meat dishes
at all prices from £6.75 to £14. Blackboard dishes of the day might
include fresh asparagus hollandaise, haddock fillet with lime and pine
kernels, and veal and pigeon pie. The super-swift lunchtime service
(much appreciated by the local business community) slows down
to a more relaxing pace at night. **Seats 140. Open** *12-2.15 & 6-11.15.*
Closed *Sun, Bank Holidays. Access, Amex, Visa.*

Leeds   Bryan's

Tel 0532 785679	Fish'n'Chips
9 Weetwood Lane Headingley Leeds West Yorkshire LS16 5LT	Map 6 C1

A modestly comfortable fish and chips restaurant serving good fresh
fish fried, in the traditional Yorkshire manner, in pure beef dripping.
Fairly standard menu with a couple of salads and special children's
section; otherwise there's a minimum charge of £4.05 per person.
Now licensed. Own parking. **Seats 116. Open** *11.30am-11.30pm (Sun
12.30-8)* **Closed** *25 & 26 Dec. Access, Visa.*

Leeds   Haley's Hotel   74%   £112

Tel 0532 784446 Fax 0532 753342	Hotel
Shire Oak Road Headingley Leeds West Yorkshire LS6 2DE	Map 6 C1

Two miles from the city centre, on a leafy lane just off the A660
Otley Road, stands a lovely Victorian house that has been transformed
into a stylish hotel. Although not large, the individually designed
bedrooms are well appointed with smart fabrics in varying styles;
attention to detail extends to a phone on both bedside and desk, shoe-
cleaning service and antique pieces. Bathrooms are bright and tiled,
and quality toiletries and bathrobes are provided. Smartly attired
young staff; 24hr room service and good breakfasts. Children under
7 stay free in parents' bedroom. There's one cot available and an extra
bed can be installed for £30. Baby-sitting and baby-listening services
available. No dogs. *Rooms* 22. *Garden. Closed 26-31 Dec. Access, Amex,
Diners, Visa.*

Restaurant   £52

A serious restaurant with a style and quality unusual for the Leeds area.
The refined, quietly elegant atmosphere is enhanced by neat table
settings, subtle lighting and smartly dressed staff. Chef Andrew Foster
cooks in a modern style, putting a classical training to good use
as a foundation on which to build. Fixed-price menus are offered for
both lunch and dinner and a seasonal carte might cover a range from
bourride with saffron and garlic mayonnaise or purple onion soup
with a puff pastry crust to trellised salmon and brill, red mullet fillets,
steamed breast of corn-fed chicken with truffle noodles, leeks and
butter sauce, and calf's liver with grapes, sultanas, almonds and
Sauternes sauce. French and British cheeses with home-made biscuits
and walnut bread, plus wines by the glass. Opinionated notes do little
to enliven a rather dull wine list. High-chairs, children's menu or small
portions and baby food are obtainable in the restaurant. *Seats* 50.
*Parties 24. Private Room. L 12.30-2 D 7.15-9.45. Closed L Sat, D Sun.
Set L £14.75 Set D £17.95/£22.50.*

Leeds   Pizza Express

Tel 0532 465207	Pizzeria
Whitecloth Hall Crown Street Leeds West Yorkshire LS2 9PF	Map 6 C1

A grade II listed building (1775) in which merchants used to trade
undyed cloth. This relatively new outlet occupies the ground floor
and mezzanine levels as well as the original large conservatory with its
York stone floors and real palm trees. Wooden floors, bare-faced brick
walls and original beams abound elsewhere. The baby grand piano
is played on Thursday and Fridays (8-11pm) and there's a resident jazz
duo on Sundays (7-10pm). Crisp, thin pizzas are served with fresh
ingredients as toppings (around £5). No-smoking area. *Seats* 150.
Open 11.30-midnight. Closed 25 & 26 Dec. Access, Visa.

Leeds   Salvo's

Tel 0532 755017	Pizzeria
115 Otley Road Headingley Leeds West Yorkshire	Map 6 C1

The 'best pizzas in the north' are the claim of this lively pizzeria.
Regulars queue outside in all weathers their wait made more pleasant
by hot crusty garlic bread served on the pavement. Pizzas include
affumicata with smoked cheese and bacon £4.75 and Kiev folded and
stuffed with chicken, garlic butter and cheese £5.35. Alternatively the

menu offers a wide range of pasta dishes and other savouries including scaloppine pizzaiola (egg-fried escalopes of beef with basil, garlic and tomato sauce served with noodles £8.35). Reservations accepted for lunch only. *Seats 45.* ***Open*** *12-2 & 5.30-11.* ***Closed*** *L Bank Holiday Mons, all Sun, 25 & 26 Dec. Access, Visa.*

Leicester   Welford Place

Tel 0533 470758	Restaurant
9 Welford Place Leicester Leicestershire	**Map 7 D4**

On entering Welford Place, you would be correct in assuming that this was previously a gentlemen's club. It's an old Victorian building with a grand sweeping staircase, large bay windows, wooden panelling and rich red walls in the bar and a bright restaurant. Breakfast is served from 8am: Continental (£4) or cooked English (£5) or individual dishes may be ordered – black pudding (£1.50). Throughout the day, the short Supplementary Menu offers inexpensive snacks – chickpea and garlic paté (£2), Parma ham and tomato sandwich (£2.50), warm steak with tarragon mustard sandwich (£5.50). There are three-course (£8.75) and two-course (£7.25) lunch menus; the former could propose cream of spinach soup, roast leg of lamb and oeufs à la neige. The à la carte menu (also available all day) has starters at £5 and main courses from £10. Traditional Sunday lunch £12. *Seats 60 (Restaurant) 40 (Bar).* ***Open*** *8am-11pm. Access, Amex, Diners, Visa.*

Leominster   Royal Oak

Tel 0568 612610	Hotel
South Street Leominster Hereford & Worcester HR6 8JA	**Map 14 A1**

The resident children here ensure that visiting children find a friendly welcome. Six sizeable family rooms and two family suites share two cots and there is storage for prams, a laundry service, baby-listening, baby-sitting on request and a supply of nappies. In the restaurant, reduced portions are available from the adult menu, which includes a vegetarian selection and a basic children's menu of fish fingers, sausages, beans and chips; food is not a strong point here. For babies there are high-chairs and bottles. Weekend breaks for families. Cot £4. *Rooms 18. Closed some Bank Holidays. Access, Amex, Diners, Visa.*

Lincoln   Moor Lodge Hotel   £70

Tel 0522 791366	Hotel
Sleaford Road Branston Lincoln Lincolnshire LN4 1HU	**Map 7 E2**

Moor Lodge is privately owned and well cared for. The hotel's genuinely flexible approach to families is summed up by their provision of an all-day children's menu, so your two-year-old, ratty because she is hungry, can be fed without fuss regardless of the time. Children can eat early with their peers but are equally welcome to join their parents in the large Parisian-style dining room, where three highchairs are provided. Both baby food and bottles are available and staff will even baby-sit on request. Seven attractive modern bedrooms, all with TV, tea-making facilities and en-suite bathrooms, are ideal for families and easily big enough to accommodate cots or an extra bed. There is also a suite comprising lounge, bedrooms and kitchen. This sleeps five and enjoys lovely rural views. Amenities include a fun pack, laundry service and a doctor on call. *Under-5s free. Rooms 25. Access, Amex, Diners, Visa.*

Lincoln   The Plaice

Tel 0522 546124	Fish'n'Chips

St Pauls Lane Lincoln Lincolnshire LN1 3AL   **Map 7 E2**

Just by the castle car parks on Westgate, John and Debbie Harris have
a prime spot for a true family chippy. Cheery waitress service to well-
spaced tables serves to emphasise that everything is cooked to order
and the quality of daily Grimsby fish supplies speaks for itself.
Haddock chips and peas (green or mushy) at £3.75 is a lunchtime
bargain: skate (£5.95), salmon salad (£5.50) and Dover soles attract
the more adventurous. Nursery puddings (Spotted Dick £1.65),
generous children's portions (from £2.40) and over half non-smoking
tables echo family commitment. *Seats 68. Open* 12-2 & 5-9.30
(*Tue/Thu/Fri to 10, Sat 12-10, Sun 12-8*). *Closed* Mon, 25 & 26 Dec.
Access, Visa.

Little Washbourne   Hobnails

Tel 0242 620237	Pub

Little Washbourne Gloucestershire   **Map 14 C1**

The licensee's family have run Hobnails for almost 250 years, which
must be some kind of record. The front bar is simply and traditionally
furnished, with a quarry-tiled floor and low beams; there's also
a modernised, carpeted rear lounge. A printed menu features a vast
selection of intriguingly filled baps (from £1.80), as well as a choice
of 35 puddings! A separate menu carries a short list of good hot home-
made specials. There are three high-chairs, a skittle alley and children's
menu. Swings and a slide in the small garden beside the car park.
Depressing, stone-floored outside loos. *Bar Food & Restaurant Meals*
12-2 & 7-10.30 (*9.30 restaurant*). *Beer* Wadworth, Whitbread, Flowers.
Garden, outdoor eating, children's play area. Family room. Access, Visa.

Liverpool   Est Est Est

Tel 051-708 6969	Restaurant

Unit 6 Edward Pavilion Albert Dock Liverpool Merseyside   **Map 6 A2**

Archetypal friendly trattoria, part of a small chain with branches
in Didsbury and Knutsford. The menu steers a familiar course from
minestrone (£1.95) and tonno e fagioli (£3.25) to a long list of pasta
(starter or main course, £2.05-£3.25/£3.95-£5.95, pizzas and
favourites such as scaloppine al limone (£9.40) and pollo principessa
(£8.05). *Seats 95. Open* 12-2.30 & 6-10.30 (*Fri & Sat to 11, Sun
12-10*) *Closed* 25 & 26 Dec, 1 Jan. Access, Amex, Visa.

Lode   Anglesey Abbey Tea Rooms

Tel 0223 811175	Tea Room

Anglesey Abbey Lode nr Cambridge Cambridgeshire CB5 9EJ   **Map 15 F1**

A great advantage here is that the all-day café and National Trust shop
are available to all without prior admission to the famous gardens. The
restaurant's success has resulted in extensions for the 1993 season
though the formula is unchanged. Counter-served coffee and cakes all
day are supplemented by the salad bar (quiche, cooked ham and
coronation chicken – all £4.50), hot lunches and vegetarian pulses
or pasta (from £3.50) at lunchtime. An extra plate or small portions
are provided for children. Two high-chairs, baby food, beakers and
cutlery are available and there's a nappy-changing table in the Ladies
toilet. Afternoon tea remains equally popular, and the enclosed garden

and play area is a summer hit with youngsters (the Abbey itself is not
really suitable for children). *Seats 150. Open 11-5. Closed 20 Dec-end
Mar, all Mon & Tue, also Wed end Oct-20 Dec. Access, Visa.*

Long Melford	**Black Lion**	**65%**	**£65**
Tel 0787 312356 Fax 0787 74557			Hotel
The Green Long Melford Sudbury Suffolk CO10 9DN			Map 10 C3

Count the Toby jugs and admire the maps and copper collection
or relax in deep sofas in the charming lounge. Bedrooms are bright
and comfortable, attractive fabrics complementing neutral walls and
carpets. Each room has antique pine furniture and an easy chair or sofa.
Rooms 9. Garden. Closed 23 Dec-2 Jan. Access, Visa.

Long Melford	**Chimneys**	**£75**
Tel 0787 79806		Restaurant
Hall Street Long Melford Sudbury Suffolk CO10 9JR		Map 10 C3

Sam Chalmers' delightful beamed restaurant offers monthly menus full
of interest and cooking in a modern style. For starters pigeon breast
in flaky pastry with basil sauce and monkfish tail in a light curry;
to follow, red mullet in Oriental spices and calf's kidneys with red
cabbage and grain mustard sauce. Some simpler cooking at lunchtimes
with traditional English puddings. Good selective wine list strong
on Alsace and the New World. *Seats 40. Parties 40. L 12-2 D 7-9.
Closed D Sun. Set L £13.95 Set D £27.50. Access, Visa.*

Louth	**Mr Chips**	
Tel 0507 603756		Fish'n'Chips
Ashwell Street Louth Lincolnshire		Map 7 F2

Just off the Market Square you'll not miss the Hagans' Union Jacks
still flying the flag of British fish. Always ready are the freshest
haddock, crunchy chips and mushy peas (they sell a ton per week!).
A la carte translates as the briefest wait for scampi and plaice cooked
to order or the salmon shantie or creamy fish pie. For vegetarians are
bubble and squeak or deep-fried courgettes, cauliflower and baby corn.
Families are especially welcomed: a mothers' comfort station and
disabled persons' toilet are all part of the service. *Seats 250.
Open 9am-11.30pm. Closed Sun, 25, 26 Dec & 1 Jan. No credit cards.*

Luccombe Chine	**Dunnose Cottage**	
Tel 0983 862585		Tea Room
Luccombe Chine nr Shanklin Isle of Wight PO37 6RH		Map 15 D4

The road winds between Shanklin and Ventnor and on a left bend
is a narrow lane signposted to a hotel and the tea rooms. In the cottage,
whose walls are adorned with china plates, ornaments and a framed
collection of cigarette cards, visitors can enjoy home-made snacks
throughout the day. Sandwiches start at £1.25, and there are scones
and cakes, ploughman's, salads and jacket potatoes. Lunch brings
cottage pie (£3.95, lasagne, home-cooked ham, burgers and basket
meals, with roasts on Sunday (£7.95 three courses). Families will have
to take a chance on the single high-chair (or else take their own);
children can wander off around the 3½ acres of gardens, but mind the
ditches! No room for changing babies in the loos. *Seats 90.
Open 10.30-5.30. Closed Mon Sept-Easter (exc. Bank Holidays).*

Lyme Regis	**Royal Lion Hotel**	**£70**
Tel 0297 445622		Hotel
Broad Street Lyme Regis Dorset DT7 3QF		Map 13 E2

Built in 1601, the Royal Lion Hotel sits well in this historic town's main street. The accommodation is simple and pubby, nothing is too grand but everything is spotlessly kept. In the restaurant, 'plain English cooking' features on the à la carte menu and small portions are offered for junior diners; children have two high-chairs, booster seats and their own menu (all £1.90) and high tea is available on request. A separate room (non smoking) in the snack bar area is also available to families. In addition to the 45′ swimming pool and gym there is a 'ball pool' for children to bounce about in. If sharing their parents' room, children under 5 pay 40% of adult rate and over 5 60% – a most unusual arrangement. *Seats 60. Open 12-2 (Bar), 7.30-9 (Restaurant). Closed 25, 26 & 27 Dec. Access, Amex, Visa.*

Lymington	**Passford House**	**70%**	**£97**
Tel 0590 682398 Fax 0590 683494			Hotel
Mount Pleasant Lane Lymington Hampshire SO41 8LS			Map 14 C4

On the edge of the New Forest between Lymington (2 miles) and Sway, this elegant white house was originally the home of Lord Arthur Cecil. Two bedroom wings and a leisure centre have since been added, but the traditional look survives in the lounges – one oak-panelled with an open fire, another with French windows opening onto a patio and ornamental pool. Upstairs there are bright and airy bedrooms with mostly white furniture; carpeted bathrooms have showers and useful toiletries. There are eight 'de luxe' rooms. Purpose-built Dolphin leisure centre has a good range of facilities. Children are catered for admirably, with cots, high chairs, a separate play area and separate meal times (high tea only in the bedrooms); no charge if sharing parents' accommodation. *Rooms 56. Garden, indoor & outdoor swimming pools, sauna, solarium, spa bath, keep-fit equipment, tennis, putting, croquet, games room, snooker, pool table. Access, Amex, Visa.*

Lympsham	**Batch Farm**	**56%**	**£56**
Tel 0934 750371			Hotel
Lympsham nr Weston-super-Mare Somerset BS24 0EX			Map 13 E1

Lympsham is easy to find, only some three miles from junction 22 of the M5. The hotel, with its 50-acre garden, stands in open farmland through which the river Axe flows. Origins of the former farmhouse are evident in the beams which adorn the bar and residents' lounges, while the neat practical bedrooms in an extension benefit from panoramic views of either the Mendip or Quantock hills. No dogs. *Rooms 8. Garden, croquet, coarse fishing. Access, Amex, Diners, Visa.*

Lyndhurst	**Lyndhurst Park**	**61%**	**£60**
Tel 0703 283923 Fax 0703 283019			Hotel
High Street Lyndhurst Hampshire SO43 7NL			Map 14 C4

The Forestdale Group's much-extended Georgian mansion is set in spacious grounds and has popular conference facilities. Bedrooms have freestanding furniture and small tiled bathrooms; cots can be provided in family rooms. Day rooms include a cocktail bar and

little lounge. Summer activity for families centres round the pool and
playground where there are swings. There's a nominal charge for
children sharing their parents' room. High-chairs and baby food
provided. *Rooms 59. Garden, outdoor swimming pool, tennis, sauna,
games room, playroom & playground. Access, Amex, Diners, Visa.*

Lytham St Anne's	Dalmeny Hotel	£68
Tel 0253 712236		Hotel
19 South Promenade Lytham St Anne's Lancashire FY8 1LX		Map 6 A1

From modest beginnings nearly 50 years ago the Dalmeny has grown
into a large family hotel with squash court, indoor pool, games room
and no less than three restaurants. For much of the year there are daily
events and amusements laid on for children and a well-equipped
playroom becomes a crèche (9am-3pm) in high season and holiday
times. Pine or light wood fitted furniture with tiled tops, feature in the
large, simply-decorated bedrooms, many with extra beds (some are
family suites with several bedrooms) and most with kitchenette. Staff
are smart, friendly and helpful. Baby-sitting/listening, cots, high-chairs,
children's menu – you name it they've got it! High tea is served in the
Carvery between 5 and 7pm; colouring pads and crayons for
artistically inclined youngsters. The hotel is still growing, with
a gymnasium and new conference rooms planned for 1993. *Rooms 90.
Indoor swimming pool, squash, sauna, beautician, hair salon. Access, Visa.*

C'est La Vie Restaurant £65

The hotel's smart eatery (there's also a Carvery and a Barbecue
restaurant) is in a vaulted basement with flagstone floor. Long-serving
chef Barry Smith can be seen in his small kitchen giving individual
care and attention to each dish from the sensibly limited, French-
inspired evening à la carte menu. There's a short, keenly-priced table
d'hote at lunchtimes. No smoking. *Seats 45. Parties 45.
Open 12.30-2.30 & 7-9. Set L from £11.50.*

Maidstone	Pizza Express	
Tel 0622 683549		Pizzeria
32 Earl Street Maidstone Kent		Map 11 C5

One of the larger Pizza Express outlets, this restaurant operates
on three floors. The balconied room upstairs is used as a jazz venue
two or three times a week (Entrance £2-£10 depending on artist.
Eating not obligatory. Reservations necessary.) Crisp, thin pizzas
(£3.15-£5.40) with fresh ingredients for the toppings. No-smoking
area. *Seats 195. Open 11.30am-midnight. Closed 25 & 26 Dec. Access,
Amex, Visa.*

Maldon	Wheelers	
Tel 0621 853647		Fish'n'Chips
13 High Street Maldon Essex		Map 11 C4

Long established family-run fish and chip restaurant and take-away
in Maldon's high street. In tea-shop surroundings they serve plaice,
cod, haddock (£3.95) and rock eel, plus skate and sole when available.
Some of the sweets are home-made, including apple pie. *Seats 52.
Open 11.30-1.45 & 6-9.30. Closed Sun, Mon, Bank Holidays.
No credit cards.*

Malmesbury	Old Bell Hotel	64%	£88
Tel 0666 822344 Fax 0666 825145			Hotel
Abbey Row Malmesbury Wiltshire SN16 0BW			Map 14 B2

Hard by the abbey, the Old Bell dates back to 1210 and therefore has claims to being England's oldest hostelry. Its wisteria-clad facade is more than a match for its spiritual neighbour. Public rooms comprise two oak-beamed bars and two lounge areas, one with a famous 800-year-old chimney. The youngest guests are welcomed with the same courtesy extended to more venerable guests. A fun pack keeps children happy while parents unpack in one of the five family rooms. Two cots are available and prams and pushchairs can be stored. Baby-sitting and baby-listening are offered. Bedrooms in the main building come in all shapes and sizes, while those in the converted stables are more uniformly modern. Families are well catered for; one child up to 10 stays free in his parents' room. Baby food is available in the restaurant, as is a children's menu and children's portions. There are two high-chairs and any accidents can soon be sorted out by the laundry service. No dogs. Clipper Hotels. **Rooms** *37. Garden. Access, Visa.*

Manchester	Cocotoo	
Tel 061-237 5458		Restaurant
57 Whitworth Street West Manchester Greater Manchester M1 5WW		Map 6 B2

Run with the enthusiasm so often displayed by Italian restaurateurs, Cocotoo is a large, well-appointed restaurant near the Palace and Green Room Theatres. The menu offers all the usual choices, including pizza, pasta (*farfalle al salmone* £4.95), variations on chicken and veal, steaks from the grill, ice creams and tiramisu. Burgers at lunchtime only. **Seats** *220.* **Open** *12-2.15 & 5.30-11.15.* **Closed** *Sun & Bank Holidays. Access, Amex, Diners, Visa.*

Manchester	Dutch Pancake House	
Tel 061-228 1851		Restaurant
St Peter's Square Manchester Greater Manchester M2 3DF		Map 6 B2

Unlike those restaurants with 'pizza' or 'burger' in their name (which usually serve other dishes as well), this is just what it claims. The menu is an exhaustive list of permutations of cheese, bacon, chicken and a great many other savoury fillings for the distinctive Dutch pancake, followed by pancakes and waffles filled for the sweetest tooth. The children's menu is a slightly smaller selection of the same, shrunk for smaller tums. There are two high-chairs and two booster seats. Subterranean restaurants seem to be a feature of Manchester, so mind the stairs. **Seats** *110.* **Open** *12-12 (Sun to 10).* **Closed** *4 days Christmas. Access, Visa.*

Manchester	Henry J Bean's Bar & Grill	
Tel 061-832 8900		Restaurant
42 Blackfriars Street Manchester M3 5EG		Map 6 B2

The menu should please most with its mix of Hank's Bar and Chicago Pizza Pie. Burgers from £4.50, pizzas from £5.40, ribs, burritos and meat or vegetable fajitas. Side orders of onion rings £1.30 and garlic bread will fill any gaps. Finish up with mud pie or chocolate fudge sundae (desserts £1.50-£2.95). Children's menu. **Seats** *80.* **Open** *11.45am-11pm, (Fri/Sat to 11.30, Sun 12-10).* **Closed** *25 & 26 Dec. Access, Amex, Diners, Visa.*

Manchester   Pizza Express

Tel 061-834 0145	Pizzeria
Old Colony House South King Street Manchester Greater Manchester	Map 6 B2

This 100-year-old York-stone building was previously a car
showroom and now benefits from floor to ceiling windows, one
of which opens up in summer. Popular with the media types from
local TV and radio stations, it's well liked for its crispy, thin-based
pizzas and generous fresh toppings (around £5). *Seats 118.*
Open 11.30am-midnight. *Closed* 25 & 26 Dec. Access, Amex, Visa.

Manchester   Victoria & Albert Hotel, Café Maigret

Tel 061-832 1188	Café
Water Street Manchester M60 9EAA	Map 6 B2

Opened in October 1992, this new hotel is located opposite the
Granada film studios and next to the Manchester Ship Canal and the
Museum of Science and Industry. The Café has dark wooden tables
and chairs, a tiled floor, potted plants, fresh flowers on the tables and
the windows are so thoroughly double-glazed that the traffic noise
is virtually eliminated. The menu changes regularly and may include
hot salmon fishcake salad with yoghurt dressing (£4.25), vegetable
curry pie and a celery sauce (£5.95) or seafood risotto with Parmesan
(£6.95), followed by apple pie and thick custard (£2.50).
A blackboard advertises the dishes of the day as well a 2- or 3-course
menu (£9.95/£12.50). Young, friendly staff are particularly attentive
to children who have their own menu – ham and pineapple pizza with
salad (£2.95), beefburger, baked beans and chips (£2.75). Baby food
or bottles will be warmed and the ladies toilet is large enough for
keeping the little one in good order. A vacant bedroom or a quiet
corner of the private lounge will be offered for nursing. Four high-
chairs and small cutlery are supplied. Buggies may be left with the
concierge. No-smoking area. Own car park. *Seats 80.*
Open 10am-10.30pm. *Closed* Dec 25. Access, Amex, Diners, Visa.

Marlborough   Polly Tea Rooms

Tel 0672 512146	Tea Room
26 High Street Marlborough Wiltshire	Map 14 C2

For many years now, the West family and the manageress have been
running these traditional tea rooms. Beams, pine dressers, pretty lace
cloths and uniformed waitresses create a splendidly traditional air and
there's a mouthwatering display of wonderful gateaux (tiramisu,
Baileys Irish coffee cream, lemon and redcurrant cheesecake) at the
entrance while inside, croissants, brioches, Danish pastries, strudels,
excellent sausage rolls, muesli scones, rows of biscuits and pastries
(from 90p) are laid out – all baked on the premises. Two set
breakfasts – country special with muesli £3.95 or a fry-up with
sautéed potatoes £5.50 – start the day; lunch offers parsnip and apple
soup (£2.50) with home-made bread, fish mousse (£5.75 with salad),
locally smoked trout and specials such as beef and Guinness pie with
dauphinois potatoes (£5.50), chicken provençale with noodles,
or spinach, cream cheese and mushroom roulade (£5.50). On weekend
afternoons only, a savoury set tea is now offered (£3.65 – quiche and
salad with a drink). The Polly Tea (three scones £3.65) and Special

Gateaux Tea are only available in the high season. Children's portions.
No-smoking area. *Seats 100*. *Open 8.30-6 (Sat 8-7, Sun 9-7)*.
Closed 25 & 26 Dec, 2nd & 3rd Fri & Sat in Oct. Access, Amex, Visa.

Marshside   Gate Inn

Tel 0227 860498	Pub
Chisley Marshside Kent CT3 4EB	Map 11 C5

Delightfully set, with picnic tables under trees, an unfenced duck pond
and a stream in the garden. Indoors, it's rustic and wholly
unpretentious, and prides itself on still being 'a talker's pub', in tandem
with a thriving bar meal trade. Fresh, local produce is the basis of
homely, honest English fare (spicy sausage hot pot £3.50, garlic
mushrooms £1.60), along with burgers and a famous black pudding
sandwich (£1.15) served with mango chutney. The menu has two
sides, one of which is green, listing healthier dishes. Small portions are
offered and food will be warmed on request. Free-range eggs and local
vegetables are also sold over the bar. A good log fire in winter. Live
jazz every Tuesday; quiz night is Thursday (when there's also a special
menu). *Bar Food 11-2.30 (Sat 11-3, Sun 12-3) & 6-11 (Sun 7-10.30);
bar snacks. Children's portions. Beer Shepherd Neame. Family room.
Outdoor play area, riverside garden, outdoor eating, summer barbecue.
No credit cards.*

Matlock   Matlock Garden Centre, Coffee Shop

Tel 0629 580500	Coffee Shop
Nottingham Road Tansley Matlock Derbyshire	Map 6 C2

Approximately 7 miles from J28 on M1 or 3 miles from Matlock
on the A615, the Coffee Shop at the Matlock Garden Waterlife and
Pet Centre attracts almost as many people as the Centre itself. It's a self-
service restaurant in bright, colourful, plant-filled surroundings where
friendly staff prepare, cook, and serve most of the food on offer. The
menu and prices are displayed on boards hanging from the ceiling:
haddock in parsley sauce, chicken fillet filled with cheese wrapped
in bacon, beef and potato pie (all £3.75), trifle (£1.45); set tea £1.95
(scone (fruit, wholemeal or plain), jam, cream and pot of tea); and
Sunday lunch features a roast (£3.99). Tables and chairs are set up on
the outdoor patio and children can play on the climbing frame in the
garden. There are highchairs, pram storage facilities, and it's possible
to change a nappy in the toilets. No-smoking area. *Seats 120 (plus
50 outside). Open Oct-Feb 10-4.30, Mar-Sep 9-5 (Sat & Sun to 5.30)
Closed 25 Dec-1 Jan. No credit cards.*

Matlock   The Strand

Tel 0629 584444	Bistro
Dale Road Matlock Derbyshire DE4 3LT	Map 6 C2

Judith and Julian Mason run a very friendly, genuine bistro
in a former Victorian draper's shop. The high-ceilinged panelled room
is lit with replica gas lamps and attractive cast-iron pillars and
balustrades lead up to more seating on the gallery. During the day, the
menu offers a variety of light, inexpensive dishes with ten different
daily specials – chef's paté (£2.95), moules marinière (£3.50), spinach
and feta cheese filo parcels (£3.50), barbecue chicken and potato pie
(£3.50), beef olives and baked potato (£4.25), Brooklyn tuna bake
£3.50. The more comprehensive evening menu changes every day.
Starters are priced between £1.80 and £4.25, and main courses £6.50

to £11.95. Families are welcome and thoughtfully considered. Two
high-chairs (with reins) are provided, while benches in booths are ideal
for older children. Half-price portions of dishes are available, although
not advertised. No baby-changing facilities and parents with children
are asked to be considerate of other diners in the evenings when live
light jazz is played on Tues, Thurs and Fri. *Seats* 72. *Open* 10-2 &
7-10. *Closed* Sun, Mon (winter only), 25 & 26 Dec, 1 Jan. Access, Visa.

Mawgan   The Yard Bistro

Tel 032622 595	Bistro
Trelowarren Estate Mawgan nr Helston Cornwall	**Map 12 B4**

Part of a stately home, the attractive Yard Bistro is housed in the old
coach house on one side of the stableyard. Being the headquarters
of the Cornish Craft Assocation, there's also a working pottery,
weaving studio, art gallery as well as outdoor theatre and garden
nursery. The bistro is open plan with granite stanchions, a bar at one
end and an open log fire at the other. Coffee only until noon, and then
the changing menu may offer Swiss chard and Brussels sprout soup
(£1.50), Stilton ploughman's (£3) with home-made pickle and bread,
grilled goat's cheese (£3.20) or a fresh pasta as well as a choice of four
hot dishes of the day (roast duck with raspberry and port sauce £6,
smoked chicken and prawn biryani with red chilis £4). Clotted cream
accompanies puddings such as warm chocolate and walnut brownies
or berry and apple crumble (both £2). A three-course roast lunch
features on Sundays (£6.50). In summer, the stable yard provides
an outdoor alternative for lunch or tea (Cornish Cream Tea in high
season only £2.50). More elaborate evening meals. Children's
portions. *Seats 45. Open* 11-2 & 7-9. *Closed* Low season: D Sun-Wed,
all Mon, all Jan & Feb, 25,26 & 31 Dec. No credit cards.

Melbourn   Pink Geranium   £85

Tel 0763 260215	Restaurant
Station Road Melbourn nr Royston Hertfordshire SG8 6DX	**Map 15 F1**

Set in an early 16th-century thatched cottage, Steven and Sally
Saunders' pretty restaurant combines a homely atmosphere with some
sophisticated cooking. Chef John Curtis produces a variety of menus
that range from relatively straightforward lunches (warm duck confit
salad, supreme of chicken with crab and sticky toffee pudding) to a
three-course *menu gourmande* (escalope of salmon with vodka and
lemon beurre blanc, venison steak with celeriac purée and port sauce,
cripsy mango tart with vanilla crème anglaise and blueberries). The
carte is involved with dishes like morel-studded terrine of guinea fowl
with toasted sesame brioche and breast of Bresse chicken filled with
salmon mousseline and served with a Szechuan peppercorn sauce.
Crispy duck with citrus fruits and a saké sauce (for two) is a house
speciality. French or English cheeses served with home-made walnut
bread. Steven is the author of a book on children's food. He scorns
sausages and other fast food but gladly serves small portions
of exquisitely presented main-menu items to young visitors. Food will
be puréed for babies and bottles warmed, beakers filled and customer's
own food warmed on request. The ladies loo is equipped with a chair
for nursing, changing table and nappy bin. Chauffeur service for those
who wish to enjoy the wine list *and* being driven home. Fenced
garden. *Seats 72. Parties 100. Private Room. L 12-2 D 7-10 (Sat
to 10.30). Closed L Sat, D Sun, all Mon. Set L £12.95/£15.95
(£16.95 Sun) Set D £24.95. Access, Amex, Visa.*

Melmerby   Village Bakery

Tel 0768 881515	Restaurant
Melmerby nr Penrith Cumbria	Map 4 C3

On the A686 Alston road, ten miles from junction 40 on the M6, the Village Bakery is in a converted barn with a bright airy conservatory and old pine furniture. Andrew and Lis Whitley organically grow their own ingredients and bake the breads and cakes in a brick oven. Vegetarians will be pleased to know that they now offer a 'vegetarian full fried breakfast': aduki bean pattie, potato and vegetable cake, egg, grilled mushrooms, tomato and fried bread (£5.75). Raspberry porridge (£2.25) and oak-smoked Inverawe kippers (£2.75) are alternatives. Lunch brings spicy lentil soup (£2.25) or chestnut and red wine paté (£2.50) as starters and as main courses, tatie pot, a local dish using organic lamb, black pudding and home-grown vegetables (£5.95) or three-layer vegetable bake with salad and garlic bread (£5.75). Another option is the baker's lunch (£4.95) – bread from the oven with cheese from the north country. Home-made puddings include carrot and cream cheese cake or hazelnut and apple cake (from £1.25) and popular biscuit slices such as a peanutter, chocolate chip cookie or Westmorland parkin should be tasted. **Seats** 45. **Open** 8.30-5 (Mon to 2.30 – snacks only, Sun 9.30-5). **Closed** 25 & 26 Dec, 1 Jan, Sun in Jan & Feb. Access, Diners, Visa.

Mere   Old Ship Hotel   £52

Tel 0747 860258 Fax 0747 860501	Inn
Castle Street Mere Wiltshire BA12 6JE	Map 14 B3

A splendid 17th-century inn with flagstones, exposed brick and stonework, log fires, panelling and beamed ceilings. Period oak furniture in the three characterful bars and the quiet residents' lounge complements the ancient fabric of the building. Bedrooms in the mainhouse have traditional furnishings while ten in the annexe are more compact and modern. Eight bedrooms not en suite share three bathrooms. Of the hotel's twelve family rooms, three are interconnecting and there are two good-quality cots. Baby-listening is available and baby-sitters can be arranged with advance notice. There is a high-chair in the restaurant, which offers small portions and baby food but no children's menu. At the rear of the hotel is a grassy play area. Laundry service. This is a popular base for touring, walking and riding. **Rooms** 23. Baby-sitting, baby-listening. Access, Visa.

Middle Wallop   Fifehead Manor   61%   £75

Tel 0264 781565 Fax 0264 781400	Hotel
Middle Wallop nr Stockbridge Hampshire SO20 8EG	Map 14 C3

Beside the busy A343 between Andover and Salisbury, the manor house stands in 3½ acres of land and has origins going back to the Middle Ages. Central to the house is the medieval dining hall with its mullioned windows and there is a small bar plus a lounge with a rather unused air. Large bedrooms in the main house have good-size bathrooms complete with resident plastic ducks; smaller singles (with showers only) are in an annexe, but have the attraction of leading out onto the rear lawn. Subdued fabrics and colour schemes are used throughout, and the furniture is mostly modern, although a few antiques help contribute to the friendly and informal atmosphere. Fine cooked breakfasts, but little choice for the more health-conscious. No accommodation charge for under-5s. The management's attitude

make this a child-friendly hotel rather than any extraordinary facilities.
Rooms 16. Garden, croquet. Closed 2 weeks Xmas/New Year. Access,
Amex, Diners, Visa.

Midsomer Norton — Mrs Pickwick

Tel 0761 414589	Tea Room
70 High Street Midsomer Norton Avon	**Map 13 F1**

Mrs Pickwick is a friendly tea room with a patio for fair-weather
snacking. Owner Pauline Towler has just built an extension on to the
back of the house thus increasing the seating capacity. Hot lunches are
taken upstairs: omelettes, cottage pie, chicken curry, macaroni cheese
(all £2.50), whilst downstairs is available for snacks, toasted
sandwiches (from £1.20) and gateaux. Clotted cream tea with home-
made scones £1.90. Children's portions available. No smoking.
Seats 44. Open 9-5.30. Closed Sun, Bank Holidays.

Milton Keynes — Friendly Hotel £77

Tel 0908 561666 Fax 0908 568303	Hotel
Monks Way Two Mile Ash Milton Keynes Buckinghamshire MK8 8LY	**Map 15 E1**

A family-friendly hotel with a small swimming pool, exercise room
and beauty treatment room. The large bedrooms have en-suite
bathrooms, televisions with three satellite channels, tea and coffee-
making facilities and in-house movies are available. At meal times,
children are given snakes & ladders place mats and a stuffed snake with
foot measurements is held up against the child who is then charged
£1 per foot for his/her meal. On Sundays, the conservatory area
is converted into a play area showing children's videos. There's
a playground outside but children will need to be supervised. Baby
food is not available on the premises but staff are happy to heat bottles.
The children's menu includes fish snakelets, forked tongue burger and
a slithering snake cake. Children under 14 stay free in their parents'
room. *Rooms 88. Access, Amex, Diners, Visa.*

Milton Keynes — Pizza Express

Tel 0908 231738	Pizzeria
396 Midsummer Boulevard Milton Keynes Buckinghamshire	**Map 15 E1**

A large outlet with a huge mural covering one entire wall, black tiling
and director-style chairs plus the more familiar white-marble topped
tables. The menu offers monthly specials such as Cajun pizza and
tonno e fagioli. Live jazz in the basement on Sunday nights. *Seats 130.*
Open 10am-midnight. Closed 25 Dec. Access, Amex, Visa.

Milton Street — Sussex Ox

Tel 0323 870340	Pub
Milton Street nr Wilmington East Sussex BN26 5RL	**Map 11 B6**

Turn left off the A27 (Eastbourne-Brighton) to get to Milton Street
and you will find the Sussex Ox. If you need one, grab a high-chair
when you arrive as there are only two and the pub is usually packed
with families. The children's menu has the usual offerings with chips
except on Sundays when there's a special roast dinner for £2.95.
Outside, there's a large garden with plenty of wooden play equipment,
a grassy area and picnic tables for warmer weather. The loos are
scruffy and you'd be better off feeding or changing a baby in the car.
Open 12-2 & 7-9.30. Closed Dec 25.

Monksilver   Notley Arms

Tel 0984 56217	Pub

Monksilver Taunton Somerset TA4 4JB — Map 13 E1

The experienced Sarah and Alistair Cade have brought inimitable flair to the white-painted roadside Notley Arms and in just a few short years built up a formidably good reputation at this previously distinctly undistinguished village pub. The interior is charmingly simple: an L-shaped bar with plain wooden furniture, black and white timbered walls, candles at night, and twin wood-burning stoves; a small but bright and cheery family room (complete with toys) leads off, and there's a stream at the bottom of the trim (and safe) cottagey garden. The big attraction here, though, is the bar food, which divides roughly into three categories – the traditional, the eastern or exotic, and the vegetarian – all given equal thought, the finest fresh ingredients, and cooked with sure-handed skill. Old favourites and four or five daily hot specials are chalked up on the blackboard: start with an excellent home-made soup (£1.50), like a well-balanced tasty lentil and vegetable, or subtle potato and dill (served with French-flour bread). For a light but satisfying lunch, choose one of the delicious pitta bread sandwiches with garlic butter, tender meats and good crispy salad. Chinese red-roast pork (£5.25) features well-marinated cubes of meat in a soy, five spice and hoisin sauce, with stir-fried pimento and courgette. The cod pie in filo pastry (£3.95), Somerset pork in cream, cider and shallots (£5.25), wild mushroom and pasta bake (£4.25) and braised beef with green peppercorn sauce (£5.75) are fine, as are puddings, with light pastry and good local cream. Despite the crowds at peak times, all runs effortlessly smoothly and with good humour. No high-chairs. *Bar Food & Restaurant Meals* 12-2 (12-1.45 Sun), 7-9.30 (7-9 Sun). *Children's portions. Beer Ruddles, Theakstons, Ushers, Wadworth. Riverside garden, outdoor eating, children's play area. Family room. No credit cards.*

Morden   Superfish

Tel 081-648 6908	Fish'n'Chips

20 London Road Morden Surrey — Map 15 E3

Part of a Surrey-based chain of above-average fish and chip restaurants. All dishes are served with well-cooked chips, French bread, pickles or sauces and 'hopefully a smile'. Beef dripping is used for frying in the traditional manner and a fillet of cod may be small, large or a Moby Dick (£3.25, £4.25 or £5.05). A children's platter of fishbites with chips costs £2.20. No reservations. *Seats* 42. *Open* 11.30-2 (Sat to 2.30, 5-10.30 (Thu-Sat to 11). *Closed* Sun, 25 & 26 Dec, 1 Jan. *Access, Visa.*

Mullion   Polurrian Hotel   65%   £168*

Tel 0326 240421 Fax 0326 240083	Hotel

Mullion Helston Cornwall TR12 7EN — Map 12 B4

A large, white-painted hotel in a commanding position atop 300ft-high cliffs. Its interior decor is in carefully muted colours and there are unparalleled westerly views from both lounge and dining room. Children's amenities are a great draw for family holidays, with an under-7s' playroom in the lively leisure club, adventure playground in the garden, and safe bathing cove, approached by a winding cliff path; baby-sitting is also available, as are baby baths, potties and nappies – the business! High tea is served 5.30-6.30pm (order before noon) and changes daily: perhaps home-made fish pie or deep-fried chicken followed by fresh fruit, jelly, yoghurt or banana custard; there are at least a dozen high-chairs in the restaurant, but tea can be served in your room. *Half-board terms only, plus self-catering family apartments. *Rooms 40. Garden, indoor & outdoor swimming pools, sauna, solarium, spa bath, keep-fit equipment, tennis, squash, badminton, putting, sea fishing, boating, snooker, coffee shop (7.30am-10pm). Closed Nov-Mar. Access, Amex, Diners, Visa.*

Needingworth   Pike & Eel Hotel

Tel 0480 63336	Pub

Overcoat Lane Needingworth nr St Ives Cambridgeshire PE17 3TW   Map 10 B2

Right on the banks of the River Ouse, in 17 acres of grounds, this popular pub bristles with families and sea-dogs, especially on Sundays. The Garden Room restaurant serves bar meals and small portions of all dishes are available at half price. It is wise to reserve one of the two high-chairs in advance as they are constantly in use. Sink into the deep comfortable chairs in the bar area in the winter and look forward to the summer when the restaurant spills out onto the terrace and into the garden. **Seats** 120. **Open** 12-2 & 7-10 (weekends to 10.30). **Closed** Dec 25, 26 & Jan 1. Access, Amex, Visa.

New Alresford   Hunters   £60

Tel 0962 732468	Restaurant

32 Broad Street New Alresford Hampshire SO24 9AQ   Map 15 D3

Wine bar/brasserie with two distinctive bow-fronted windows, awnings and candlelight within, run by the Birmingham family. Promising food from a young, enthusiastic chef: sautéed foie gras on toasted brioche with oranges and pan-fried fillet steak with creamy cep sauce and roast potatoes typify the top end of the menu; simpler offerings might include a salad of avocado and toasted chèvre or steamed salmon with mashed potatoes and a watercress butter sauce. Friendly, laid-back service and good-value wines. Children are made welcome with high-chairs and smaller portions. **Seats** 30. **Parties** 80. Private Room. L 12-2 D 7-10. Closed D Sun, 24-27 Dec. Access, Visa.

Rooms   £48

Three rooms in an old Georgian building, all with shower and WC en suite. No phones in rooms. **Rooms** 3.

Newmarket   Horseracing Museum Restaurant

Tel 0638 667331	Restaurant

99 High Street Newmarket Suffolk CB8 8JL   Map 10 B3

An excellent and popular spot for lunch and tea where you can choose your eating area between a marquee (from Mar-Oct, seating 50), the newly extended restaurant and a large safe garden with a fine old carriage to admire. The restaurant is self-service and there is a range of salads and home-made hot dishes that should suit all but the youngest of babies. There are no high-chairs but changing and nursing can be done in the spacious, immaculate loos. Ask to use those in the museum as they are larger than those in the restaurant. **Seats** 60. **Open** 10-4.30 (2-5 Sun Mar-June, Sept-Dec, 12-5 July & Aug). **Closed** Mon out of season, mid Jan-March & Xmas.

Newquay — Atlantic Hotel — £98

Tel 0637 872244	Hotel
Dane Road Newquay Cornwall TR7 1EN	Map 12 B3

Built in 1892 and still standing firm against the wind blowing across the headland on which it stands, the Atlantic has been totally refurbished over the last four years. Family rooms with cots are available and between 7 and 9pm children can be left (without charge) in the supervised crèche. A new playground, overlooking the sea, contains swings, roundabouts, and a tree house. Similarly, children now have their own games room complete with table tennis, video machines and pool table. Small children can have their own meal at 5.30pm. Breakfast time is relaxed, with high-chairs and booster seats provided. However, so that everyone stays happy, it is worth remembering that many guests are elderly and enjoy a certain degree of formality. Children can eat and/or stay for free depending on age and season – ring ahead for details. *Rooms 90. Open all year. Access, Visa.*

Newquay — Hotel Riviera — 63% — £78

Tel 0637 874251 Fax 0637 850823	Hotel
Lusty Glaze Road Newquay Cornwall TR7 3AA	Map 12 B3

Popular for family holidays, functions and conferences (for around 150), this well-appointed modern hotel overlooks a lovely stretch of coastline (a small supplement is charged for rooms with a sea view). Three bars, a lounge and a garden provide plenty of space to relax, and in summer there's evening entertainment (every Saturday during the rest of the year). Children's suppers are served 6-6.15pm in La Piazza 'night spot' area or at 7pm with their parents in the dining room. *Rooms 50. Outdoor swimming pool & children's pool, games room, snooker, sauna, squash, racquetball, children's playroom and play area. Access, Amex, Visa.*

Norden — The Manor

Tel 0706 50027	Pub
Edenfield Road Norden nr Rochdale Lancashire OL12 7TW	Map 6 B2

The management of this Victorian Gothic pub have gone all out to attract families and have made such a success of it that the place is now regularly used for children's parties. Two well-designed adventure playgrounds (one for under-4s, the other for older children) keep the kids happy in the fenced garden with picnic tables. Inside, in a family area is a Lego table. Children have their own menu and six high-chairs are provided. An excellent mothers' room has a changing area, nursing chair and microwave for heating baby foods. No-smoking area. *Open Bar Food 11.30-10 (Sun from 12). Access, Visa.*

North Cerney — Bathurst Arms

Tel 0285 831281	Pub
North Cerney nr Cirencester Gloucestershire GL7 7BZ	Map 14 C2

17th-century coaching inn alongside the A435, not far from Cotswold Water Park. Rustic unspoilt bar with flagged floor, good reliable food from an ever-changing blackboard selection, which might include dressed crab (£4.95), deep-fried whitebait (£3.20), salmon with fennel and Pernod (£6.50) or coronation chicken (£4); local goat's cheese made in North Cerney. The seven bedrooms are light and

pretty, each rather tweely named after an English flower. **Bar Food &**
Restaurant Meals 12-2.15 (12-2 Sun), 6.30-9.15 (7-9.15 Sun).
Children's portions. Free house. **Beer** *Archers, Boddingtons, Hook Norton,*
Tetley, Wadworth. Walled riverside garden, outdoor eating. Access, Visa.

Northallerton   Bettys

Tel 0609 775154	Tea Room

188 High Street Northallerton North Yorkshire	Map 5 E3

In a long terrace of houses, Bettys is the traditional tea shop that every
town deserves. The day begins with breakfast – warm Yorkshire
oatcakes (£1.40), mushroom and bacon omelette (£4.80), rösti
potatoes (£3.10) or simply two croissants or brioches with jam and
butter (£1.65). Light lunches bring sandwiches (from £2.35), salads
(corn-fed chicken £4.98), grills, omelettes, hot dishes such as haddock
and prawns au gratin and the speciality of the house, rarebit made
with Theakston's Yorkshire Ale served with apple or tomato chutney
(£5.45). Bettys famous warm Yorkshire fat rascal (£1.90), buttered
pikelets (98p) and banana and walnut loaf (£1.10) are some of the tea
breads. Cream tea £3.55. Various ices (from £2.05), desserts (toffee
and brandy snap fanfare £4.20) and cakes (from £1.78 – chocolate
brandy roulade, Yorkshire curd tart). Rare coffees and a selection
of teas. Children's portions. No-smoking area. **Seats 58. Open** 9-5.30
(Sun from 10). **Closed** 25 & 26 Dec, 1 Jan. Access, Visa.

Norwich   Airport Ambassador Hotel   65%   £76

Tel 0603 410544 Fax 0603 789935	Hotel

Cromer Road Norwich Airport Norwich Norfolk NR6 6JA	Map 10 C1

Modern redbrick hotel whose aeronautical associations include the
Concorde Bar and a replica Spitfire in the garden. Practical
accommodation in decent-sized bedrooms; the honeymoon suites
feature four-poster beds and jacuzzis. Purpose-built conference facility.
Nappies, a laundry service and baby-listening are provided and
at mealtimes 14 high-chairs and children's portions are on offer.
Rooms 108. *Gymnasium, indoor swimming pool, sauna, steam room,*
whirlpool bath. Access, Amex, Diners, Visa.

Norwich   Britons Arms Coffee House

Tel 0603 623367	Coffee Shop

9 Elm Hill Norwich Norfolk	Map 10 C1

Built in 1420 from second-hand materials by seven women, this
ancient half-timbered house is a popular all-day restaurant/tea room.
It's on two floors, with three rooms (two non-smoking) and alfresco
eating (lunchtime only) in the garden terrace off the first-floor room.
Coffee, tea and light snacks are served until 12.15. There's one hot dish
per day (all £3.70) – mild spiced lamb with dahl rice, Baltic fish cakes
or salmon and broccoli gratin, as well as quiches (£3.30), pies
(£3.40 –chicken and leek, Norfolk pork and apple) and jacket potatoes
(£2.70). Working partners Gilly Mixer and Sue Skipper make their
own puddings (cranberry and walnut pudding or raspberry and
hazelnut meringue – both £1.65) as well as scones and cakes (lemon
and honey, prune and walnut loaf) – all £1. £2.20 minimum charge
between 12.15 and 2pm. Children under 8 not allowed in stepped
garden. Children's portions. No-smoking area. **Seats 65. Open** 9.30-5.
Closed *Sun, Bank Holidays. No credit cards.*

Norwich   Café La Tienda

Tel 0603 629122	Café
10 St Gregory's Alley Norwich Norfolk NR2 1ER	Map 10 C1

Overlooking a churchyard and trees and serving imaginative
vegetarian wholefood dishes, Café La Tienda is a real refuge from the
bustle of Norwich. Seating is on two floors and decor is simple with
scrubbed pine tables, no tablecloths and a wall of flysheets highlighting
the proprietor's interest in environmental issues. There is plenty
of room to tuck a pushchair in beside your table and there is also one
clip-on high-chair. The food is good, the varied selection supplemented
by daily blackboard specials such as courgette and hazelnut bake
or crispy mushroom layer (£3.50). Regular menu items include soup
(cream of leek £2), vegetable and cashew nut paté (£2.80) and hot
filled pitta breads (houmus, spicy bean £3). Finish with ice creams,
apple and apricot crumble or pecan pie (all £2.50). No children's
menu but small portions of most dishes can be provided. Plenty
of room for nappy changing in the second-floor loo. No smoking.
Open 11-2.30 (Sat to 3.30). **Closed** Sun, Bank Holidays. No credit cards.

Norwich   Calendars

Tel 0603 748068	Restaurant
26 Jarrold Way Bowthorpe Norwich Norfolk NR5 9JD	Map 10 C1

You can eat and drink all through the day in an atmosphere of high
kitsch at this American café, bar and restaurant. The food is a catholic
mix of all-American favourites and Tex-Mex specials. Ten high-chairs
demonstrate a positive attitude to children and it is a splendid venue
for birthday parties. There is plenty for children to look at, and service
is very friendly, although a notice (quite reasonably) requests that
children remain seated while eating. Balloons, straws, numerous
napkins and finger bowls are provided. 'Little League' portions are
available as well as a separate children's menu. No-smoking area.
Owned by Taylor Walker, the brewers, with branches in Watford,
Reading, Kingston, Birmingham and Poole. **Seats** 235. **Open**
noon-11.30, Sun 10.30am-11.30pm. Access, Amex, Diners, Visa.

Norwich   Clarke's

Tel 0603 880241	Restaurant
Dereham Road Easton Norwich Norfolk NR9 5EH	Map 10 C1

Chintzy furnishings, wheelback chairs and oak beams make a cheerful
setting for enjoying decent wholesome food. The seasonal menu may
include cauliflower mousse £4, stilton and celery soup £2.50
or lamb's liver with a cream and French mustard sauce, while main
courses are typified by lasagne, grilled salmon, veal Roman-style and
pesto-sauced tomato quiche. Pavlova £4, hot raspberry soufflé
or bread-and-butter pudding £3.25 to finish. Various set menus,
à la carte. Traditional Sunday lunch. No smoking in the dining room,
but desperate puffers can escape to the bar. **Seats** 50. **Open** 12-2 & 7-9.
Closed D Sun, all Mon, 1 Jan. Access, Amex, Diners, Visa.

Norwich   Norwich Sport Village Hotel   63%   £69

Tel 0603 788898 Fax 0603 406845	Hotel
Drayton High Road Hellesdon Norwich Norfolk NR6 5DU	Map 10 C1

Practical, roomy bedrooms are at the centre of a very extensive sports
complex situated just off the outer Norwich ring road on the A1067

to Fakenham. All the rooms have en-suite facilities, half showers, half tubs. Sporting facilities are the most impressive feature. They include seven squash courts and no less than a dozen tennis courts, seven of them indoors. The Aquapark is most impressive and includes a competition pool, a shallow, warm, playpool with two slides and rapids and a paddling pool for toddlers. There's a soft play area for the very young. All the rooms are suitable for families and cots, potties, nappies, high-chairs and baby food can be provided. Hotel guests share the lively open-plan bar, bistro and restaurant with the other users of the complex. No dogs. Conference facilities for 2000! *Rooms 55.* *Garden, indoor swimming pool, steam baths, whirlpool bath, sauna, solarium, gymnasium, multi-sports hall, aerobics, beauty clinics, hairdressing, squash, tennis, badminton, snooker, coffee shop (10am-10.30pm). Access, Amex, Diners, Visa.*

Norwich   Pizza Express

Tel 0603 622157	Pizzeria
15 Benedict Street Norwich Norfolk	Map 10 C1

A cheerful outlet of this popular pizza chain. The menu includes the usual selection of crisp-based thin pizzas like *fiorentina* with spinach, free-range egg, Parmesan, olives, mozzarella and tomato (around £5). Good espresso. *Seats 100. Open 11.30am-midnight. Closed 25 Dec. Access, Amex, Visa.*

Nottingham   Loopers Restaurant

Tel 0602 632175	Restaurant
Model Aviation Centre Goosedale Farm Moor Rd Bestwood Nottingham Notts NG6 8UJ	Map 7 D3

A converted 17th-century barn housing the country's largest collection of working model aircraft and, separated by a windowed partition, a popular daytime restaurant and bakery, the latter also supplying local businesses. Large hot scones (60p) and vine-fruit-packed cake (80p) are joined at lunch by traditional fare ranging from prawn cocktail (£2.25) and soup of the day (£1.70), to chicken Kiev (£7) and plain grilled steaks (from £7.50). Self-service with friendly, helpful staff. Popular with families, especially for the traditional Sunday roast. No smoking. Bookable evening dinners. Signposted from the A60 Nottingham-Mansfield road. *Seats 150. Open 10-5.30. Closed Tues in Dec, 25 & 26 Dec. No credit cards.*

Nunton   Radnor Arms

Tel 0722 329722	Pub
Nunton nr Salisbury Wiltshire SP5 4HS	Map 14 C3

Unpretentious little ivy-clad pub with honest, hearty home-made food on offer. The same food can be eaten throughout the pub (in bar or dining room). Although there is no restaurant, there is a separate evening meal menu with a large selection of à la carte dishes. Some ideas might be broccoli and spring onion soup (£1.90) or sliced smoked trout to start, with devilled kidney beans (£4.25), smoked chicken and mushroom tagliatelle (£5.50), American style rib-eye steak (£7.25) or a choice of fresh fish (from Poole or Grimsby) – skate wings with caper sauce (£5.75) – to follow. Treacle tart and lemon crunch flan are popular puddings (£2). One high-chair. When the sun shines, families make for the large enclosed garden where there are plenty of picnic tables, climbing frames, tree swings and a wide, well-kept lawn. The disabled loo is large enough for nappy changing. *Bar Food* 12-2, 7-9.30. *Children's menu (£2 per dish)/portions.* *Beer* *Hall & Woodhouse Tanglefoot, Badger Best, Hard Tackle, Charles Wells IPA. Garden, outdoor eating, children's play area. No credit cards.*

Oakham	**Whipper-In Hotel**	70%	£80

Tel 0572 756971 Fax 0572 757759	Hotel

Market Place Oakham Rutland Leicestershire LE15 6DT	Map 7 E3

Standing in the market square of Rutland's old county town, this relaxed, rural hotel dates back to the 17th century. A flagstone-floored foyer leads through to a low-beamed bar-lounge that is popular with the locals. Bedrooms, two of which boast four-poster beds, are neat and individually decorated with comfortable seating areas and a few antiques. Children up to 14 free in parents' room. High-chairs, cots, baby-listening, baby-sitting and room service are all offered. *Rooms 25. Access, Visa.*

Odiham	**Blubeckers**	

Tel 0256 702953	Restaurant

The Mill House Odiham Hampshire RG25 1ET	Map 15 D3

Blubeckers is in a magnificent old mill house where in the restaurant, you can still see the huge wheel churning round. Half of the restaurant is set aside for families. The children's menu is excellent value and features nasty sounding cocktails like 'Dracula's dribble' and 'slime juice'. Adults are offered char-grilled steaks and burgers, and 'old favourites' like chicken and Stilton crumble or smoked haddock and spinach pie. The long list of puddings ranges from Baileys hot chocolate cake to grandma's hot walnut pud and maple syrup mountain; ask for at least a couple of spoons! High-chairs are set with baby cutlery and a helium balloon is tied to all children's chairs, threatening to pull them up, up and away. Children are invited to enter the menu-colouring and awful joke contest and prizes are awarded each month. At one end of the room there is a 'dungeon' where children can escape to when mealtime formality becomes too much. Outside there is boating on the pond, a Wendy House, climbing frame, swings and a vast, green lawn. *Seats 150. Open 12.30-2 (Sat until 2.15, Sun until 3) & 6.30-9.45 Fri until 10.45, Sun from 6, Sat 6-10.45). Closed Xmas. Access, Amex, Diners, Visa.*
Also at:
Chobham Blubeckers at the White Hart Chobham Surrey Tel 0276 857580.   Map 15 E3
Shepperton Blubeckers Eating House Shepperton Middlesex Tel 0932 243377. (See Entry)   Map 15 E2

Orford	**Old Warehouse**	

Tel 0394 450210	Café

The Quay Orford Suffolk	Map 10 D3

A fine old warehouse on Orford Quay, with splendid views from the flowery terrace over the quay. The narrow entrance and steep stairs are a bit of a struggle but worth the effort. Downstairs is a shop selling yachting gear, upstairs a roomy café offering a range of tasty home-prepared food: thick vegetable and smoked sausage soup £1.95, Welsh rarebit £2.50, potted shrimps, quiche, spaghetti bolognese (£3.95). On Sunday comes a roast beef lunch (£6.50) with all the trimmings and a drink. There are two high-chairs but unfortunately no room for

changing or breastfeeding. *Seats* 42. *Open* 10-6 (*in winter 10-5 Sat &
Sun only*). *Closed* 25 & 26 Dec. Access, Visa.

| Ormesby St Margaret | **Ormesby Lodge** | **58%** | **£46** |

| Tel 0493 730910   Fax 0493 733103 | | | Hotel |

Decoy Rd Ormesby St Margaret nr Great Yarmouth Norfolk NR29 3LG   **Map 10 D1**

A small family-run hotel five miles north of Great Yarmouth and
within a mile or so of several beaches. The building is Victorian, and
some of the original feel survives in the bar/lounge. All the bedrooms
have private bathroom facilities and vary in their decor but all are
in good order and have plenty of space for a cot and an extra bed. The
restaurant will go to great lengths to please its smaller diners and small
portions will cheerfully be prepared. *Rooms 9.* Garden. Access, Amex,
Diners, Visa.

| Oswestry | **Wynnstay Hotel** | **68%** | **£83** |

| Tel 0691 655261   Fax 0691 670606 | | | Hotel |

Church Street Oswestry Shropshire SY11 2SZ   **Map 8 D2**

Town-centre Georgian hotel with stylish day rooms. Besides the
restaurant and lounge there are conference facilities plus a 200-year-old
crown bowling green as an unusual leisure offering. Best of the
bedrooms have whirlpool baths. Children up to 16 accommodated
free in their parents' room; meals for under-2s free of charge. Baby-
sitting and listening arranged in advance. *Rooms* 27. Garden, bowling,
coffee shop (9am-midnight). Access, Amex, Diners, Visa.

| Over Stratton | **Royal Oak** | | |

| Tel 0460 40906 | | | Pub |

Over Stratton South Petherton Somerset TA13 5LQ   **Map 13 F2**

Although now a pub, this row of three 400-year-old thatched cottages
still merges with its neighbours in the main street of the village and,
but for the pub sign, it would be easy to miss altogether. Cottage
atmosphere is still the secret of an interior with a real sense of style.
Features like old beams, hamstone and flag floors plus stone pillars
blend successfully with dark rag-rolled walls, scrubbed wooden tables,
a polished granite bar counter and extensive displays of dried flowers,
hops and strings of garlic. A globe-trotting menu takes its inspiration
from you name where: croissants from France, Hawaiian pineapple
and prawns (£4.95), Polynesian lamb kebabs (£5.65), steak and
kidney pie (£5.95) from Blighty and much else besides. Non-fans
of McDonald's should give the Royal Oak's own home-made chargrilled burger (£5.75) a try; this is as good as a burger can be. Fat,
moist, succulent and laced with onions, it comes with a piquant
barbecue sauce, a generous amount of varied salad and crisp, plump,
golden chips. Landlady Lyn Holland is not only charming but also full
of good ideas, like the Booty Box (£2.75) on the children's menu, full
of goodies including a wholemeal sandwich, cheese, fruit, crisps and
a crunchy bar in a special box children can take away with them. The
adult equivalent is a barbecue pack (£8.50) containing a pair of lamb
cutlets, sausage, gammon steak and a chicken drumstick (along with
salad and jacket potato) that, weather permitting, is cooked on the grill
outdoors. Other choices include squid platter (£4.95), baked avocado
with crab (£5.95), veal escalope in Calvados (£11.95) or garlic fried
chicken (£7.95). One high-chair is provided; no children in the bar.
Beyond the barbecue, there are swings, a junior assault course and

no less than three trampolines to keep the kids amused. *Bar Food &
Restaurant Meals 12-1.45, 7-10 (7-9.30 Sun). Children's portions. Beer
Hall & Woodhouse. Garden, outdoor eating, children's play area.
Access, Visa.*

Oxford   **Blue Coyote**

Tel 0865 241431	Restaurant
36/37 St Clements Street Oxford Oxfordshire	**Map 15 D2**

Mexican and American specialities are served in generous portions and
cheerful surroundings in a family-friendly restaurant near the Plain.
*Seats 68. Open 12-3 & 6-11 (Sat 12-12, Sun 12-11). Closed Bank
Holidays. Access, Visa.*

Oxford   **Browns**   £30

Tel 0865 511995 Fax 0865 52347	Restaurant
5-11 Woodstock Road Oxford Oxfordshire OX2 6HA	**Map 15 D2**

All-day value-for-money eating in one of Oxford's most popular
restaurants. Spaghetti, salads, savoury pies, steaks, burgers and hot
sandwiches are the basis of the menu, the last including double egg and
bacon, club and vegetarian. Lots of puddings, late-morning breakfasts
(Mon-Sat), traditional teas and Sunday lunchtime is clearly a family
affair when children have their own menu. The 12 high-chairs are
ingenious items which tuck neatly under the table so that the baby can
really join in. There is a mother and baby room. Other branches
in Cambridge, Brighton and now Bristol. *Seats 240. Parties 50. Private
Room. Meals 11am-11.30pm (Sun & Bank Holidays from 12). Closed
25 Dec. Access, Visa.*

Oxford   **Pizza Express**

Tel 0865 790442	Pizzeria
The Golden Cross Cornmarket Street Oxford Oxfordshire	**Map 15 D2**

A Pizza Express outlet with a difference – occupying a grade one listed
building and boasting a champagne bar and conservatory on the
ground floor plus an upstairs restaurant with long oak refectory-style
tables, wood panelling and carefully preserved 16th-century al fresco
paintings. In addition to the successful range of pizzas (£3.15-£5.30)
there's the King Edward – a potato-based pizza with four cheeses,
rosemary, tomato and Parmesan (£4.60), a range of salads (including
fresh prawn and crab) and sandwiches made to order. *Seats 110.
Open 11am-midnight. Closed 25 & 26 Dec. Access, Amex, Diners, Visa.*

Penshurst   **Fir Tree House Tea Rooms**

Tel 0892 870382	Tea Room
Penshurst nr Tonbridge Kent	**Map 11 B5**

Mrs Fuller-Rowell's traditional tea room with a delightful garden
is still a firm favourite with both families and those after
straightforward afternoon teas from a past era. Home-baked tea breads
(40p a slice), an array of delectable cakes (from 75p), sandwiches (£1)
and, whenever possible, home-made jams continue to please, with set
cream (£2.50) and traditional (£4.25) teas as popular as ever. A good
selection of loose-leaf teas too. No smoking. *Seats 45. Open 3-5.45 Apr
to Oct, 2.30-5.30 Sat & Sun only Jan to Mar. Closed Mon except Bank
Holidays, Tues following Bank Holidays, all Nov & Dec. No credit cards.*

Peterborough   **Butterfly Hotel**   63%   £70

Tel 0733 64240 Fax 0733 65538	Hotel

Thorpe Meadows Longthorpe Parkway Peterborough Cambridgeshire PE3 6GA   **Map 7 E4**

One of a small chain of modern, low-rise East Anglian hotels (the
others are in Bury St Edmunds, Colchester and King's Lynn) built
to a formula. Peterborough's Butterfly sits at the water's edge,
overlooking a rowing lake. Neat, practical accommodation ranges
from studio singles to four suites and double or family rooms will
be supplied with cots and Z-beds on request (children up to eight stay
free). Baby-sitting and baby-listening can be arranged in advance and
Walt's place, the open-plan, pine-clad restaurant overlooking the lake,
offers a simple children's menu. Good breakfasts. No amusements
in the hotel, but nearby Belvoir provides good family entertainment.
Rooms 70. *Access, Amex, Diners, Visa.*

Petts Wood   **Ming**

Tel 0689 820427	Restaurant

23 Station Square Petts Wood nr Orpington Kent BR5 1LY   **Map 11 B5**

Traditionally a family event, Sunday lunch is an ideal time to visit
Ming. The Sunday buffet is a relaxed, informal affair where you can
enjoy a choice of twenty or so dishes for £10 a head or £5 for
children. With lacquered furnishings and peach table linen, this
is a very smart restaurant but the friendly staff, who obviously enjoy
children, make sure that it is never intimidating. There are no high-
chairs but room is made at the table for pushchairs. There is space
at the rear of the restaurant to feed a baby in comfort, and baby food
and bottles will be heated on request. *Seats* 70. *Open* 12-2.30 &
6-11.30. *Closed* Dec 25 & 26. *Access, Amex, Visa.*

Poole   **New Inn**

Tel 0202 674442	Pub

Wimborne Road Poole Dorset BH15 2EL   **Map 14 C4**

A pub, complete with family room, known for its unqualified
welcome to children. An impressive climbing frame dominates the
enclosed play area, which has a woodchip floor and picnic tables. The
children's menu is written up daily. The ladies toilet has a changing
shelf, piped music while you go to work and also a child's toilet. Three
high-chairs. Non-smoking area. *Open* 11-2 (*Sun from* 12) 6-9 (*Sun
from* 7). *Closed* Xmas evening. *Access, Visa.*

Poole   **Sandbanks Hotel**   59%   £110

Tel 0202 707377 Fax 0202 708885	Hotel

15 Banks Road Sandbanks Poole Dorset BH13 3PS   **Map 14 C4**

Ideal for families, with an attractive patio and garden leading onto the
surprisingly clean sandy beach (winner of an EEC Blue Flag Award),
and complete holiday services that include organised activities and
a nursery. Four tiers of balconied bedrooms look either out to sea
or across Poole Bay. Winter trade is boosted by conference business
when the open-plan bar, vast sun lounge and dining rooms afford little
privacy for individual hotel guests – so enquire in advance. 20 larger
rooms in the original hotel building are designated as family rooms.
No dogs. Children under the age of 12 accommodated free in parents'
room (except in high season – July to Sept); separate children's
restaurant. The provision of 16 high-chairs shows that children are

an integral part of the hotel's business. Sand-filled play areas feature climbing frames and a pirate ship. Baby-sitting and listening are available on request. ***Rooms*** *105. Garden, indoor swimming pool, sauna, steam room, solarium, spa bath, gymnasium, crèche (daily in summer). Access, Amex, Diners, Visa.*

Powerstock   Three Horseshoes Inn   £50

Tel 0308 85328	Pub

Powerstock Bridport Dorset DT6 3TF   **Map 14 A4**

The Three Horseshoes is a stone and thatch country inn with simple country furnishings and open fires, reached by narrow winding lanes. Its restaurant comprises two pine-panelled rooms, one small and cosy, the other more roomy and airy. Fish is what chef-licensee Pat Ferguson is best known for, and the blackboard menu can include anything from freshly boiled crab or grilled lobster to fish pie, bourride and sea bass cooked in a paper bag. Meat and game dishes, too: garlic-studded rack of lamb, kidneys turbigo, venison pie; plus traditional British puddings. Must book for busy Sunday lunches in winter. Tables in the garden for summer eating. Not really suitable for very young children, except in summer. ***Seats*** *60. Private Room. L 12-2 D 7-10 (Sun 7.30-8.30). Set L £7.50 & £10.50 (Sun only). Access, Amex, Visa.*

Rooms   £55

Large, traditionally styled rooms have central heating, en-suite bathrooms and lovely views. Delightful garden. Families with children are welcome, with cots available. ***Rooms*** *4.*

Reading   Pizza Express

Tel 0734 391920	Pizzeria

56 St Mary's Butts Reading Berkshire   **Map 15 D2**

The oldest building in Reading with a Tudor exterior and simple black and white interior decoration in keeping with the facade. Dining on three split levels with the usual thin, crisp-based pizza menu and a good range of Italian wines. ***Seats*** *92.* ***Open*** *12-12.* ***Closed*** *25 & 26 Dec. Access, Amex, Visa.*

Repton   Brook Farm Tea Rooms

Tel 0283 702215	Tea Room

Brook End Repton Derbyshire   **Map 6 C3**

Brook Farm is a working dairy and arable farm and the Tea Rooms are housed in an old sandstone and brick barn beside a trout brook. There's a large, lawned and walled garden which has bench seating for summer eating. The lunchtime menu is written up on the blackboard and offers such choices as sweet and sour pork, asparagus pancakes or fisherman's pie (all £3.65) and home-made cakes and puddings (treacle tart £1.10, apple crumble £1.10). The Brook Farm Cream Tea (£1.95 – two scones with jam, cream and pot of tea) and Farmhouse Tea (£2.15 – round of sandwiches, scone with butter and jam, pot of tea) are tea-time options or there's a choice of toasted teacakes (60p), crumpet (45p) or 10 flavours of locally-made dairy ice cream (£1). Children's menu (£1.10) or portions available. Two highchairs are supplied and nappy changing is feasible in the ladies loo. After tea, take a stroll by the brook or explore Repton whose history goes back to 653 A.D. ***Seats*** *54.* ***Open*** *10.15-5.* ***Closed*** *25 Dec for 1 week. No credit cards.*

Richmond   Café Rouge

Tel 081-332 2423	Brasserie
7a Petersham Road Richmond Surrey	Map 15 E2

Café complet (£2.75), petit déjeuner 'Café Rouge' (£5) and pain
au chocolat begin the day at this very French café/restaurant which,
decor-wise, is more back-street Les Halles than Champs Elysées. Tables
near the entrance tend to be kept for those just buying a coffee or glass
of wine with more serious eaters venturing further back or to a small
room downstairs. The main menu ranges from *croque monsieur*
(£3.95), *baguette poulet* (4.65) and *soupe au pistou* (£2.25) to *marmite
dieppoise* (£6.95 – Normandy fish soup), *entrecote béarnaise* with
pommes frites (£8.95) and *carré d'agneau au romarin* with *gratin
dauphinois* (£7.95). A shorter version of the full menu operates
between 3 and 6pm except on Sundays when the main menu
is available all day. There's a fixed-price (£9.95) menu lunchtimes and
evenings and a budget set lunch (£6.95) weekdays. **Seats** 50.
Open *10am-11pm (Sun to 10.30). Access, Visa.*

Richmond   Pizza Express

Tel 081-940 8951	Pizzeria
20 Hill Street Richmond Surrey	Map 15 E2

Close to the cinema and always busy at weekends, it's just a hop from
the lovely Thamesside promenade where children can let off steam
after a good helping of crisp pizza (around £5) and sticky chocolate
cake. **Seats** 90. **Open** *11.30-midnight.* **Closed** *25 & 26 Dec. Access,
Amex, Visa.*

Richmond   Refectory

Tel 081-940 6264	Restaurant
6 Church Walk Richmond Surrey TW9 1SN	Map 15 E2

You can leave the gag at home when you come to lunch at the
Refectory. Most of the tables are taken by families and the babble and
chatter is reassuringly vigorous without ever becoming intrusive.
When the sun shines you can eat in the pretty little courtyard but
more often you will opt to sit inside at the mellow pine tables. The
Steels cater very well for children and provide four high-chairs,
a booster seat, storage for prams and pushchairs and a changing/
breastfeeding area. The food is served speedily but it is certainly not
fast food. Children may have small portions of the traditional British
dishes like chicken and mushroom pie with buttered cabbage and
creamed cauliflower, and to drink, perhaps a glass of elderflower
cordial. No smoking. **Seats** 44. **Open** *12-2 only.* **Closed** *Mon, 1 week
Christmas. Access, Visa.*

Rochdale   Egerton Arms

Tel 0706 46183	Pub
Ashworth Road Rochdale Lancashire OL11 5UP	Map 6 B1

A lovely old pub in the Ashworth Valley surrounded by fields, the
Egerton Arms offers a daily-changing, varied and fresh bill of fare.
Adventurous children might enjoy sampling small portions of chicken
tikka, Javanese satay or seafood vol-au-vent. On Sundays a more
predictable children's menu is available. Three high-chairs are
provided and baby bottles or food will be warmed. Staff are

welcoming and nobody seems to mind if a tot toddles out on a tour of inspection or a mum nurses at the table. **Open** *Bar food 12-2 (Sun until 3.45) & 6-9.* **Closed** *a few days early New Year. Access, Visa.*

Rochester   The Knowle

Tel 0474 822262	Restaurant

School Lane Higham Rochester Kent ME3 7HP   Map 11 B5

A discreet sign from the road is the only indication that this imposing Victorian country house is a popular, family-run restaurant. From the moment you sink into the deep leather sofas in the mahogany-panelled bar you feel cosseted and cared for. The traditional English cooking produces dishes made with the best fresh ingredients, prepared with care. Children can have half-price though apparently not half-size meals and the waitresses cannot do enough, whether it is offering bowls of mashed vegetables for the children or heating bottles for a baby; under-6s eat free! Two high-chairs provided. Children can play in the three acres of gardens, well away from the road. **Open** *12-1.30 & 7-10.30.* **Closed** *D Mon, L Sat, D Sun. Access, Visa.*

Romsey   Cobweb Tea Room

Tel 0794 516434	Tea Room

49 The Hundred Romsey Hampshire SO5 18DF   Map 14 C3

Angela Webley's tea room is a homely place with beams, green tablecloths, cheery service and a little patio at the back. Temptingly displayed baking includes old-style madeleines (75p), chocolate truffles and a delicious apricot Bakewell tart (£1.50), plus various sponge gateaux. Light lunches offer toasted sandwiches (from £1.50), baked potatoes (from £2.25) or hot dishes such as chicken and broccoli crumble, courgette and walnut bake, steak and mushroom pie or chicken curry (all £3.75). Pavlova, date and apple crumble and tiramisu are popular puddings (all £1.50). Cream teas £2.50. Children's portions. No-smoking area. **Seats** *36.* **Open** *10-5.30 (Bank Holiday Mon from 12. Sun prior to Bank Holiday Monday from 2.30).* **Closed** *Other Sun, Mon, 1 week Christmas, 2 weeks end Sep/early Oct. No credit cards.*

Romsey   Latimer Coffee House

Tel 0794 513832	Coffee Shop

11 Latimer Street Romsey Hampshire   Map 14 C3

Good quality home-baking at this characterful coffee house just off the High Street. New owners plan improvements. Friendly staff. Tables outside in fine weather. **Seats** *76.* **Open** *9.15-5.* **Closed** *Sun, 25 & 26 Dec. No credit cards.*

Ross-on-Wye   Meader's

Tel 0989 62803	Restaurant

1 Copse Cross Street Ross-on-Wye Hereford & Worcester HR9 5P9   Map 14 B1

Hungarian-born Andras Weinhardt offers hearty lunchtime dishes from his native land like ham and bean soup (£2), layered cabbage (£4.50) and beef stroganoff with rice (£6.50). The set evening menu (£19 for two including a bottle of Hungarian wine) comprises a main course and dessert: chicken in paprika or mushroom goulash could be followed by apple strudel or a pancake with lemon, sugar and cottage cheese. The evening carte offers starters at £2.50, main courses at £7.50 and desserts at £2. Children's menu £3.50; there are two high-chairs and the friendly staff will warm food and find a room for breast-feeding and nappy-changing. No-smoking area. *Seats 45.* ***Open*** *10-2.30 & 7-9.30.* ***Closed*** *Sun, Mon, 25 & 26 Dec, 1 Jan. No credit cards.*

Ross-on-Wye	Pengethley Manor	67%	£114
Tel 098 987 211 Fax 098 987 238			Hotel
Harewood End Ross-on-Wye Hereford & Worcester HR9 6LL			Map 14 B1

Fifteen acres of estate with pitch-and-putt golf course, trout lake and landscaped gardens enhance Pengethley's tranquil country setting: while there is plenty of activity for sportsmen and families (under-14s staying free in parents' room). There are purpose-built, family rooms in converted stables, some with their own lounges and sofa beds. Baby-sitting/listening and a laundry service are all available. Conference rooms are kept discreetly separate. The garden offers plenty of space for letting off steam and high-chairs, baby food and bottles are provided at mealtimes. *Rooms 24. Garden, croquet, outdoor swimming pool, snooker, outdoor chess, 9-hole improver's golf course, fishing. Access, Amex, Diners, Visa.*

Ryton-on-Dunsmore	Ryton Gardens Café	
Tel 0203 303517		Café
Wolston Lane Ryton-on-Dunsmore Warwickshire		Map 7 D4

Wholefood dishes using organic ingredients are the speciality: not unsurprisingly, as it is part of the National Centre for Organic Gardening. A typical menu lists tomato soup £1.10, walnut and mushroom stroganoff £3.95, courgette and sweetcorn provençale £3.95 and Cheshire fidget pie £3.95. Cakes include sticky prune cake, carrot cake, vegan fruit cake and ginger cake from 80p. *Seats 24.* ***Open*** *9-4.30 Oct-Mar, 9-5.30 Apr-Sept.* ***Closed*** *25 & 26 Dec. Access, Visa.*

St Albans	Sopwell House Hotel & Country Club	65%	£115
Tel 0727 864477 Fax 0727 44741			Hotel
Cottonmill Lane Sopwell St Albans Hertfordshire AL1 2HQ			Map 15 E2

A new country club is the centrepiece of this much extended 18th-century house. There are plenty of ways to pamper yourself – indoor pool plus toddler pool, supervised gymnasium, beautician and hairdressing. You will be well looked after, in tasteful and stylish surroundings, by efficient staff who are genuinely welcoming to families. The Brasserie offers informal meals in a conservatory setting and the kitchen will gladly fulfil orders of boiled eggs and soldiers for smaller diners, as well as small portions of most dishes on the menu. Cots are supplied and baby-sitting and baby-listening can be arranged. *Rooms 84. Garden, gymnasium, indoor swimming pool, sauna, solarium, spa bath, steam room, beautician, hairdressing, snooker. Access, Amex, Diners, Visa.*

St Dominick	The Edgcumbe Arms at Cotehele Quay	
Tel 0579 50024		Pub
The Quay Cotehele St Dominick nr Saltash Cornwall PL12 6TA		Map 12 C3

A stretch of woodland, containing a chapel built by Richard Edgcumbe during the Wars of the Roses, separates Cotehele Quay from Cotehele House (near the village of Callington). Along the quayside, amid a row of 18th and 19th-century houses, The National Trust's Edgcumbe Arms sited in a former lime worker's cottage which became a public house. They look out on to the Shamrock, the sole surviving stone-carrying Tamar barge, and the River Tamar. Drinks and light refreshments are available all day: home-made soup (£1.95), paté, ploughmans, fisherman's lunch (£3.90 – smoked mackerel fillet), jacket potatoes (£2.75), home-made fruit pie and clotted cream (£2.15), various cakes and biscuits, and traditional Cornish Cream Tea (£2.75) with Cornish splits (soft white yeast buns). A quarter of a mile up the hill at the late-Medieval Cotehele House, the converted barn in the terraced grounds is now **The Barn** restaurant serving a variety of inexpensive hot and cold dishes. (In season, visitors are required to pay a grounds only entrance fee (£2.50) to eat at the restaurant). The Edgcumbe Arms had been granted a provisional drinks license at the time of going to press. Wall seating outside overlooking river. Children's portions. No smoking. *Seats 76.* *Open 11-5.30 (Apr-Oct), 11-4 (Sat & Sun only in Nov, Wed-Sun in December, Sun only Jan, Feb, Mar). Access, Amex, Visa.*

St Ives	Slepe Hall	61%	£65
Tel 0480 63122 Fax 0480 300706			Hotel
Ramsey Road St Ives Cambridgeshire PE17 4RB			Map 10 B2

An intimate hotel, housed in what was once a small private boarding school for girls, kept in good order by the house-proud Stapleton family. Several bedrooms feature four-poster beds and all but a couple have en-suite bathrooms; one family room has a double and single bed plus further room for a cot. Children stay free in their parents' room. The Brunel Suite and conference room provide adaptable facilities for up to 220, so ask in advance about wedding receptions at weekends. Children are offered a special menu in the bar and half portions in the dining room; four high-chairs are provided. Sunday lunch is popular. *Rooms 16. Closed 25 & 26 Dec. Access, Amex, Diners, Visa.*

St Martin's	St Martin's Hotel	69%	£196*
Tel 0720 22092 Fax 0720 22298			Hotel
St Martin's Isles of Scilly TR25 OQW			Map 12 A2

Hotel launch and Suzuki 4-wheel drive provide transport for arrivals, so make your travel arrangements when booking. St Martin's provides the ultimate escape for solitude seekers, an equally novel activity centre for families (under-14s stay free in parents' room) and the last word in privacy for a conference or private dinner. Public rooms include the first-floor sunset lounge which affords wonderful views westward towards Tresco. Under the same ownership as the Polurrian Hotel in Mullion, Cornwall. *Half-board terms only. **Rooms** 24. Garden, croquet, indoor swimming pool, fishing, snooker, sailing and scuba-diving instruction, baby-sitting, baby-listening. Closed Nov-Mar. Access, Amex, Diners, Visa.*

Restaurant   £55

Table d'hote dinners make good use of fish and shellfish, game and home-grown vegetables. Many special dishes attract a supplement to the fixed-price menus. Simple sweets – pear crumble, profiteroles, baked cherry cheesecake. Lighter bar lunches. *Seats 80. Parties 80. Private Room. L in bar only D 7.15-9. Set D £22.*

St Michael's Mount   The Sail Loft Restaurant

Tel 0736 710748	Restaurant

St Michael's Mount Marazion Cornwall TR17 0IT   Map 12 A4

Take the ferry at high tide or walk across a cobbled causeway for
a meal at The National Trust's converted boat store and carpenter's
shop. Hot lunches -with local fish a feature – include the Hobbler's
Choice (the island ferrymen are known as Hobblers), seafood casserole
of fresh fish, vegetables, prawns and mussels (£4.50), jacket potatoes
(from £2.55) and mushrooms in a lemon and tarragon sauce with rice
(£3.60). Alternatively, the Smuggler's lunch – smoked mackerel fillet
with horseradish sauce and side salad (£4.25), the Ferryman's (£3.35),
and the Sail Loft salad (£2.55) are the cold dishes. Good choice
of home-made cakes, biscuits and puddings with the traditional
Cornish Cream Tea featuring splits (soft white yeast buns) instead
of scones (£2.60). No smoking. *Seats 88. Open 10.30-5.30.*
Closed Nov-Mar. Access, Amex, Visa.

Salcombe	Soar Mill Cove	65%	£128
Tel 0548 561566 Fax 0548 561223			Hotel

Soar Mill Cove Salcombe Devon TQ7 3DS   Map 13 D3

Spectacular coastal location and unrivalled sea views make for
a memorable holiday hotel. The closeness of 14 bedrooms, all
at ground level with neighbouring patios, readily engenders a house
party atmosphere, much in keeping with the Makepeace family's
philosophy, and to which the staff contribute willingly. Thoroughly
comfortable bedrooms, close carpeted through to equally adequate
bathrooms, provide essential ingredients for a peaceful stay. The
National Trust beach and cliff walks prove highly popular diurnal
activities. Families with young children are admirably catered for;
high tea between 5 and 5.30pm (high-chairs and baby food provided)
is designed to leave residents in peace during dinner. *Rooms 14.*
Garden, indoor & outdoor swimming pools, tennis, putting, games room,
laundry room. Closed Jan-mid Feb. Access, Amex, Visa.

Restaurant   £70

Residents order in advance from their rooms, arriving for the main
event at immaculately prepared tables in the dining room. A typical
menu might offer a choice of four dishes at each course – hot terrine
of veal and mushroom with a dill sauce, followed by tenderloin
of pork glazed with a light Stilton sabayon. Laden dessert and cheese
trolleys, followed by coffee in the lounge, continue the communal
flavour. Suitable for residents only. *Seats 40. L 12.30-2 D 7.30-9.30.*
Set D £28.

Salcombe	South Sands	61%	£138*
Tel 0548 843741 Fax 0548 842112			Hotel

Cliff Road Salcombe Devon TQ8 8LL   Map 13 D3

New owners (the same as the Tides Reach) have taken over this well-
maintained holiday hotel, which stands directly on a sandy South
Sands beach, a mile south of the town. Public areas include
a bar/lounge with log-burning stove and a popular buttery bar. Pine-
furnished bedrooms include several that interconnect for family use.
Families are well catered for, with high tea, baby-listening and
a supervised crèche in high season. *Half-board terms only, but B&B
in early and late season. A fine location for a classic British seaside

holiday without the promenade and day-trippers; a regular chug-chug boat goes directly from the beach into town and there are wonderful cliff-top walks over the Bolt Head – the kids will really think they've had a holiday here. **Rooms** *32. Indoor swimming pool, solarium whirlpool bath, steam bath, moorings, coffee shop (noon-8.30pm). Access, Visa.*

Salisbury   Harpers

Tel 0722 333118	Restaurant
6 Ox Row Market Place Salisbury Wiltshire	Map 14 C3

Providing you order something more than just tea or coffee, there's no minimum charge at this friendly first-floor restaurant overlooking the Market Square. Various set and à la carte menus offer good value and a wide choice that ranges from beefsteak casseroled in vegetables with parsley dumplings (£4.50), cream of mussel soup with dill (£2.90) and scrumpy pork (£7.50) to breadcrumbed plaice with tartare sauce (£4.50) and Harpers nut loaf (£7.90) – there are always plenty of vegetarian options. Everything is home-cooked with Adrian Harper in the kitchen and wife Ann running front of house. **Seats** *60.* **Open** *12-2 & 6.30-10 (Sat to 10.30).* **Closed** *Sun (except for D in summer), 25 & Dec, 1 Jan. Access, Diners, Visa.*

Salisbury   Michael Snell Tea Rooms

Tel 0722 336037	Tea Room
8 St Thomas's Square Salisbury Wiltshire SP1 1BA	Map 14 C3

Michael Snell's splendid establishment is a former school, tucked between St. Thomas' church and a rushing weir. In addition to the two rooms and outside eating areas, there's a shop selling cakes and chocolates. The regular snacks on the substantial menu are supplemented by a dish of the day such as steak and kidney pie (£5.50 with vegetables), moonraker vegetable pie (£5.35). Michael bakes the ham for salad (£5.95) as well as the many gateaux and pastries (£1.20-£2.60). A Wiltshire Cream Tea is served (£3.35) with a selection of teas or home-roasted coffee. At busy lunchtimes, there's a £4 minimum charge in the school tea room. Under-10s have their own menu. No-smoking areas. **Seats** *112.* **Open** *9-5 (Sat from 8.30).* **Closed** *Sun, Bank Holidays. No credit cards.*

Salisbury   Old Castle

Tel 0722 328703	Pub
Old Castle Road Salisbury Wiltshire	Map 14 C3

Average food with a children's choice of the usual top ten plus chips. However, the venue itself is excellent for families. The large Garden Room with its wicker furniture and matching high-chairs is for family use, as are the terraced gardens with their fine views of Salisbury and playground with a long slippery slide and bouncy castle in summer. **Open** *11-3 & 5.30-10 (from 7 Sun). Access, Amex, Visa.*

Salisbury   Redcoats Tea Rooms

Tel 0722 414536	Tea Room
58 The Close Salisbury Wiltshire	Map 14 C3

Within the ancient museum of The Duke of Edinburgh's Royal Regiment in the north west corner of the cathedral close, this tiny tea room, offers a good range of sandwiches (from £1.20), salads (from £3), ploughmans and light lunches such as home-made soup, pasties, quiche (£3.50) and, from noon, jacket potatoes with various fillings (from £2). Home baking includes banana cake (70p), passion cake (95p), and various slices. In summer, eat out on the charming, walled patio or picnic (with food purchased from the tea room only) on the extensive lawns that reach down to the river. No smoking. *Seats 30.* *Open 10-4.15* (Fri to 4). *No credit cards.*

Saunton	**Saunton Sands**	67%	£124
Tel 0271 890212 Fax 0271 890145			Hotel
Saunton nr Braunton Devon EX33 1LQ			Map 12 C2

An ideal, family-oriented resort hotel, where you may park your car for a week and never need to use it; Saunton Sands commands panoramic views over the North Devon coastline. Five miles of golden sands stretch past the door; within, the leisure facilities are as abundant as are the sporting and aquatic activities without. Bedrooms are neat, light and airy, with Laura Ashley-style fabrics. Childrens' facilities include a crèche (10am-6pm), play areas, plenty of cots, baby-sitting, baby-listening and high teas (5-6pm). No dogs. *Rooms 96. Garden, tennis, squash, indoor swimming pool, spa bath, sauna, solarium, snooker, hairdressing. Access, Amex, Diners, Visa.*

Seaview	**Seaview Hotel**	
Tel 0983 612711		Hotel Bar Snacks
High Street Seaview Isle of Wight PO34 5EX		Map 15 D4

Nick and Nicky Hayward's charming seaside hotel is the sort of place families go back to year after year. Two heavily nautical bars (the front one is very cramped) and two terraces (front and rear) in fine weather provide the setting for enjoyable bar snacks, from rich local crab soup with crusty bread (£2.95), pork and parsley terrine (£3.25) and herring roes on toasted muffins (£3.50) to tandoori-marinated chicken leg with fenugreek potatoes (£4.95), seafood quiche topped with prawns and cheese (£4.95) and, on Sundays, roast beef with Yorkshire pud and all the trimmings (£4.95). Treacle sponge (£2.75) or apple pie and cream (£2.40) to finish. *Seats 32. Open 12-2 & 7-9.30. Closed 25 Dec. Access, Amex, Diners, Visa.*

Selling	**White Lion**	
Tel 0227 752211		Pub
The Street Selling nr Faversham Kent ME13 9RQ		Map 11 C5

The 300-year-old building has seen many customers including, local legend has it, highwaymen on their way to plunder the rich folk. These days you can eat here in safety, as long as you keep an eye on the well-kept, fenced-in garden where there are pets. Food is mainly steaks, fish, sandwiches or ploughman's, but surprisingly there is also a good selection of Indian dishes (Monday night is curry night); good home-made puds like lemon meringue and mince and rum tart. No high-chairs, beakers or small cutlery, so take your own. There is a chair in the ladies so nursing is manageable, but changing is less so. Leave the pushchair in the car as there is no storage space. *Open 12-2.15* (Sun 2.30) *& 7-9* (weekends 9.30). *Closed Dec 25. Access, Amex, Diners, Visa.*

Shaftesbury   **Royal Chase Hotel**   60%   £84

Tel 0747 53355   Fax 0747 51969   Hotel

Shaftesbury Dorset SP7 8DB   Map 14 B3

Former monastery with 35 bedrooms and purpose-built conference
facilities. Families are well catered for, particularly in holiday periods –
both summer and winter (ring ahead for details of crèche facilities and
baby-sitting/listening). Family rooms close to the pool where parents
can sit at tables and watch their water babies. Flexible eating
arrangements; high-chairs are provided and there's a mix of children's
favourites (Heinz tomato soup, fish fingers, pizza and beans on toast)
and smaller main-course portions (chicken chasseur, chili, seafood
crumble) from which to choose. Outside meal times there's a large
garden plus videos and games indoors to keep the youngsters amused.
*Rooms 35. Garden, indoor swimming pool, solarium, steam room. Access,
Amex, Diners, Visa.*

Shanklin   **Cliff Tops Hotel**   64%   £99

Tel 0983 863262   Fax 0983 867139   Hotel

Park Road Shanklin Isle of Wight PO37 6BB   Map 15 D4

The Isle of Wight's largest hotel enjoys panoramic views from its
position on the cliff above Sandown Bay (a public lift down to the
seafront is right alongside). There's a choice of bars, a leisure club,
conference rooms and plenty of facilities for children; cots are
available. Most of the bedrooms have balconies. Children up to 14 stay
free in parents' room (50% discount in their own room). All children
join the Sammy Seagull Club on arrival and given a fun case and
badge; high tea (5-6pm), separate dining area with video
entertainment, supervised crèche during school holidays, aquaglide
in the indoor pool, baby-listening and high chairs are all on offer.
*Rooms 88. Indoor swimming pool, gymnasium, sauna, steam room, spa
bath, solarium, beauty & hair salon, snooker, children's play area.
Access, Amex, Diners, Visa.*

Shanklin   **Hambledon Hotel**

Tel 0983 862403   Hotel

Queens Road Shanklin Isle of Wight PO37 6AW   Map 15 D4

A home from home is what Beryl and Norman Birch aim to provide
at their comfortable family hotel close to the beach. Two suites and
five large rooms have ample space for the cots provided and amenities
include high-chairs, boosters, toys and children's books. Nappies and
baby clothes placed in a special bucket in the bedroom will be washed,
dried and returned the same day and by night there is a baby-listening
service and patrol by a qualified nursery nurse. All bedrooms have en-
suite showers but a bathroom is provided for children who prefer
something in which they can sail a rubber duck. Children may eat
with parents or take early tea at 5pm. Special diets are catered for and
food will be puréed for babies. Outside is a safe garden, with slide.
£145 per person per 7 day stay. Under-1s £2.50 per day. 1-3s
£5-£6.50. *Rooms 11. Access, Visa.*

Sheffield   **Brasserie Leo**

Tel 0742 589411	Brasserie

Charwood Hotel Sharrow Lane Sheffield South Yorkshire S11 1AA   **Map 6 C2**

A recent change of chef, but suitably Belle Epoque-designed second
restaurant (access also from London Road) in true brasserie style
remains an exemplary operation in the Kings' much praised Charwood
Hotel, and one which many establishments would do well to emulate.
Although separate breakfast and tea menus take precedence
at appropriate times of day, they, along with the main carte, are
available throughout the opening hours. Therefore, bamboo-steamed
king prawns with hoisin sauce (£4.95), venison medallion with a port
and orange jus (£11.50) and crème brulée with rhubarb (£2.95)
could be had for breakfast if you so wished. As if this was not enough,
you could also chose from a selection of light bites – Leo's club
sandwich (£5.70) or Spanish omelette (£4.75) are typical – or (from
midday) the daily blackboard menu which offers four choices
of starter, main and sweet, all for £10. Crisp, friendly, professional
service. **Seats 56. Open** *7am-1pm.* **Closed** *24, 25 & 26 Dec evenings.*
Access, Amex, Diners, Visa.

Shepperton   **Blubeckers Eating House**

Tel 0932 243377	

Church Square Shepperton Middlesex TW17 9JY   **Map 15 E2**

Not quite matching the stylish country mill setting of its sister outlet
in Odiham, Hants (our 1992 Family Restaurant of the Year), this well-
established restaurant is right on a bend in the road opposite
Shepperton's pretty church square. The old building contains a warren
of rooms filled with check tablecloths and high-chairs with balloons
tied to them. Almost as soon as one sits down the helpful, efficient staff
produce a jokey children's menu, along with a cup of wax crayons.
The children's choice is standard fare: half-pint burger, fish sticks,
scampi, kids ribs and Mexican sauce, hot sausage dog (from £1.95-
£3.75); puddings include smartie smacker, chocolate dipper and hot
fudgey chocolate cake (£1.45-£1.95); humdinger, slime juice and
dracula's dribble kids cocktails should also raise a laugh. Sunday lunch
is a real bargain – £7.75 for three courses with a choice of any starter
or pudding from the normal dinner menu. Good ribs, burgers, fine
haddock and spinach potato-topped pie plus desserts that should test
even the finest of trenchermen! There is no room in the Ladies
to change a baby, but otherwise this a fine destination for a family
outing, albeit a little cramped and underlit. After lunch a short stroll
past the Warren Lodge Hotel will take you to the edge of the Thames
where ducks will delight younger children. **Seats** *85.* **Open** *L Sun only
(also every day during December), D 6.15-10.30 (from 6 Fri-Sun,
to 11 Fri & Sat).* **Closed** *3 days Christmas.*

Sherborne   **Eastbury Hotel**   67%   £98

Tel 0935 813131 Fax 0935 817296	Hotel

Long Street Sherborne Dorset DT9 3BY   **Map 14 B3**

Built in 1740, the Eastbury is a fine Georgian town house with well-
proportioned rooms. Public areas comprise an elegant entrance hall,
a comfortably furnished lounge, a library amd an intimate cocktail bar
with an ornately carved counter. Bedrooms, three of which are in an
adjacent building, have smart polished-wood furniture and pretty
fabrics. Bathrooms offer showers and tubs, plus good soaps and

toiletries. No dogs. Families are well catered for – children up to
16 stay free in parents' room. Large conservatory restaurant
overlooking the garden. Clipper Hotels. **Rooms** *15. Garden.*
Access, Visa.

Shrewsbury   The Good Life

Tel 0743 350455	Restaurant
Barracks Passage Wyle Cop Shrewsbury Shropshire SY1 1XA	**Map 6 A3**

A narrow passage off Wyle Cop leads to this informal vegetarian
restaurant in three rooms of a restored 14th-century building. Upstairs
is the no-smoking area and downstairs offers counter service providing
fresh food throughout the day: various quiches – asparagus, sweetcorn
and cheese (from £1.45) or hot specials like lasagne, spinach moussaka
or savoury cheese vegetable bake (all £1.95). Home-made puddings
(£1.50), cakes and scones are also available. **Seats** *65.* **Open** *9.30-3.30*
(Sat to 4.30). **Closed** *Sun, Bank Holidays. No credit cards.*

Sidcup   Mama Carmen

Tel 081-300 5233	Restaurant
9 Marechal Neil Parade Main Road Sidcup Kent DA14 6QF	**Map 11 B5**

Like a sleepy Spanish courtyard, with terracotta tiles, a fountain and
bright geraniums, the dining room conjures up one's best memories
of Spain. Fish dishes are a speciality. The food is beautifully presented
and no less care is taken with the children's portions. There are two
clip-on high-chairs plus children's cutlery, colouring books and
crayons are all provided. Babies can be changed and nursed in an
upstairs room. Branch at No 5 Market Street, Dartford, Kent Tel 0322
289749. **Open** *12-3 & 6-11.* **Closed** *L Sat & Mon, D Sun. Access, Amex,*
Visa.

Sidmouth   Victoria Hotel   67%   £120

Tel 0395 512651 Fax 0395 579154	Hotel
The Esplanade Sidmouth Devon EX10 8RY	**Map 13 E2**

Although named after Queen Victoria (a frequent visitor to her
neighbouring residence), the hotel was actually opened early in the
reign of Edward VII. Lounges are roomy and relaxing, and most
of the well-appointed bedrooms face the sea (many have French
windows leading to private balconies). Families are well catered for
with good leisure facilities, baby-sitting and considerations for children
in the dining room. Room service is available at any hour. No dogs.
Only really suitable for children during Christmas and high summer
season (when entertainment is provided), as the rest of the year sees
mainly elderly folk enjoying the sea breezes. **Rooms** *65. Garden,*
putting, indoor & outdoor swimming pools, keep-fit equipment, squash,
tennis, spa bath, sauna, solarium, snooker & games room, hairdressing,
dinner dance (Saturdays), lock-up garages. Access, Amex, Diners, Visa.

Sissinghurst   Granary Restaurant

Tel 0580 712850	Restaurant
Sissinghurst Castle Sissinghurst nr Cranbook Kent TN17 2AB	**Map 11 C5**

An ancient cow-shed has been turned into an attractive restaurant with
exposed beams, wooden floors and huge picture windows overlooking
fields. Few visitors can pass it by and queues frequently form so be
prepared to wait or plan to eat early. Children are welcome and staff
will warm baby food and bottles. Small portions of salads,

ploughman's lunches and filled jacket potatoes are available from the self-service counter, as are cream teas, cakes and pastries. Four smart high-chairs (without reins) are provided. On sunny days children can play on a grassy area outside. Ring before travelling to check opening hours. No smoking. *Open 12-6 (Sat and Sun from 10). Closed all Mon & Oct 15-Good Friday (except Oct 23-Dec 23 when open Wed-Sat 11-4).*

Skelwith Bridge   Chesters

Tel 05394 32553	Café
Skelwith Bridge nr Ambleside Cumbria	**Map 4 C3**

Enjoying a pretty riverside setting next to Skelwith Bridge, this appealing café shares space with the showroom and shop of a restored slate works. An impressive array of home baking (55p-£1.80) includes chocolate fudge cake, John Peel pie, Tiffins, carrot cake with fudge topping, lemon yoghurt cake , orange and coconut cake, date slices, flapjacks and several puddings (sticky toffee, hot lemon, cherry pie – £1.45). Given the popularity of Karen Lawrence's cakes, the savoury menu is kept small – home-made soup (curried parsnip or mushroom and split pea -£1.75), quiches (leek, cheese and broccoli £2.95), selection of rolls (from £1.50) or walnut and Stilton paté (£2.25). Terrace in front for summer days. Children's portions of savoury items. *Seats 50. Open 9.30-5.30 (winter to 4.45). Closed 24-26 Dec, 1 Jan, 1 week Jan. No credit cards.*

Skipton   Randell's Hotel   65%   £95

Tel 0756 700100 Fax 0756 700107	Hotel
Keighley Road Snaygill Skipton North Yorkshire BD23 2TA	**Map 6 C1**

A purpose-built hotel, just south of the town centre, standing by the Liverpool to Leeds canal. Spacious bedrooms are light and contemporary with fully-tiled private facilities. Children under 14 stay free in parents' rooms and cots are available. Day rooms include an open-plan lobby and a first-floor bar. There's also a well-equipped leisure centre which offers splendid facilities for over-7s in the form of the Young Adventurers' Club as well as a baby pool. The hotel's supervised nursery/crèche for under-7s is open from 8am-6pm weekdays, 10-2 Sat and 11-3 Sun and is equipped with table toys, games, house corner and paints. Babies can rest in a separate quiet room. Changing facilities (including baby wipes and nappies) are also provided. Children can either eat in the nursery or with their parents and can choose from the children's menu. Ten high-chairs are provided together with booster seats, beakers and cutlery. The hotel's restaurant has a fenced off terrace overlooking the canal. Special childrens' weekends are planned for 1993. *Rooms 61. Indoor swimming pool, gymnasium, spa bath, sauna, solarium, beautician, hair salon, squash, snooker, coffee shop (7am-10pm). Access, Amex, Diners, Visa.*

South Holmwood   Gourmet Pizza Company

Tel 0306 889712	Restaurant
Horsham Road South Holmwood nr Dorking Surrey	**Map 15 E3**

The pizzas (if not the puds) live up to the name with generous amounts of topping – made from fresh ingredients – in some unusual combinations. Chinese duck (£7.75) with Peking duck, hoisin and plum sauce; smoked Edam, broccoli, spring onions, coriander and ginger; English Breakfast (£4.95) with Cumberland sausage, smoked

bacon, tomatoes, mushrooms and two eggs; and Cajun prawn and
chicken (£7.70) among other more classic varieties. There are also
some good salads and a handful of pasta dishes. The seventh in a small
chain, this one is about two miles south of Dorking on the A24.
Ample parking. **Seats** 85. **Open** *noon-11pm (Fri & Sat to 11.30).*
Closed *25 & 26 Dec. Access, Visa.*

South Molton   Corn Dolly

No telephone	Tea Room

115a East Street South Molton Devon   Map 13 D2

Tracy Dodd and her friendly crew continue their commendable
reliance on local produce, free-range eggs and fine home baking at her
"Real Tea Shop" attached to a tiny craft and gift centre where
speciality teas, coffees and Devon relishes are also sold. By keeping the
menu selection simple, the quality is assured: King's Ransom (£4.25) –
a grilled Stilton-covered teacake – is a perennial favourite; Seafarer's
Tea (£3.45) features locally smoked mackerel, soup (carrot and pulse
£1.35) is a regular winter warmer. **Seats** 20. **Open** *9.30-5 (Mon from
10, Wed to 2, Sat 10-5.30).* **Closed** *Sun. No credit cards.*

Southsea   Pizza Express

Tel 0705 293938	Restaurant

41 Osborne Road Southsea Hampshire   Map 15 D4

This particular branch of the popular pizza chain has a nautical look,
with life belts and flags on the wall and ship-type rails on the upper
floor. More than a dozen varieties of pizza, plus a couple of main-
course salads. **Seats** 80. **Open** *11.30am-midnight.* **Closed** *25 & 26 Dec.
Access, Amex, Visa.*

Southwold   The Swan   65%   £82

Tel 0502 722186 Fax 0502 724800	Hotel

Market Place Southwold Suffolk IP18 6EG   Map 10 D2

The ancient Swan (rebuilt in 1660 and remodelled in the 1820s) faces
the market place of a most charming seaside town. An old long-case
clock and fresh flowers grace the flagstoned foyer and an abundance
of sofas the period drawing room. Main-house bedrooms are
traditional in style with freestanding furniture, including the odd
antique, while simpler chalet-style rooms surround a garden to the
rear. The adjacent brewery can occasionally disturb the peace during
the day. **Rooms** 45. Access, Amex, Visa.

Restaurant   £65

An elegant, pink dining room and a choice of fixed-price only menus
offering an interesting mix ranging from chicken and bacon terrine
on a green herb sauce to sautéed Cromer skate wing with mixed
pepper sauce and Spotted Dick with clotted cream. **Seats** 50. *Private
Room. L 12.15-1.45 (Sun to 1.30) D 7-9.30 (Sun to 9). Closed D 3rd
Sun in Jan. Set L £10.50/£13.95 Set D £15.95-£25.50.*

Sowerby Bridge   The Hobbit

Tel 0422 832202	Pub

Hob Lane Sowerby Bridge Norland West Yorkshire HX6 3QL   Map 6 C1

The Hobbit serves food and drinks all day and the Bilbo's Bistro
menu offers a huge selection of dishes including tandoori chicken,
deep-pan pizzas and home-made lasagne. All are available in reduced

portions and there is also a children's menu until 9pm (particularly popular 4-6.30pm). In the evenings the dining room menu lists good-value dishes such as prawn-filled salmon with a cream, wine and watercress sauce. High-chairs are available and staff will heat customers' bottles and food, or liquidise to suit all tastes. Children are given a funpack on arrival. There is space to change a nappy and to stow a push-chair. A relaxed and welcoming establishment. *Bar Food 11.30am-11pm. Access, Amex, Visa.*

Stafford   Soup Kitchen

Tel 0785 54775	Tea Room
Church Lane Stafford Staffordshire	**Map 6 B3**

Tucked away down a cobbled lane between St Mary's Church and Mill Lane, the Sandy family's cottagey, 16th-century tea rooms reveal within a veritable warren of comfortable interlinked rooms, with plenty of no-smoking areas and a choice of waitress service. Production of home baking through the day is prodigious, and the choice of lunches – from three soups (£1.05) through cottage pie and vegetable lasagne (£3.15) to daily roasts and pies – is both extensive and predictable. Young Duncan Sandy regularly mans the door to meet and seat the hordes, and epitomises the friendly eagerness to please of all his staff. "Families welcome: children and grannies adored" is their highly appropriate motto. *Seats 170. Open 10-5 (Sat from 9.30). Closed Sun and Bank Holidays. No credit cards.*

Staines   Pizza Express

Tel 0784 456522	Pizzeria
12-16 Clarence Street Staines Middlesex	**Map 15 E2**

Spacious, modern design with conservatory eating at the front and balcony tables with a view over the river to the rear. The menu includes a choice of reliably good, crispy pizzas (from £3.15) with fresh toppings as well as salads, lasagne and cannelloni. *Seats 105. Open 11.30am-midnight. Closed 25 Dec. Access, Amex, Visa.*

Stanstead Abbots   Briggens House Hotel   70%   £102

Tel 0279 792416 Fax 0279 793685	Hotel
Stanstead Road Stanstead Abbots nr Ware Hertfordshire SG12 8LD	**Map 15 F2**

A large, stately home-from-home, a few miles off the M11, set in 45 acres of grounds with its own 9-hole golf course. High standards of service are typified by the smart, uniformed doormen. A magnificent carved wood staircase leads up from the entrance hall with its glass chandelier to 22 bedrooms in the main house; 32 more are in the converted coach house and have lower ceilings, but all are equally tastefully decorated with a good range of extras included as standard. Swagged drapes and elegant reproduction antiques give an elegant air. In summer, tables are set on the expansive lawns outside the French windows leading off the lounge. A fun pack is provided for children and there are four cots, with bedding, for the five family rooms. Baby-listening/sitting is offered. Children may have high tea in the restaurant (high-chairs/half portions) or eat in their rooms but they are not allowed in thedining room at night. Large gardens with a pond and an unheated swimming pool. Laundry service. Queens Moat Houses. *Rooms 54. Garden, outdoor swimming pool, tennis, 9-hole golf course, croquet, bowls, fishing. Closed 1 wk Xmas. Access, Amex, Diners, Visa.*

Stonham Aspal   **Stonham Barns**

Tel 0449 711755	Restaurant
Pettaugh Road Stonham Aspel Stowmarket Suffolk IP14 6AU	Map 10 C3

The restaurant is part of a complex based around a garden centre.
Considerable effort has gone into making the complex attractive
to families, with lots of diversions for children so that adults can
browse unflustered. The restaurant, a converted barn with open
brickwork and high beamed ceiling, is an impressive setting. There is a
conservatory with Lego, paper and colours, and outside there is a small
adventure playground with sandpit, slide and swing. Food
is unadventurous but it is home-cooked, there are daily specials and
a self-service salad bar.The staff are happy to provide for babies
as necessary and will find you a quiet place for changing and
breastfeeding as the toilets are not suitable. Children's parties can
be arranged. *Open 10-5.30 (4.30 Oct-Mar). Closed 25 & 26 Dec.
Access, Visa.*

Stow-on-the-Wold   **Fosse Manor**   60%   £90

Tel 0451 30354 Fax 0451 32486	Hotel
Fosse Way Stow-on-the-Wold Gloucestershire GL54 1JX	Map 14 C1

Long-standing resident proprietors Bob and Yvonne Johnston and
their loyal staff run a family haven that attracts many repeat visits.
Built in the style of a Cotswold manor house, it stands in its ivy coat
in grounds set back from the A429. Bedrooms (including ten equipped
for family use – cots provided) overlook colourful gardens and the
Fosse Way; the bright look of the day rooms is enhanced throughout
by potted plants, fresh flowers and spotless housekeeping. Family
facilities include supervised play times for children in a playroom and
playground on high days and holidays; children's menu with a theme
and high-chairs, too. There are toys in the drawing room and even the
bar 'powder-room' has a changing area, complete with nappies and
wipes. *Rooms 20. Garden, croquet, sauna, solarium, spa bath, beauty salon.
Closed 22-30 Dec. Access, Amex, Diners, Visa.*

Stratford-upon-Avon   **Grosvenor House Hotel**   £91

Tel 0789 269213 Fax 0789 266087	Hotel
12-14 Warwick Road Stratford-upon-Avon Warwickshire CV37 6YT	Map 14 C1

A friendly, unpretentious hotel which has undergone a programme
of improvement. There are eight family suites with pretty co-
ordinating fabrics and light restful colours. Three cots are provided for
babies and there is a laundry service. In the restaurant, children under
14 can choose from a special menu and early suppers can be arranged.
Parents can book a baby-sitter and then head for the theatre.
Under-15s stay free in their parents' room. *Rooms 40. Access, Amex,
Diners, Visa.*

Stratford-upon-Avon   **Piccolino's Pizzeria**

Tel 0789 267067	Restaurant
7 Greenhill Street Stratford-upon-Avon Warwickshire	Map 14 C1

Arguably worth the extra walk to the unfashionable end of Greenhill
Street, here's a dependable alternative to the high street pizza chains.
One of a family-owned group of three pizzerias (see also entries under
Warwick and Leamington Spa), the cooking is reliable and portions

generous. Cooked-to-order pizzas (*napolitana* £4.85; *quattro formaggi* £5.60) are notably good, pasta alternatives (*ravioli di pomodoro* £4.95; *tagliatelle alla marinara* £5.85) richly sauced, and there are steaks (*pizzaiola* £9.75) for those wishing to splash out more. Functional decor suggests their heart lies in the kitchen: they're family-friendly, too. **Seats** 70. **Open** *12-2.30 & 5.30-11 (Fri to 11.30, Sat 12-11.30, Sun to 10.30). **Closed** 25 & 26 Dec. Access, Visa.*

Stratford-upon-Avon	Windmill Park	64%	£89
Tel 0789 731173 Fax 0789 731131			Hotel
Warwick Road Stratford-upon-Avon Warwickshire CV37 0PY			Map 14 C1

Four linked blocks provide practical accommodation in a modern yellow-brick hotel on the A439 (leave the M40 at junction 15) with a well-equipped leisure centre. Many large family and interconnecting bedrooms, with under-12s staying free in their parents' room. You need to take your own potty and nappies but the non-slip bath is fine for babies and there is a baby-listening service and a baby-sitter can be arranged. Pushchairs and prams are no problem in the public areas or dining room which also has four high-chairs. Children have their own menu (or smaller portions), but bring your own baby food, which is willingly reheated. **Rooms** *100. Indoor swimming pool, gymnasium, sauna, steam room, spa bath. Access, Amex, Diners, Visa.*

Stretton	Ram Jam Inn		£57
Tel 0780 410776 Fax 0780 410361			Inn
Great North Rd Stretton nr Oakham Rutland Leicestershire LE15 7QX			Map 7 E3

Hard by a service station on the northbound lanes of the A1 (southbound drivers take the B668 exit to Oakham and follow signs), nine miles north of Stamford, a very pleasing alternative to the mass of commercial hotels along the A1. Public rooms are devoted completely to informal, yet smartly furnished eating areas (bar, snack, outdoor terrace and restaurant areas). All the bedrooms overlooking the garden and orchard are individually and tastefully decorated with limed pine furniture, and surprisingly quiet considering the proximity to the road. Cots and high-chairs are available for youngsters. The Ladies loo has changing facilities. **Rooms** *10. Garden, coffee shop (7am-10pm). Closed 25 Dec. Access, Amex, Visa.*

Restaurant   £35

Straightforward menu in a pleasingly light dining room overlooking the orchard; children are given colouring books and crayons on arriving and a children's menu is provided. Home-made soup, half a pint of prawns with crusty bread, a choice of pasta, braised Rutland venison with glazed vegetables and new potatoes, chargrilled steak or leg of lamb, stir-fried pork and good desserts like treacle tart with praline ice cream or blackberry and apple compote with a pastry hat and custard. Well-priced wines with regular bin ends and useful tasting notes. Great snacks in an informal snack area include breakfast from 7am, one-inch-thick home-made burgers and giant granary baps. Open all day, the Inn also offers a selection of home-baked cookies and scones for tea. Outdoor terrace overlooking an orchard for snacking in good weather. No-smoking area. On a road dominated by fast food outlets, it's well worth slowing down for the extraordinary Ram Jam Inn. **Seats** *40. Parties 40. Private Room. L 12-2.30 D 7-10 (light meals 7am-10pm).*

Stroud   The Old Lady Tea Shop

Tel 0453 762441	Tea Room
1 Threadneedle Street Stroud Gloucestershire	**Map 14 B2**

The Walker family have owned the bakery below this pleasant first-floor tea shop for thirty years. Don Walker runs the bakery while his wife looks after the airy, plant-filled tea shop. There's a small menu of light snacks (toasted sandwich from £1.20, pizza £1.50, ploughman's £2, jacket potato from £1.75) and an understandably good choice of cakes, flapjacks, lardies, cream cakes, doughnuts, gingerbread men, iced buns and excellent light scones (cream tea £2). Unlicensed. *Seats 32. Open 9.30-4.30 (Mon & Thu to 4). Closed Sun, Bank Holidays. No credit cards.*

Studland Bay   Knoll House   61%   £154*

Tel 092 944 251 Fax 092 944 423	Hotel
Studland Bay nr Swanage Dorset BH19 3AH	**Map 14 C4**

Progeny-free holidaymakers and families are equally well catered for at the Fergusons' hotel, which won our 1991 Family Hotel of the Year award. There's an adventure playground, indoor play rooms, family suites with interconnecting rooms and even a children's dining room with a separate kitchen to keep the little ones happy, while the wooded grounds, a nearby bird sanctuary and a safe, sandy beach provide peaceful diversions for other guests. There's plenty of comfortable lounge space, and bedrooms – neither large nor small – are plain and practical. TVs may be hired. *Half-board terms only. *Rooms 80. Garden, outdoor swimming pool, sauna, solarium, whirlpool bath, steam room, keep-fit equipment, tennis, 9-hole golf course, boutique. Closed Nov-Easter. No credit cards.*

Sutton   Pizza Express

Tel 081 643 4725	Pizzeria
6 High Street Sutton Surrey	**Map 15 E3**

One of many popular pizza restaurants in a well-run chain. Crisp, thin pizzas (around £5) and fresh ingredients used for the toppings. *Seats 140. Open 11.30-midnight. Closed 25 & 26 Dec. Access, Amex, Diners, Visa.*

Sutton Benger   Bell House Hotel

Tel 0249 720401	Hotel
High Street Sutton Benger Wiltshire SN15 4RH	**Map 14 B2**

Friendly staff create a cheerful, relaxed atmosphere at this much extended and modernised hotel which was originally a 15th-century house. There are three bedrooms suitable for families, two cots and a baby-listening service. A children's menu (2 course for £6.95) can be provided in the restaurant as well as small portions and there are two high-chairs. The garden is large but there is no specific play area. Under-10s free. *Rooms 14. Access, Amex, Diners, Visa.*

Swindon   Blunsdon House Hotel   69%   £93

Tel 0793 721701 Fax 0793 721056	Hotel
Blunsdon Swindon Wiltshire SN2 4AD	**Map 14 C2**

A farm guest house in 1958, a country club in 1960, and a fully licensed hotel since 1962 – and the Clifford family have been here from the beginning. It's a popular conference rendezvous with

extensive leisure club facilities that even extend to a toddlers' splash
pool. Guests are provided with a good standard of comfort in the form
of gardens, formal and casual bars, a residents' lounge, two restaurants
and porterage; younger guests have their own play room and whizz
kids can relax in the Big Lad's computer room. All the bedrooms are
reasonably roomy and many have pleasant views. Decoration and
appointments are of smart modern business standard, and bathrooms
all have shower attachments and ample toiletries; some have spa baths.
Latest opening date for the nine-hole golf course is early 1993.
Families are well catered for; children up to 13 stay free in parents'
room; baby-sitting/listening available (arrange in advance). There are
plenty of high-chairs and children's tea is provided by room service.
No dogs. *Rooms 88. Garden, tennis, croquet, putting, indoor swimming
pool, squash, sauna, solarium, gymnasium, spa bath, beautician, hairdressing,
games room, snooker, crèche. Access, Amex, Diners, Visa.*

Tewkesbury	**Tewkesbury Park**	**62%**	**£89**
Tel 0684 295405 Fax 0684 292386			Hotel
Lincoln Green Lane Tewkesbury Gloucestershire GL20 7DN			Map 14 B1

Built around an 18th-century mansion, but the atmosphere today
is more country club than country house and conferences are big
business. Well-appointed bedrooms afford views of the Malvern Hills.
Good facilities for families with a supervised crèche in the leisure club
at weekends; children are encouraged to eat in the club restaurant,
although high-chairs and children's portions are provided in the dining
room. Children's playroom and playground. No dogs. Country Club
Hotels. *Rooms 78. Garden, indoor swimming pool, keep-fit equipment, spa
bath, sauna, solarium, squash, tennis, golf, beautician, hairdressing, snooker,
coffee shop (10am-10.30pm). Access, Amex, Diners, Visa.*

Threshfield	**Old Hall Inn**	
Tel 0756 752441		Pub
Threshfield nr Grassington North Yorkshire BD23 5HB		Map 6 C1

The Old Hall Inn is an exceptionally family-friendly pub in the
peaceful village of Threshfield in the Yorkshire Dales. Tremendously
popular, the atmosphere is really welcoming, there are always plenty
of children about and being sociable is almost compulsory. The quality
of the food is impressive – excellent fresh ingredients and a constantly
changing blackboard list of daily specials; children can have small
portions of anything on the menu. There are no high-chairs but there
is room to change a baby on the vanity unit in the ladies. The family
dining area opens out onto a pretty, well-stocked garden, with a patio
and bird garden. You may also like to visit nearby Kilnsey Park with
its trout farm, adventure playground and large aquarium.
Open 12-2 & 6.30-9.30 (Sun 7-9). No credit cards.

Thurlestone	**Thurlestone Hotel**	**69%**	**£152**
Tel 0548 560382 Fax 0548 561069			Hotel
Thurlestone Kingsbridge Devon TQ7 3NN			Map 13 D3

The elegance of the 20s combines with the amenities of the 90s
in a handsome family-owned hotel in a lovely setting with spectacular
sea views and close to sandy beaches. Splendidly geared to family
holidays, particularly at Easter and half-term times with special
programmes organised that include magician, film shows, outdoor
sports, cartoons, cabaret and competitions (including crosswords!).
It also has an off-peak trade in small conferences. Day rooms make the
most of the location, likewise half the smart, well-equipped bedrooms.
Baby-sitting/listening can be arranged to allow parents flexibility
to enjoy the adult facilities; early-evening children's suppers are also
offered. Children up to 16 can stay free of charge in their parents'
room. Extensive gardens with swings, climbing frames and climbing
net. Riding and sailing can be organised locally for older children.
Toddlers will enjoy the indoor paddling pool, nursery menus, cots
in family bedrooms and high-chairs. *Rooms 68. Garden, 9-hole golf
course, putting, squash, tennis, badminton, indoor & outdoor swimming
pools, keep-fit equipment, sauna, solarium, beauty salon, hairdressing,
snooker, table tennis, coffee shop (8am-10pm). Access, Visa.*

Tickton	**Tickton Grange Hotel**	**62%**	**£73**
Tel 0964 543666 Fax 0964 542556			Hotel
Tickton nr Beverley Humberside HU17 9SH			Map 7 E1

A family-owned Georgian house standing in 3½ acres of rose gardens,
where afternoon teas are served in the summer. Day rooms retain
a traditional appeal, and bedrooms are decorated in a fresh, light style.
There are two suites, one with a Georgian four-poster bed. Tickton
truffles are offered as a welcome. The Whymant family run the hotel
along friendly and informal lines, offering a particularly warm
welcome to families. There are five family-size rooms and baby baths,
potties, nappies, bottles and baby food are all stocked. In addition,
there are swings, a nursery slide and a climbing frame in a safely
enclosed courtyard with plenty of lawned areas. *Rooms 16. Garden.
Access, Amex, Diners, Visa.*

Tivetshall St Mary	**Old Ram**	
Tel 0379 608228 (tables)/676794 (accommodation)		Pub
Ipswich Road (A140) Tivetshall St Mary Norfolk NR15 2DE		Map 10 C2

Five 'luxury' en-suite rooms are on offer at this popular roadside
family dining pub, parts of which date back to the 17th century.
In one of the larger rooms there are two bunk beds for family use
(children are charged at £10 per night). On the eating side, try the
daily seafood specials like crab, lobster or jumbo cod in batter (£6.50).
Good traditional features and a warming fire in the main bar, which
has a framework of ancient pillars and beams and a brick floor;
alongside is a lounge bar and beyond that a family room. Weather
permitting you could also eat in the small enclosed garden. There are
two high-chairs but no changing facilities. *Bar Meals 7.30am-10pm.
Children's portions. Free House. Beer Adnams, Greene King, Ruddles.
Garden, outdoor eating. Family room (coach house). Accommodation
5 bedrooms, all en suite, £54. Children welcome overnight. No dogs.
Access, Visa.*

Tolworth   Superfish

Tel 081-390 2868	Fish'n'Chips
59 The Broadway Tolworth Surrey	**Map 15 E2**

Part of a Surrey-based chain of above-average fish and chip restaurants.
A few steps away from the large Marks & Spencer underneath the
distinctive tower block by the A3. See Morden entry for more details.
*Seats 36. Open 11.30-2 (Sat to 2.30), 5-10.30 (Thu-Sat to 11). Closed
Sun, 25 & 26 Dec, 1 Jan. Access, Visa.*

Tormarton   Compass Inn

Tel 0454 218242	Pub
Tormarton nr Badminton Avon GL9 IJB	**Map 13 F1**

Busy creeper-clad former coaching inn one minute north of junction
18 of the M4 (the exit for Bath). Pleasant conservatory (ideal for
families) and garden. Good-sized bedrooms in two modern extensions.
*Beer Archers, Bass, Smiles. Garden. Children's play area.
Family room.*

Torquay   Livermead Cliff Hotel   60%   £86

Tel 0803 299666 Fax 0803 294496	Hotel
Sea Front Torquay Devon TQ2 6RQ	**Map 13 D3**

Right by the sea, with direct access to the beach and popular for
family holidays. Also geared up to the conference trade, so it's quite
a busy place all year round. Picture windows in the lounge look out
to sea. Parents with offspring are well catered for with cots, baby-
sitting, baby-listening and children's high tea available. Good
housekeeping, friendly staff. Lovely outdoor pool and garden
overlooking the bay. *Rooms 64. Garden, outdoor swimming pool,
solarium, laundry room. Access, Amex, Diners, Visa.*

Torquay   Palace Hotel   68%   £128

Tel 0803 200200 Fax 0803 299899	Hotel
Babbacombe Road Torquay Devon TQ1 3TG	**Map 13 D3**

A much-extended Victorian hotel set in 25 acres of gardens and
woodland running down to the sea. Very much a family holiday place
in summer, it's more concerned with conferences at other times. Public
rooms are vast, with elegant pillars and moulded ceilings. Six large
suites have splendid views, individual decor and good-quality
furniture; ordinary rooms are simple but comfortable, with handsome
period bathrooms. Children up to 12 stay free in parents' room. Cots,
baby-sitting/listening, high-chairs provided; high tea and nanny
in high season. No dogs. *Rooms 140. Garden, indoor & outdoor
swimming pools, sauna, hairdressing, indoor & outdoor tennis, squash,
9-hole golf course, snooker, children's play room, nanny (resident in high
season). Access, Diners, Visa.*

Totnes   **Willow**

Tel 0803 862605	Restaurant
87 High Street Totnes Devon	Map 13 D3

Fran Goldsworthy and Maha Roberts boldly fly the vegetarian flag from the Willow masthead. Their cakes and pastries throughout the day range from the 'relatively healthy' to the 'luscious but naughty', with organic milk ices and soya ice dream always to hand. Daily-changing lunch menus ensure a steady stream of regulars to sample carrot and coriander soup (£1.10), parsley, lemon and tofu dip (£2.20) and perhaps spicy Ghanaian stew (£2.95). Evening dishes served with few salads might be cauliflower marranca (£5.30), chili bean casserole (£5.20) and organic spinach filo pie (£5.70). Wednesday night is exclusively Indian, and Friday live music night. Organic wines and bottled beers; take-away also available. Children's menu and garden: no credit cards. **Seats** 60. **Open** 10-5 & 6.30-10. **Closed** D Mon/Tue & winter Thu, all Sun. No credit cards.

Trent   **Rose & Crown**

Tel 0935 850776	Pub
Trent nr Sherborne Dorset DT9 4SL	Map 13 F2

Initially two separate thatched cottages, the Rose & Crown is refreshingly unpretentious within, simply furnished, with a rug-strewn stone floor and roaring log fires in winter. No pub games, fruit machines or music. A great emphasis on good fresh food, making good use of local gardens and farms. The 40-seat conservatory restaurant serves dishes such as smoked pigeon breast with kiwi and lime sauce (£2.50) and half a roast duck with apricot and ginger sauce (£7.95). Regular bar food is also all home-made: cheese and sirloin steak sandwich (£4.95), prawn and garlic pizza (£4.25). Excellent local cheeses. No children in the bar, but plenty of room in the family room and extension. Children's menu/portions; one high-chair. **Bar Food & Restaurant** 12-2, 7-9.30 (10 Sat/Sun). **Beer** Boddington, Fullers, Hook Norton. Garden, outdoor eating. Family room. Access, Visa.

Tresco   **Island Hotel**   67%   £170★

Tel 0720 22883 Fax 0720 23008	Hotel
Tresco Isles of Scilly Cornwall TR24 0PU	Map 12 A2

Tresco, England's "Island of Flowers", is privately owned and maintained with, incidentally, a total ban on cats and dogs. Guests arriving at the quay or heliport (from Penzance) are transported by tractor-drawn charabanc to the island's only hotel, set in beautifully tended gardens. Picture windows make the most of this spectacular location and the panoramic sea views: should the mists close in there's a Terrace Bar (where local fish and seafood feature prominently on the light lunch menu and on the blackboard-listed specials) and a Quiet Room stacked with books, magazines and games. Under-14s stay free in parents' room. Special holiday packages for gardeners. ★Half-board terms only. **Rooms 40.** Garden, croquet, outdoor swimming pool, fishing, boating, bowling green, games room. Closed 6 weeks Oct/Nov. Access, Amex, Visa.

Restaurant   £60

Table d'hote and à la carte menus place strong emphasis on local seafood (Scillonian scallops, Bryher crab), and there's Devonshire beef and veal from the grill. Traditional farmhouse cheeses. Luxurious

Sunday buffet (including lobster). Children can eat half-price from the carte. No smoking. *Seats 95. Parties 40. L 12-2 D 7-9.30. Set D £22.50.*

Twickenham   **Pizza Express**

Tel 081-891 4126	Pizeria
21 York Street Twickenham Middlesex	**Map 15 E2**

A corner location, next door to Norma's Deli Diner, with bright and airy decor using a white-tiled floor and mirrors and prints on the walls. Reliably good, crisp pizzas are served with fresh toppings. Live jazz Wed evenings. No-smoking area. *Seats 70. Open 11.30-midnight. Closed 24 & 25 Dec. Access, Amex, Visa.*

Ullswater   **Old Church Hotel**   67%   £120

Tel 076 84 86204 Fax 076 84 86368	Hotel
Watermillock Penrith Cumbria CA11 0JN	**Map 4 C3**

A stylish water's-edge hotel where residents are greeted very much as Kevin and Maureen Whitemore's house guests. Both lounges are built for relaxation and packed with board games and periodicals; in the library a TV rarely comes into play. Maureen's bold colour schemes brighten the bedrooms (priced according to the view), with crown canopies and half-testers framing really comfortable beds; cots and baby-listening are provided. By contrast, bathrooms are on the cramped side. Breakfasts deserve to be taken seriously, ranging from Lakeland yoghurts and home-made muesli to Manx kippers, Cumberland sausage and mixed grill with black pudding. No dogs. *Rooms 10. Garden, croquet, fishing, boating. Closed Dec-Feb. Visa.*

Restaurant   £70

The smaller lounge doubles as an aperitif bar where guests gather prior to dinner at 8 (non-residents must book). There's a limited choice of first and main courses, four dishes at each stage, with perhaps mushrooms with Stilton and port sauce or grilled goat's cheese with mustard and fried apples followed by noisettes of lamb with parsley pepper crust and rosemary gravy or roast loin of pork with sage stuffing, crackling and plum sauce. An inter-course dish of soup (typically Norman potato and shallot soup with shredded carrot) is optional. Traditional desserts are given a modern twist. Lighter lunches are also served daily. The stunning view of Ullswater is the icing on the cake. *Seats 30. Parties 10. Private Room. L 12.30-1.45 D 7.30 for 8. Set D £28.50.*

Ventnor   **Royal Hotel**   60%   £76

Tel 0983 852186 Fax 0983 855395	Hotel
Belgrave Road Ventnor Isle of Wight PO38 1JJ	**Map 15 D4**

Neat gardens and a small children's swimming pool front this Victorian sandstone hotel owned by Forte. The rattan-furnished conservatory entrance hall is a favourite seating area, as is a cosy bar. Elderly lightwood fitted units and rather neutral colour schemes in the bedrooms are enlivened only by a variety of colourful floral curtains; cots are provided. Children are well catered for with a games room, ice cream parlour and nanny during school summer holidays. *Rooms 54. Garden, croquet, outdoor swimming pool, games room. Access, Amex, Diners, Visa.*

Walberswick   **Mary's Restaurant**

Tel 0502 723243	Restaurant
Walberswick Suffolk IP18 6UG	**Map 10 D2**

Just north of this small coastal village is the river Blyth, which still shelters working fishing boats. These are the daily source for much of the restaurant's menu. In addition to fresh food, the Jelliffs' rambling restaurant provides a charming place to eat with a separate room for those who smoke, and tables in the garden. Much of the adult menu will make a very healthy children's portion, and something will always be found for little ones who are finished while their parents are tackling three courses. A secluded room will be found for breast-feeding mums and a large bathroom does for nappy changing. One clip-on baby chair provided. *Open 10-6, 7.15-9 (Fri & Sat), 7 days Aug* *Closed Mon-Thurs Nov-Easter, all Mon Easter-end July & Sept.*

Wantage   **Vale & Downland Museum Centre**

Tel 0235 771447	Café
Church Street Wantage Oxfordshire OX12 8BL	**Map 14 C2**

A museum of past and present local life set in a 17th-century cloth merchant's house. In the coffee shop, good home baking is the showpiece, from chocolate cake, date slice and Boston brownie at 45p, down to ginger animals at 3p each. The lunchtime menu runs from soup to jacket potatoes, quiche, lasagne and vegetable hot pot (£1.70). If you've forgotten the lidded beaker, bib or even the baby's food, don't worry – all are stocked. The garden, complete with Henrietta a sociable hen, is an added bonus. Drawing paper and pens keep youngsters amused or they can have a go at brass-rubbing. There is an area for nursing in the restaurant and a pull-down changing shelf in the disabled loo. Unlicensed. No smoking. *Seats 50.* *Open 10.30-4.30, Sun 2.30-5. Closed Mon, 25 Dec, 1 Jan.* *No credit cards.*

Warminster   **Jenner's Restaurant**

Tel 0985 213385	Restaurant
45 Market Place Warminster Wiltshire BA12 9AZ	**Map 14 B3**

A cheerful wholefood restaurant right in the centre of town, with pine tables and chairs and a tempting display of dishes to eat in or take away. The menu, supplemented by daily specials, is mainly vegetarian: stuffed jacket potatoes (from £1.85), toasted sandwiches, salads, cauliflower cheese bake (£3.45), beany goulash; recently, one meat dish was introduced – steak and kidney pie (£3.45). Pecan pie, bread pudding and fruit crumble are good accompaniments to the 'everlasting' coffee (60p). Two set teas – Old Fashioned and Cream (both £2.75). Organic wine. Children's portions. No smoking. *Seats 60. Open 9.30-5.30. Closed Sun Oct-Mar. No credit cards.*

Warwick   **Piccolino's Pizzeria**

Tel 0926 491020	Restaurant
31 South Street Warwick Warwickshire	**Map 14 C1**

A dependable alternative to the larger high street chains (there are branches also in Stratford and Leamington Spa – see entries). Piccolino's is family-owned and family-friendly too. Cooked-to-order pizzas (*napolitana* £4.85, *quattro formaggi* £5.60) are notably good, pasta alternatives (*ravioli di pomodoro* £4.95, *tagliatelle alla marinara*

£5.85) richly sauced, and there are steaks (*pizzaiola* £9.75) for those
wishing to splash out more. Despite somewhat functional decor,
suggesting that the heart of the operation lies firmly in the kitchen;
service is typically relaxed and informal. **Seats** *70.* **Open** *12-2.30 &
5.30-11 (Fri to 11.30, Sun to 10.30, Sat 12-11.30).* **Closed** *25 & 26 Dec.
Access, Visa.*

Warwick   The Racehorse

Tel 0926 496705	Pub

Stratford Road Warwick Warwickshire CV34 6AP   Map 14 C1

Food is basic, the deep-fat fryer is the main cooking tool and chips
come with everything. Outside there is an adventure playground,
a bouncing castle at weekends, and a tuck shop tucked with sweets,
drinks and ice creams. There are two high-chairs, two boosters, bibs,
plastic dishes and spoons and jars of baby food. The children's menu
is designed to look like a comic, filled with cartoons and jokes about
food. The £1.99 special includes a main course of funny fish bites and
wobbly jelly trifle. Finally, the nappy-changing room not only has
a pull-down changing table and a supply of wipes, nappies, tissues etc,
but is also large enough for you to sit and feed a baby. Storage for
push-chairs and no-smoking area. Owned by Everards brewery.
Open *12-10.15, Sun 12-2 & 7-10.* **Closed** *25 Dec eve. Access, Amex,
Diners, Visa.*

Welbeck   Dukeries Garden Centre,
Welbeck Coffee Shop

Tel 0909 476506	Coffee Shop

Welbeck nr Worksop Nottinghamshire   Map 7 D2

Situated in the walled gardens of historic Welbeck Abbey, the coffee
shop is housed in restored Victorian greenhouses with exposed beams
and bare brick walls. All the food is made on the premises and may
include daily specials such as turkey curry £2.99, lasagne or macaroni
cheese. Cakes and gateaux (45p-£1.85) or hot toffee pudding £1.45.
Roast Sunday lunch £3.95-£4.50. Children's portions and many
supervised amusements on offer in the garden centre complex.
Seats *140.* **Open** *10-6 (Nov-end Feb till 5).* **Closed** *4 days Christmas.
Access, Visa.*

Wellesbourne   King's Head

Tel 0789 840206	Pub

Warwick Road Wellesbourne Warwickshire CV35 9LX   Map 14 C1

The King's Head is a carefully renovated, listed building with owners
who are keen to provide a welcoming stopover for families. Staff are
attentive and will do what they can to help. On the first floor, the
family rooms are of a good size, pleasantly decorated and comfortable;
push-chair porterage is not a problem but they can be stored
downstairs if you prefer. There is only one cot (ring ahead to reserve
it or take your own) and children can stay free in their parents' room.
The two family rooms can accommodate four people. Parents with
push-chairs will find plenty of space for parking beside the tables
in the bar but there is space to store them away if a high-chair
is preferred. Baby food and bottles are not provided but staff are
happy enough to heat customers' own. A jolly children's menu offers

the usual chips and burger fare with the likes of jumbo torpedo
sausage or chicken nuggets, both offered with tomato soup for £2.25,
and reduced portions are available from the main menu. There is a
garden in which to play and the toilets are nicely furnished, allowing
for easy changing and nursing. No-smoking area. **Open** (Bar food)
12-2 & 6-10 (Sat until 10.30), Sun 12-2.30 & 6-9.45. **Accommodation**
9 rooms, £60 (£90 for four in a family room). Access, Visa.

Wembley   **Pizza Express**

Tel 081-902 4918   Pizzeria

456 High Road Wembley Middx   Map 15 E2

A busy pizza outlet with the usual crisp-based pizzas cooked
in an open-to-view oven and a not-so-usual selection of Italian liqueurs
such as strega, sambucca and grappa. **Seats** *60.* **Open** *12-12.*
Closed *25 Dec. Access, Amex, Visa.*

West Bexington   **Manor Hotel**   **59%**   **£75**

Tel 0308 897785   Fax 0308 897035   Hotel

Beach Road West Bexington nr Bridport Dorset DT2 9DF   Map 14 B4

"Where country meets coast", says their literature, and indeed Richard
and Jayne Childs' small stone house stands in a garden on a gentle slope
near the famous Chesil Bank shingle beach. Stone walls and oak
panelling are much in evidence. Day rooms include lounge/reading
room, cellar bar, restaurant and conservatory. Pretty, cottagey
bedrooms, most with sea views, are furnished with old pine and
enhanced with books and ornaments; three rooms suitable for families
(children charged for) and cots provided. Snacks and teas (3-6pm)
in their cellar bar, the pretty conservatory or the garden, which offers
a view of the sea. Families are very well catered for with high tea
on request, high-chairs and baby food indoors, Wendy House and slide
outdoors. Changing facilities only in the rooms. **Rooms** *13. Garden,
children's playground. Access, Amex, Diners, Visa.*

West Byfleet   **Superfish**

Tel 0932 340366   Fish'n'Chips

51 Old Woking Road West Byfleet Surrey   Map 15 E3

Part of a Surrey-based chain of above-average fish and chip restaurants.
Jane's Upstairs offers 'fish and chips with style' (booking advisable Tel
0932 345789). See Morden entry for more details. **Seats** *30.*
Open *11.30-2 (Sat to 2.30), 5-10.30 (Thu-Sat to 11).* **Closed** *Sun, 25 &
26 Dec, 1 Jan. Access, Visa.*

Westcliff-on-Sea   **Oldham's**

Tel 0702 346736   Fish'n'Chips

13 West Road Westcliff-on-Sea Essex   Map 11 C4

Licensed fish restaurant opposite the Palace Theatre. Specialities are
plaice, sole, scampi, cod cuts and 'supreme fish special' with a selection
of fried fish (£5.50). Ice creams and home-made apple pie to finish,
or the daily special (Spotted Dick on our latest visit). Children's
portions. **Seats** *80.* **Open** *11-9.30 (Sun to 9).* **Closed** *25 & 26 Dec.
No credit cards.*

Westerham   **Spinning Wheel**

Tel 0959 572622	Pub

Grays Road Horley Road Westerham Kent TN16 2HX   Map 11 B5

With its thatched roof, the Spinning Wheel has long been a landmark
on the main road between Biggin Hill and Westerham. Now owned
by the Brewers Fayre group, the emphasis here is firmly on family
dining. Clearly visible and accessible, the playroom is at one end of the
restaurant. A huge, sturdy climbing frame dominates the room, soon
to become an even more of a fun factory. On warm summer evenings
you can eat outside where there's also a climbing frame. There
is a mother and baby room with a pull-down changer, complimentary
nappies, baby powder and room to breast-feed. There are at least
14 high-chairs. *Open 11.30-10 (Sun 12-10). Closed Dec 26. Access,
Visa.*

Westgate-on-Sea   **Ivyside Hotel**

Tel 0843 831082 Fax 0843 831082	Hotel

25 Sea Road Westgate-on-Sea Isle of Thanet Kent   Map 11 D5

Family facilities are a priority at this friendly hotel. Accommodation
is basic but spotless. What you will find is: a playroom, indoor and
outdoor pools (with paddling pools), a mother and baby room,
a garden with play equipment and a bouncy castle and in high season
a magician, organised beach competitions, outings and a disco. There
are 35 family rooms with connecting doors to children's rooms
equipped with beds or bunks; under-11s free if sharing with their
parents' room; 11 to 15-year-olds are charged half rate. Cots will
be provided, as will night lights. A small chemist's shop provides
nappies and there is even a toy shop. In the restaurant there are
20 high-chairs and 15 booster seats. £72 half-board for a double room.
Rooms 70. Access, Amex, Visa.

Whitby   **Elizabeth Botham & Sons**

Tel 0947 602823	Tea Room

Skinner Street Whitby North Yorkshire YO21 3AH   Map 5 F3

Situated up a steep flight of stairs, above a bakery that provides much
of the produce available on the large menu, is this traditional, rather
old-fashioned seaside tea shop. An all-day breakfast (£3.30), various
things-on-toast (from £1.50), filled baked potatoes (£1.95), home-
made pork pie and tomato chutney (£3.05), fish and chips (£4) and
a wealth of fresh cream cakes and gateaux paint the picture. Best value
is the special meal of the day (£4.55) which includes soup and a sweet.
Also at 30 Baxtergate in Whitby (Tel 0947 602823) – a contrastingly
modern branch with smaller menu but the same food; more suitable
for younger children. *Seats 120. Open 10-4.30 (9-5.30 high season).
Closed Mon (except high season), Sun, Bank Holidays.*

Whitby   **Magpie Café**

Tel 0947 602058	Restaurant

14 Pier Road Whitby North Yorkshire YO21 3PJ   Map 5 F3

A lovely café overlooking the fishing quay, from where much of the
superb fresh fish is delivered. The McKenzie family have run it for
over 40 years, and still go about their daily tasks with enthusiasm. It's
three floors (there's a view of the harbour from the second) with
autographed celebrity photographs decorating the white walls and

uniformed waitresses providing a very friendly and efficient service.
Fish can be fried, grilled or poached – try Whitby crab, cod (in cream
and tarragon sauce £5.25), haddock, plaice, sole, lobster (£8.95),
salmon, monkfish (grilled skewers £8.95) – you name it, they serve it.
There are five set menus at lunchtime (£7.25 to £10.95) – the
Magpie de Luxe Lunch offers Whitby crab and prawns, lemon sole,
pudding and cheese. Vegetarian meals are always avaialble (mushroom
and butter bean stroganoff (£4.35) and there's a children's menu
at £2.95. 27 home-made puddings (Jamaican fudge slice, bread-and-
butter pudding, lemon layer pudding, Yorkshire curd cheesecake,
sherry trifle – all £1.95) include gluten-free, wholefood, fat-free and
vegetarian. The home baking is again emphasised at teatime with
biscuits, cakes and fruit cakes (cream tea £1.75, afternoon tea £3.25).
No-smoking area. **Seats** 80. **Open** 11.30-6.30. **Closed** 3rd week
Nov-mid-Mar. Access, Visa.

Whitney-on-Wye   Rhydspence Inn

Tel 04973 262	Pub

Whitney-on-Wye nr Hay-on-Wye Hereford & Worcester HR3 6EU   Map 9 D4

Well-loved, reliably entertaining old inn set in the heart of Kilvert
country, on the A438 about a mile out of Whitney-on-Wye.
Delightful timbered interior and two attractive bars, with real fires,
old furniture and beams aplenty. Nice touches include magazines and
newspapers, creating an atmosphere in keeping with the old library
chairs. The charming dining room and restaurant overlook the garden.
Five comfortable bedrooms have beams, sloping floors, plus
an armchair at the least; some rooms are more romantic, others more
modern in style, one has a four-poster. Staff are happiest when there
are only a couple of children staying at any one time. A put-up bed can
be moved into either of the two larger bedrooms but there is no cot.
While it is expected that any children (or grown-ups) who stay at the
inn will behave themselves there is no stiff or starchy atmosphere. Bar
food suggestions include spinach and mozzarella crunch (£4.95),
braised liver and onion (£5.75), and seafood platter (£6.50). The
longer restaurant menu is as varied: ricotta and spinach pancake
(£4.85), Bavarois smoked salmon (£5.75), monkfish and salmon
brochette (£12.95), fillet of steak with Stilton (£13.50), plus
an excellent choice of farmhouse cheeses. A 3-course traditional Sunday
lunch is available in the restaurant (£10.95, children almost half
price). **Bar Food & Restaurant Food** 11-2 (12-2 Sun lunch
in restaurant), 7-9.30. Children's portions. Free House. **Beer** Bass,
Robinson, Marston's. **Cider** Dunkerton. Garden, outdoor eating. Family
room. **Accommodation** 5 bedrooms, all en suite, £55. Children welcome
overnight, additional beds (£12.50). No dogs. Access, Amex, Visa.

Willerby   Grange Park Hotel   67%   £87

Tel 0482 656488 Fax 0482 655848	Hotel

Main Street Willerby nr Hull Humberside HU10 6EA   Map 7 E1

Four miles from Hull and four from Beverley, Grange Park is a much-
extended Victorian house standing in 12 acres of grounds. Besides
comfortable modern accommodation it offers extensive purpose-built
conference facilities and a fine health and leisure centre (Club
Tamarisk) equipped with indoor swimming pool and whirlpool bath.
Families are well catered for with crèche facilities and a children's
playground; children's accommodation is free with two adults.
A playroom crèche is supervised by NNEB nurses on Monday,

Wednesday and Friday mornings. Cots and baby-listening are provided, baby-sitting can be arranged. There's a children's menu in the Cedars Restaurant and a climbing frame and swing in the garden. *Rooms 109. Garden, indoor swimming pool, gymnasium, sauna, steam room, solarium, beautician, hair salon, helipad. Access, Amex, Diners, Visa.*

Wimborne Minster   Quinneys Coffee House

Tel 0202 883518	Coffee Shop
26 West Borough Wimborne Minster Dorset BH21 1NF	Map 14 C4

The emphasis at Quinneys is now that of a coffee shop and bakery. The owners offer over 15 kinds of coffee and a selection of 8-9 teas. The coffee house has expanded upstairs and the menu extended. The 25-year-old bakery continues to produce home-made cakes (tiffin cake 65p, Eccles cakes 70p) and interesting sandwiches and home-cooked hot dishes provide a wide choice for children. There is plenty of room for nappy-changing and nursing mothers. *Seats 44. Open 8-4.30. Closed Sun, between Christmas and New Year. No credit cards.*

Winchester   Lainston House   75%   £134

Tel 0962 863588 Fax 0962 72672	Hotel
Sparsholt Winchester Hampshire SO21 2LJ	Map 15 D3

63 acres of majestic parkland surround Lainston House, an elegant William and Mary building dating from 1668. That it's an impressive establishment is clear from the moment you enter the parquet-floored foyer, which is dominated by a large fireplace decorated with fine Delft tiles. Flowers, paintings, books and ornaments make the comfortable lounge homely and relaxing and there's a splendid bar panelled with carved cedar. Main-house bedrooms are of grand proportions, with quality soft furnishings, period furniture and harmonious colour schemes; annexe rooms in Chudleigh Court are smaller but were refurbished last year. Swings and see-saws in the grounds; high-chairs and high tea in the dining room. *Rooms 32. Garden, tennis, croquet, coarse fishing, helipad. Access, Amex, Diners, Visa.*

Winchester   Pizza Express

Tel 0962 841845	Restaurant
1 Bridge Street Winchester Hampshire	Map 15 D3

Part of the long-running and reliable chain of pizza restaurants with the usual range of pizzas including the classic margherita (just mozzarella and tomato), the cheeseless marinara and the great favourite American hot. *Seats 84. Open 11.30am-midnight. Closed 25 & 26 Dec. Access, Amex, Visa.*

Winterborne Kingston   Greyhound Inn

Tel 0929 471332	Pub
Winterborne Kingston nr Blandford Dorset DT11 9AZ	Map 14 B4

An unadulterated pub with a tempting tractor and climbing frame in the garden. Bar staff are usually engaging and courteous, and food arrives quickly. Choices on the menu are unexceptional for pub food, particularly in the children's selection, but it is all fresh, largely home-made, and who complains about pub portion control? The carvery meal, served in the evening and for Sunday lunch, is good value at £6.95 including a sweet, and scaled down might provide an alternative for children. There is one high-chair and baby bottles will be heated on request. *Open 11-2 & 6.30-10 (Sun 12-2.30, 7-9.30). No credit cards.*

Wirksworth   Crown Yard Kitchen Restaurant

Tel 0629 822020	Restaurant
Crown Yard Market Place Wirksworth Derbyshire	Map 6 C3

Look for the Heritage Museum sign, walk through the arch and up the winding slope where you will find this bright, airy restaurant. In addition to the menu which features home-made pies (from £3.50), pizzas (£3), lasagne (£3.70) and curries (£3.50) together with jacket potatoes (from £1.30), sandwiches (80p) and salads (£3). Having visited the Heritage Centre, tired children can be treated to a home-made biscuit or cake, toasted teacake (45p) or even set cream tea (£1.75). If they can't sit still, there's a box of toys to capture their attention. Children's portions, high-chairs and beakers are available. Seating on a terrace in summer. Smoking is not allowed between 12 and 2.30pm. *Seats 32. Open 9-5 (Sun from 10). Closed 25 & 26 Dec, 3 weeks Jan. Access, Visa.*

Wisley   Conservatory Café & Terrace Restaurant

Tel 0483 225329	Café
The Royal Horticultural Society's Garden Wisley Surrey	Map 15 E3

Everything in the garden is lovely, and that includes the Conservatory Café (run by Cadogan Caterers) which manages to maintain creditably high standards despite serving upwards of 4,000 customers on a busy day. Virtually everything for the light, airy café with its large terrace, is made on site – light sponges oozing fresh cream (£1.95), tea cakes, Chelsea buns (both 50p), almond florentines (62p), lemon meringue pie (£1.45), salads, sandwiches (from £1.55), well-filled Cornish pasties (£1.55), quiches (£1.30) and, at lunchtime, various hot vegetarian dishes at £3.75. The table-service Terrace restaurant offers traditional English breakfasts until 11.30 then (from noon) set lunches (£11.75) and, in the afternoon, a choice of set teas from £3.95. Within The Royal Horticultural Society's Garden (adult entrance fee was £3.95 in 1992), the café and restaurant are open from 9.30am on Sundays, but only to RHS members. Children's portions. *Seats 500. Open 10-5.30 (winter to 4). Closed Sun, except to RHS members. Access, Visa.*

Woodbridge   Seckford Hall   68%   £90

Tel 0394 385678 Fax 0394 380610	Hotel
Woodbridge Suffolk IP13 6NU	Map 10 D3

Look out for the hotel sign on the A12 Woodbridge by-pass (don't turn off into the town) to find this imposing Elizabethan manor house set in extensive gardens which include an ornamental fountain and lawns leading down to a willow-fringed lake. Inside, period features abound with linen-fold panelling and heavily beamed ceiling in the Great Hall (lounge), huge stone fireplaces and carved doors. Bedrooms are comfortably furnished more in private-house than hotel style, four have four-poster beds (one dates back to 1587) and some are in a courtyard complex that includes an inspired conversion of an old tithe barn into a delightful heated swimming pool. *Rooms 35. Garden, indoor swimming pool, solarium, whirlpool bath, mini-gym, clay-pigeon shooting. Closed 25 Dec. Access, Amex, Diners, Visa.*

Woodstock   Brothertons Brasserie

Tel 0993 811114	Brasserie

High Street Woodstock Oxfordshire   **Map 15 D2**

The informal, relaxed atmosphere of this popular town-centre brasserie
is perfect for enjoying a morning coffee, lunch, tea or evening meal.
The printed menu keeps regular favourites like Brothertons smokies
(£3.95), deep-fried Brie with cranberry sauce (£3.25), large
Mediterranean prawns with garlic (£4.85) and crepes (chicken with
mushrooms and parsley £6.95), supplemented by specials that change
daily like chicken supreme with mustard sauce (£8.25) or mushroom
stroganoff (£5.95). Traditional English puddings to finish. Scones and
jam for tea (£1.60) and a roast dish on Sundays (£4.95-£6.50).
*Seats 65. Open 10.30am-10.30pm. Closed 25 & 26 Dec, 1 Jan. Access,
Amex, Diners, Visa.*

Woolacombe   Woolacombe Bay Hotel   66%   £175★

Tel 0271 870388 Fax ext 437	Hotel

South Street Woolacombe Devon EX34 7BN   **Map 12 C1**

Family summer holidays, winter breaks and conferences are the main
business at this imposing Edwardian hotel, whose lawns and gardens
reach down to long, lifeguard-patrolled golden beaches. Public rooms
are fairly grand, bedrooms bright and roomy, with mostly modern
furnishings. There are also self-catering suites, apartments and flats.
Cots, baby-sitting/listening, 50 high-chairs, children's menu and baby
food are all provided; the basement contains a cavernous playroom.
Children's supper (for up to 8s) 5.15-6pm and supervised
crèche/playtime (7.30-9.30pm) during holiday periods. No dogs.
★Half-board terms only. *Rooms 61. Garden, indoor & outdoor swimming
pools, floodlit all-weather tennis, pitch & putt, squash, keep-fit equipment,
shortmat bowling, snooker, table tennis, hairdressing, children's playroom
and organiser. Closed Jan. Access, Amex, Diners, Visa.*

Worthing   Pizza Express

Tel 0903 821133	Pizzeria

Stanford Square Warwick Street Worthing West Sussex   **Map 11 A6**

The overriding feature of this Pizza Express is the large conservatory
looking out on to a walled garden where alfresco eating is possible
in summer. Crisp, thin pizzas (£3.15-£5.40) and fresh ingredients are
used for the toppings. *Seats 150. Open 11.30am-midnight. Closed 25 &
26 Dec. Access, Amex, Visa.*

Yarm   The Coffee Shop

Tel 0642 791234	Coffee Shop

44 High Street Yarm Cleveland TS15 9AE   **Map 5 E3**

A haven of wholesome, home-prepared food on the first floor
of a small family-run department store; a visit with a push-chair could
be perilous, but careful children are well catered for. Wholemeal flour
abounds, in scones (69p), in home-baked bread for sandwiches and in
the pasta for the lasagne verdi (£4.99). Hot dishes appear throughout
the morning: mini quiches, perhaps prawn and mushroom (£4.35),
and broccoli bake (£3.79), and equally tempting desserts include
hazelnut meringue (£2.19). There's a courtyard for use in fine
weather. *Seats 50. Open 9-5.30. Closed 25 & 26 Dec. Access, Visa.*

Yarmouth   Jireh House

Tel 0983 760513	Café

St James's Square Yarmouth Isle of Wight   Map 14 C4

Cosy, comfortable tea rooms in a 17th-century building. The
atmosphere is homely and relaxing, making it a popular spot for
enjoying a range of straightforward snacks that are available all day
long. Coconut and cherry slice, rock cakes, gateaux and crumbles are
priced from 55p, and there are two set afternoon teas. Also on the
menu are ploughman's, jacket potatoes, salads and hot specials such
as macaroni cheese, shepherds pie and vegetable bake. No smoking.
Seats 48. Open 8am-10.30pm (Oct-Feb to 6.30). No credit cards.

Yattendon   Royal Oak

Tel 0635 201325 Fax 0635 201926	Pub

The Square Yattendon nr Newbury Berkshire RG16 0UF   Map 15 D2

Dating back to the days of Oliver Cromwell, the creeper-clad Royal
Oak is only ten minutes from junction 13 of the M4, at the heart of a
pretty Berkshire village. Food continues to be the main attraction
in both the busy beamed bar (where all tables are set for diners) and
in the calmer dining room (featured in our *1993 Hotels & Restaurants
Guide*). A new door now leads straight out from the tiny bar counter
into a walled garden where a few tables nestle under vine-clad trellises;
in summer this is a delightful spot for a drink, particularly with
a toddler who can crawl around the garden. Chef Dominique Orizet
offers an extensive hand-written bar menu that is changed daily and
usually lists up to 25 dishes, both small and large. The prices veer
towards those of a restaurant, but one feels no compulsion to order
anything more than one dish. Snack-type dishes range from fish soup
with rouille or crispy duck with frisée salad (£5.25/£8.50) to popular
favourites like asparagus hollandaise (£6.75) and fine ploughman's
lunches (served with an interesting selection of cheeses £5). The choice
of more substantial dishes always includes good fish. There's usually
a good selection of quality bottles of wine open behind the bar for
serving by the glass. Upstairs, three of the five bedrooms have smart
en-suite bathrooms (the other two have their own private bathrooms
across the hallway) and feature king-size beds; generous towelling and
thoughtful extras like quality toiletries and mineral water bring the
rooms up to a good hotel standard. A travel cot can be provided. Some
rooms overlook the small garden, others the historic village centre.
Good, leisurely breakfasts are served in the dining room where a lone
high-chair is provided – book it for the bar area if you're making
a special journey. The Royal Oak is an exceptional combination
of local pub, friendly inn and smart restaurant; on the one hand it's
small enough not to have to worry about baby-sitting (you can nip
upstairs from the dining room to check on the little one) and the
cooking's easily good enough to warrant a special journey, but on the
other hand it's also small enough to upset other guests if a 1½-year-old
junior *Egon Ronay's Guides* inspector decides to cut a new tooth
at 3.30am! Owner Julie Huff won't bat an eyelid, but other guests
might not appreciate the disruption to their romantic weekend away.
*Bar Food & Restaurant Meals 12-2, 7-10. Children's portions. Free
House. Beer Wadworth, Adnams, Burton's. Garden, outdoor eating.
Accommodation 5 rooms, 3 en-suite, £80. Children welcome overnight,
cots available. Access, Amex, Diners, Visa.*

York	**Abbey Park Resort Hotel**	57%	£86

Tel 0904 658301   Fax 0904 621224 · Hotel
The Mount York North Yorkshire YO2 2BN · Map 7 D1

One mile from the city centre, this hotel offers modern facilities
behind a Georgian facade. Families are made to feel very welcome and
there are four cots to share between the seven family rooms. Storage
space for pushchairs and a laundry service are both provided and
a regular baby-sitter can be summoned when the baby-listening service
won't suffice. Four high-chairs are supplied in the restaurant and the
waitresses love to fuss over children. Customers' bottles can be heated
and there is a well-planned children's menu as well as reduced portions.
Children up to 14 stay free in parents' room. *Rooms 85. Access, Amex,
Diners, Visa.*

York	**Bettys**		

Tel 0904 659142 · Tea Shop
6 St Helens Square York North Yorkshire · Map 7 D1

Unashamedly old-fashioned dishes, made with quality ingredients, are
served by neatly uniformed waitresses. Ceiling fans hum leisurely
to the refrains of the evening pianist evoke a bygone era. The day
begins with breakfast – warm Yorkshire oatcakes (£1.40), mushroom
and bacon omelette (£4.80), rösti potatoes (£3.10) or simply two
croissants or brioches with jam and butter (£1.65). Light lunches
bring sandwiches (from £2.35), salads (corn-fed chicken £4.98), grills,
omelettes, hot dishes such as haddock and prawns au gratin and the
speciality of the house, rarebit made with Theakston's Yorkshire Ale
served with apple or tomato chutney (£5.45). A wide choice of teas
and rare coffees accompanies buttered pikelets (98p), banana and
walnut loaf (£1.10) or a warm Yorkshire fat rascal (£1.90) at tea
time. On the evening menu, smoked Wensleydale cheese croquettes
(£2.98) and seafood vol-au-vents (£3.60) are served as starters, and
haddock and prawn croustades (£5.85) or mushroom and chestnut
roulade with casserole red cabbage (£4.55) as a main course. Various
ices (from £2.05), desserts (toffee and brandy snap fanfare) and cakes
(from £1.78 – chocolate brandy roulade, Yorkshire curd tart)
to follow. Children's menu. No-smoking area. *Seats 174. **Open** 9-9.
Closed 25 & 26 Dec, 1 Jan. Access, Visa.*

York	**Four Seasons**		

Tel 0904 633787 · Restaurant
45 Goodramgate York North Yorkshire YO1 2LS · Map 7 D1

Run with pride by Jean and Alan Medd, the Four Seasons is a popular
choice for families. In traditional surroundings which date back to the
16th century the menu offers home-made specialities like steak,
mushroom and ale pie as well as a tempting array of afternoon treats
such as carrot cake, scones and walnut cake. The staff are extremely
friendly and attentive. No one shudders at breast-feeding in the
restaurant but if you prefer, there's a sofa upstairs with a screen
if required. Changing facilities with mats and wipes are not
exclusively sited in the ladies loo, hurrah! Books and toys are also
provided. ***Open** 10-10. **Closed** Dec 25 & 26, Jan 1. Access, Amex,
Diners, Visa.*

York	Hill Hotel	58%	£59

Tel 0904 790777   Hotel
60 York Road Acomb York North Yorkshire YO2 5LW   Map 7 D1

Two miles from the centre of York, this handsome Georgian house
stands in just under an acre of walled garden. Owners Peter and
Debbie Blackburn are welcoming hosts to families and relaxation
is easy in the comfortably traditional lounge and little bar. Half the
bedrooms are suitable for family occupation; cots available. High-
chairs are provided for high tea (5-6pm) and Peter will cook almost
anything on request. Baby food is provided; children can play in the
spare lounge. Parents can enjoy a relaxed evening in the dining room
courtesy of the baby-listening service. Children will enjoy the walled
garden with its pet rabbit and friendly dog. **Rooms** 10. Garden. *Closed*
4 weeks Dec/Jan. Access, Amex, Visa.

York   Miller's Yard Vegetarian Café

Tel 0904 610676   Café
Gillygate York North Yorkshire YO3 7EB   Map 7 D1

A workers' co-operative with wholefood bakery, takeaway and
a sparsely decorated, counter-service split-level vegetarian and vegan
café. Hearty portions of wholesome produce draw the crowds. Filled
jacket potatoes (£1.50), pizza (£1.50), vegan items such as mushroom
and nut pasty (80p) and tofuburger (60p), and a daily hot dish, like
a cashewnut loaf with an asparagus-based sauce (£2.70) full of flavour,
use organic produce wherever possible and offer excellent value for
money. Equally filling sweets such as Tassajara cake (£1.35) to finish.
No smoking. BYO licence (80p corkage). Pavement tables in fine
weather. **Seats** 60. **Open** 10-4 (*summer to 4.30*). **Closed** *Sun, 25 &*
26 Dec. No credit cards.

York   National Trust Tea Rooms

Tel 0904 659282   Tea Room
30 Goodramgate York North Yorkshire YO1 2LG   Map 7 D1

Round the corner from the National Trust shop and about 200 yards
from the minster, the tea rooms are well kept and efficiently run.
Profits from the catering contribute to the upkeep of the Treasurer's
House (qv). The menu covers morning coffee and afternoon tea
(cheese scone 75p, cakes from 90p); all-day breakfasts; open
sandwiches; salads; savoury snacks; and dishes of the day such
as Yorkshire pudding filled with chili con carne and served with
a jacket potato and salad (£4.95). Plenty of children's choices. Note the
selection of Yorkshire fruit wines (to be consumed with meals only).
No smoking. **Seats** 50. **Open** 9.30-5.30 (*Mon from 10.30*). **Closed** *Sun,*
25 & 26 Dec. Access, Visa.

York   Spurriergate Centre

Tel 0904 629393   Restaurant
St Michael's Church Spurriergate York North Yorkshire YO1 1QR   Map 7 D1

Spiritual food in a carefully renovated and converted redundant
church by one of York's most historic crossroads. Paved stone and
notable 15th-century stained glass lend bags of atmosphere, and there's
plenty of wholesome food to feed the body. Breakfast, perhaps a bacon
sandwich or croissant, is supplemented by hot daily specials from 11.30
such as filled Yorkshire puddings (£2.20), mushroom stroganoff

(£3.25) or harvest pie (£3.25), with sandwiches (£1.95), filled jacket potatoes (£1.95) and generously portioned cakes the mainstay of the menu. No smoking throughout. *Seats 90. Open 10-5. Closed Sun, Bank Holidays, 2nd Tue of each month.*

York   Taylor's Tea Rooms & Coffee Shop

Tel 0904 622865	Tea Room
46 Stonegate York North Yorkshire YO1 2AS	Map 7 D1

Quintessential tearooms, part of the estimable Bettys group, at the top of steep stairs in a listed city-centre building. An exceptional range of fine teas and coffees, available here by pot or cafetière, have been sold on lower floors for over 100 years. There is also much good quality eating to be had, from an all-day breakfast grill (£5.90 for the works) or cream tea (£3.55), via various sandwiches – plain (from £2.35), toasted (£2.95) and open (£5.65) – to salads (£1.95 per portion) and hot dishes such as omelettes (£4.68) and rarebits (£5.45). Sweet things include a myriad of gateaux and tarts, and the speciality Yorkshire fat rascal (£1.90), a warm, thick scone packed with vine fruits and smothered with butter. Traditionally attired staff provide quick, friendly service. Children are served first and care is taken to serve their food at the right temperature and with small cutlery. A baby changing room is separate from the toilets and has a raised shelf, a changing mat, nappies, baby wipes and a potty. In addition, high-chairs, disposable bibs, feeding dishes, rattles, free jars of baby food and beakers all combine to make Taylor's an excellent place for a young family. Unlicensed. Three rooms no-smoking. *Seats 65. Open 9-5.30. Closed 25 & 26 Dec, 1 Jan. Access, Visa.*

York   Treasurer's House

Tel 0904 646757	Tea Room
Minster Yard York North Yorkshire YO1 3JD	Map 7 D1

A National Trust property, originally home to the medieval treasurer's of York Minster and largely rebuilt in the 17th century, with the basement cellars converted into a neat and tidy tea room. Friendly, helpful staff dispense good quality home-baking such as ginger parkin, apricot and nutmeg cake and treacle tart (from 80p), with savoury choices ranging from a daily flan, perhaps Stilton, celery and walnut (£3.95), to York ham sandwich (£2). Round things off with apple and cinnamon sponge pudding and lump-free custard (£1.85). Fruit wines available by the glass. No smoking. *Seats 60. Open 10.30-5. Closed Nov-end Mar. No credit cards.*

York   Viking Hotel   69%   £105

Tel 0904 659822 Fax 0904 641793	Hotel
North Street York North Yorkshire YO1 1JF	Map 7 D1

Tall, modern Queens Moat Houses hotel by the river between the two main bridges in the city centre. Plenty of style and comfort and a major conference venue. Leisure facilities include a well-equipped, supervised gymnasium. Handily placed for the Jorvik Viking Centre and the Waxwork Museum, the Viking welcomes families with open doors. Most of the spacious double rooms will accommodate a cot or extra bed and seven suites serve larger families. The restaurant, which offers high-chairs, a children's menu and small portions opens at 5.30pm for parents who prefer to get their charges fed and bedded early. No dogs. *Rooms 188. Gymnasium, sauna, solarium, spa bath, golf practice net. Access, Amex, Diners, Visa.*

Other 1993 Egon Ronay's Guides published by Pan Books Ltd

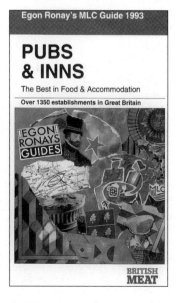

cellnet
The nearest phone.

With a mobile phone, your family can always be together, even when you're apart.

Imagine how reassuring that would be.

A phone constantly by your side. Not just for emergencies, but for when you have some good news you can't wait to tell. Or to make last minute arrangements. Or let someone know you're delayed.

With Lifetime, it's now easily affordable.

Lifetime is a special new service from Cellnet (the world's largest network operator), which can significantly reduce the cost of using a mobile phone.

To find out more about Lifetime, get together with your mobile phone centre, leading electrical retailers or a service provider, where you can be connected in minutes.

Or call 0800 21 4000.

Scotland

Aberdeen   Henry J Bean's Bar & Grill

Tel 0224 574134	Restaurant

Windmill Brae (almost under the bridge) Aberdeen Grampian   Map 3 D4

Of the plethora of American-themed burger joints, this is up with the
best, success due severally to relaxed but lively surroundings, slick
service, good value (particularly during daytime hours), and a better
than average product, namely burgers grilled to order 'without cheese,
no extra charge' – the chili version (£3.15), BBQ ribs and bibs
(£2.95) and fried chicken (£2.95). Happy hours bring prices down
further. Drink coffee from 'bottomless' mugs, or designer beers.
*Seats 50. Open 11am-10.30pm (Sun 6.30-11). Closed L Sun, 25 Dec.
No credit cards.*

Alexandria   Cameron House   81%   £138

Tel 0389 55565 Fax 0389 59522	Hotel

Loch Lomond Alexandria Strathclyde G83 8QZ   Map 3 B5

Expensive refurbishment and a sympathetic extension have turned
a Georgian house into an elegant hotel with most impressive leisure
facilities. Just off the A82, it enjoys a splendid location by Loch
Lomond on a large estate that includes time-share lodges. Peaceful,
country house-style day rooms in the original house contrast with the
more lively bar that overlooks the leisure club. Spacious bedrooms are
individually decorated with stylish fabrics and boast comfortable
armchairs; there are huge, soft towels and bathrobes in the bathrooms.
Families are well catered for and there are excellent leisure facilities
including a daily crèche (normally to 5pm, but extended to 9pm
on Thurs & Fri) and baby-sitting available. Supervised children's
activities such as nature trails, treasure hunts and day trips are also
organised. Staff offer a warm welcome and high standards of service.
The brasserie provides high chairs, a children's menu (melon boats
with orange sails, beans, burgers, spaghetti hoops, corn on the cob,
omelette, milk shakes, banana split etc) and there's a changing/breast-
feeding area. No dogs. *Rooms 68. Indoor swimming pools, steam room,
sauna, solarium, spa bath, squash, badminton, snooker, gymnasium,
hairdressing, beauty salon, crèche, kiosk, 9-hole golf course, tennis, croquet,
clay-pigeon shooting, watersports centre, marina, fishing, mountain bikes.
Access, Amex, Visa, Diners.*

Georgian Room   £75

Sparkling chandeliers, rich drapes and quality silverware create a
luxurious setting for Jeff Bland's serious, sophisticated cooking; the
short à la carte menu seems to have learned something from the decor.
Casserole of langoustines with woodland mushrooms and black,
ginger-flavoured noodles and a lobster and lentil sauce; supreme
of chicken with leek and truffle ravioli, and geranium and
blackcurrant parfait served with a praline basket of fruits are indicative
of the involved style. An imaginative, six-course Celebration menu
is also offered – for those wishing to become even more involved, plus
fixed-price daily menus. *Seats 60. L 12-3 D 7-10. Set L from £15.50
Set D from £27.50.*

Almondbank   **Almondbank Inn**

Tel 0738 832242   Pub
Main Street Almondbank Tayside PH1 3NJ   Map 3 C5

Just off the A85 to the west of Perth, on the village main street, the
whitewashed Almondbank Inn enjoys fine views over the River
Almond from its small well-kept rear garden. It's not a quiet pub:
a juke box in the bar regularly pumps out the latest hits, and there's
a pool table on the first floor. Food is taken fairly seriously, however,
and the Birdcage Bistro, despite some rather gimmicky descriptions
produces generally pleasing food, the majority of it from fresh
produce. The menu itself is long, running from first courses like "name
that tuna" and deep-fried Camembert with cranberry sauce (£2.50),
to main courses such as steak and onion pie (£3.85), chicken in a
creamy curry sauce (£4.65), and a whole list of Angus minute steaks
with a variety of sauces. Puddings are largely ice-cream based.
On Friday and Saturday evenings, a slightly different menu is heavy
on steak (Bonnie Prince Charlie sirloin steak £10.25) and chicken
dishes. **Bar Food** 12-2.15, 5-8.30 (6.30-10 Fri/Sat). *Children's menu
(£1.65 per dish). Free House. **Beer** Greenmantle, Tennents. Riverside
Garden (River Almond), outdoor eating. Access, Visa.*

Ardentinny   **Ardentinny Hotel**   59%   £76

Tel 036 981 209   Fax 036 981 345   Hotel
Loch Long Ardentinny nr Dunoon Strathclyde PA23 8TR   Map 3 B5

50 yards from the beach, the Ardentinny is an old west-coast droving
inn by Loch Long in the Argyll Forest Park; not least of its claims
to fame is that Harry Lauder was born there. It has a buttery, two
popular public bars with stunning loch views, and a hotel dining
room that features much local produce – particularly strong
on venison, lamb and seafood. Good honest home-prepared food
is served in the buttery and bars (except on Sundays): venison sausages
with onion gravy and minced tatties (£3.95), salmon and broccoli fish
cakes (£4.50) and Musselburgh pie (£6.75). The restaurant table
d'hote menu (£19.50) offers local wild salmon tartare, tomato and red
pepper tartlet, Molly Malone pie, roast spatchcock marinated in Arran
mustard, and venison casserole with juniper berries. For those who
keep right on to the end of the road there's a good choice of Scottish
cheeses and home-made sweets, perhaps steamed pudding and custard
(£2). Good wine list. Popular with Clyde yachtsmen at weekends and
fishermen. Bedrooms are good-sized, neat and bright, with white units
or period furniture; some have showers only. **Bar Food** 12-2.30 (12-3
Sat), 6-10. **Restaurant Meals** 7.30-9.30. *Children's menu (£2 per dish).
Children allowed in bar to eat. Free House. **Beer** Websters Yorkshire,
McEwans Export. Seaside garden, outdoor eating. Family room.*
Accommodation *11 bedrooms, all en suite, from £49 (single £24).
Children welcome overnight, additional beds (£7), cots supplied (£3).
Hotel closed Nov-mid March. Access, Amex, Diners, Visa.*

Arisaig   **Old Library Lodge & Restaurant**

Tel 06875 651   Restaurant
Arisaig Highland PH39 4NH   Map 3 A4

Alan and Angela Broadhurst are coming up for ten years at the Old
Library, a 200-year-old stable converted into a restaurant and guest
house. It stands in an area of great natural beauty, commanding fine
views over Loch Nan Ceall and the Inner Hebrides. Lunchtime is the

time for snacking, from a menu typified by bacon and lentil soup with
home-baked bread (£1.35), smoked trout salad (£4.60), spaghetti
bolognese (£3.80) and pot roast of lamb provençale (£4.95).
Toasted sandwiches are £1.50 a round. The evening table d'hote
menu is £18.50 and B&B costs £28 per person in the six bedrooms.
There are three tables out on the patio. *Seats 28. Open 11.30-2.30 &
6.30-9.30. Closed end Oct-week before Easter. Access, Visa.*

Auchmithie   But'n'Ben

Tel 0241 77223	Restaurant

Auchmithie by Arbroath Tayside   Map 3 D5

Margaret and Iain Horn's simple, friendly cottage restaurant, 3 miles
north-east of Arbroath, offers good local produce with a distinct
Scottish flavour from midday, with mussels in wine and garlic (£3),
poached salmon salad (£4.20), Angus sirloin steak (£6.80) and sweets
from the trolley, but those turning up early will always get
a welcoming cup of coffee. A hearty Scottish high tea from 4-5.30 pm
brings a choice of perhaps Grandma Horn's meat-roll salad, Arbroath
smokie pancake or local fried haddock in oatmeal, with wholemeal
bread, home-made scones, cake and tea for £5.50. The choice widens
in the evenings when more substantial dinners are served. Smoking
in sitting rooms only. *Seats 40. Open 12-9.30 (Sun to 5.30).
Closed Tue. Access, Visa.*

Auchterhouse   Old Mansion House   68%   £90

Tel 082 626 366 Fax 082 626 400	Hotel

Auchterhouse by Dundee Tayside DD3 0QN   Map 3 C5

Seven miles from Dundee on the B954, a 16th-century Scottish
baronial house has been skilfully converted by Nigel and Eva Bell
to a charming and relaxed hotel. Some nice architectural features
include the vaulted entrance hall, an open Jacobean fireplace and
a splendidly ornate 17th-century plasterwork ceiling. Pleasantly
furnished bedrooms – two are family suites with separate children's
bedrooms – have good bathrooms well stocked with toiletries.
Baby-sitting can be arranged, baby-listening is offered; 7pm curfew
for children in the bar and restaurant. The heated outdoor pool
is fenced. *Rooms 6. Garden, croquet, outdoor swimming pool, squash,
tennis. Closed Xmas, 1 week Jan. Access, Amex, Diners, Visa.*

Restaurant   £66

Much local produce is used for the varied carte that is supplemented
by a separate vegetarian menu. No under-10s at night. No smoking.
*Seats 50. Parties 20. Private Room. L 12-2 D 7-9.30 (Sun to 9).
Set L £10.95.*

Ayr   Fouters Bistro

Tel 0292 261391	Bistro

2a Academy Street Ayr Strathclyde KA7 1HS   Map 4 A1

A cheerful bistro in a converted vaulted basement; staff will be only
too happy to give a helping hand down the stairs for mums with
pushchairs – tables are also set aside in corner areas for buggies
to be placed by their side. Scottish produce is cooked in French style
with consistently enjoyable results. There are good-value lunchtime
menus – 1-3 courses £4.95-£8.50. Starters may include smoked
chicken crepe, home-made patés or soup, followed by casserole of local
lamb with wild mushrooms, taste of Scotland platter or puff pastry

pithiviers with broccoli and Brie in cream sauce. Home-made ice creams feature on the dessert menu along with their popular bread-and-butter pudding and sticky toffee pudding. Ploughman's with mixed cheeses, a loaf, fresh fruit and nuts (£4.95). More robust Provençal food is served in the evenings and the two-course bistro menu is £9.90. Children's menu and portions – perhaps goujons of sole or chicken with pommes frites, peas and tomato sauce (£2.95); two highchairs and beakers provided. *Seats 39. Open 12-2 & 6.30-10.30. Closed L Sun, all Mon, 2 days Christmas, 2 days New Year. Access, Amex, Diners, Visa.*

Ayr   The Stables

Tel 0292 283 704	Coffee Shop
Queen's Court 41 Sandgate Ayr Strathclyde KA7 1BD	Map 4 A1

A characterful wine bar-cum-coffee shop in a charming shopping area formed out of some old buildings near the town centre. The menu, which has a strong Scottish flavour, ranges from freshly-baked scones, cakes and sandwiches to steaks, roast chicken breast and pies like ham and haddie (£6.50), and steak with pickled walnut (£7). Smoked salmon, eel, venison and duck breast come from the family's own smoke house and there is always a small selection of Scottish farmhouse cheeses. The wine list includes a selection of traditional country wines (silver birch, elderflower, blackberry) and there is a good range of single malt whiskies. There's no special children's menu but dishes like macaroni cheese, haggis and chicken stovies come in junior portions as do their own ices. A couple of high-chairs cope with the really young ones (for whom they will liquidise something in the kitchen or heat up customers' own baby food and bottles) and there is a little menagerie of toy animals and some picture books to keep the little ones amused. Outdoor eating. *Seats 52. Open 10-10 (Mon to 5). Closed Sun, 25 & 26 Dec, 1 & 2 Jan. Access, Amex, Diners, Visa.*

Ballachulish   Ballachulish Hotel   60%   £69

Tel 085 52 606 Fax 085 52 629	Hotel
Ballachulish Argyll Highland PA39 4JY	Map 3 B4

An imposing inn set below rugged mountains which sweep down to Loch Linnhe. Impressive views are shared by restaurant, cocktail bar and baronial residents' lounge. There's a "local" atmosphere in the Ferry Bars. Bedrooms are called Lairds or Chieftains, the latter enjoying the best of the light, space and views. Guests have free use of the leisure centre at the sister hotel The Isles of Glencoe about two miles away. Families are well catered for by child-friendly staff; the garden's farm area is an added attraction. *Rooms 30. Garden, sea fishing. Access, Visa.*

Banchory   Raemoir House   71%   £105

Tel 033 02 4884 Fax 033 02 2171	Hotel
Raemoir Banchory Grampian AB31 4ED	Map 3 D4

Three generations of the Sabin family have built friendly hospitality into the fabric of their hotel, an 18th-century mansion set in a 3500 acre estate. Rich red brocade chairs, panelled walls and well-worn antiques enhance the traditional look of the morning room, and the bar is fashioned from a Tudor four-poster. Bedrooms are all different in size and character, but most have inviting chaises longues, day beds or armchairs. Five rooms are in the historic 16th-century Ha'Hoose immediately behind the mansion. There are some self-catering apartments converted from the original coach-house and stables. Very much a family hotel with nearly all mother and baby's requirements provided on request – from potties and baby baths to baby-listening and laundry. *Rooms 25. Croquet, sauna, solarium, keep-fit equipment, tennis, game fishing, 9-hole mini golf, shooting, helipad. Closed 1 week Jan. Access, Amex, Diners, Visa.*

Restaurant £68

Top-quality produce is cooked without undue elaboration and served in generous portions by friendly staff. Chicken and ham paté, goujons of lemon sole or golden game consommé precede Dee salmon, pan-fried brill, sautéed breast of pheasant or a Raemoir special – a tiny joint of three lamb chops served with a traditional garnish. There's a long choice for vegetarians, plus homely sweets. *Seats 64. Parties 85. Private Room. L by arrangement on Sun 12.30-2 D 7.30-9. Set L £12.75 Set D £21.50.*

Banchory	Tor-na-Coille Hotel	66%	£75
Tel 033 02 2242 Fax 033 02 4012			Hotel
Inchmarlo Road Banchory Grampian AB3 4AB			Map 3 D4

Built as a private house in 1873 and a hotel since the turn of the century, Tor-na-Coille retains much of its Victorian character. Roxanne Sloan is continuing a programme of refurbishment in the antique-furnished bedrooms, and the lounge has also been redecorated. The hotel copes very well with children (under-10s stay free in parents' room) with cots, baby baths, potties, changing mats, baby-sitting and baby-listening. Baby food, children's menu and cutlery are also provided; a small charge is made for cots and under-15s. Further facilities are offered during Summer school holidays (ring for details). Laundry service on site. *Rooms 25. Garden, croquet, squash, playground, baby-sitting, baby-listening, crèche (8-4, Mon-Fri). Closed 25 & 26 Dec. Access, Amex, Diners, Visa.*

Beauly	Priory Hotel	
Tel 0463 782309		Pub
The Square Beauly Highland IV4 7BX		Map 2 B3

Bustling, friendly local hotel/inn in the main square, close to the ancient priory ruins. *Children's play area. Family room.*

Busta	Busta House Hotel	
Tel 080 622 506		Pub
Busta Brae Shetland Islands ZE2 9QN		Map 2 D1

Tremendously civilised hotel in a wild place. A 16th-century former laird's home overlooking the sea, simply furnished in Scottish rural style and, beyond its rather formidable exterior, open to non-residents for good home-cooked bar lunches and suppers – marinated Shetland herring and oatcakes (£2.25), Shetland lamb cutlets (£4.85), broccoli and mushroom quiche (£4.20), steak, red wine and mushroom pie (£4.95), grilled Shetland salmon with cheddar and onion sauce (£5.25). The restaurant offers a 5-course daily-changing fixed-price menu (£19.50). A roast dish (£5.25) is available on Sundays in winter. 136 malt whiskies on offer! Four acres of walled garden, small private sea harbour, and holiday packages of the fly/sail and drive kind. *Bar Food 12-2 (12.30-2 Sun)-2, 6-9 (6-9.30 summer). Restaurant Meals 7-9. Children's portions. Children are allowed to eat in the bar. Free House. Beer Orkney Raven Ale, McEwans. Garden, outdoor eating.*

Accommodation 20 bedrooms, all en suite, £73. Children welcome overnight, additional beds (£10), cots supplied. Pub and accommodation closed Christmas week. Access, Amex, Diners, Visa.

Carbost   Old Inn

Tel 047 842 205	Pub
Carbost Isle of Skye Highland IV47 8SR	Map 2 A3

Next to the loch, and near the Talisker distillery, a charming, chatty little island cottage, popular as a walkers' base. *Family Room. Children's play area, lochside patio/terrace. Children welcome overnight. No credit cards.*

Coylton   Finlayson Arms Hotel

Tel 0292 570298	Pub
Coylton nr Ayr Strathclyde KA6 6JT	Map 4 A1

Easy to spot with its brilliant white exterior, the Finlayson Arms stands on the A70 six miles from the birthplace of Robbie Burns and just four from Ayr racecourse. It is also an ideal place for golfers and T-off times are arranged free of charge. The bright, well-kept look continues both in the lively bar and in the neat little bedrooms. Murdo Munro personally prepares a hearty breakfast – guaranteed to start your day well. *Free House. **Beer** Broughton. Garden, children's play area. **Accommodation** 9 bedrooms, all en suite, £55. Children welcome overnight, additional beds and cots available, no charge for children under 12. Access, Amex, Diners, Visa.*

Crieff   Crieff Hydro   62%   £83*

Tel 0764 65555 Fax 0764 653087	Hotel
Crieff Tayside PH7 3LQ	Map 3 C5

An enormous, Victorian building, now a family hotel par excellence with an impressive range of leisure activities to keep everyone busy and fit – from indoor cinema and table tennis room to outdoor riding school and golf course. Most of the bedrooms are of a decent size, furnished with either lightwood units or more traditional and antique pieces; some family rooms have bunk beds in a separate alcove; family suites, baby-listening and cots (free for under-2s) are also available. Banqueting and conference facilities for up to 400 delegates keep the place busy during the week; some sporting facilities are reserved for competitions during bowls and tennis weeks. Breakfast, lunch and supper for the under-10s are taken in the nursery where high-chairs, and baby food are provided; a playroom adjoins the nursery. Nine whitewashed two-storey family apartments are also close to the hotel; the sitting rooms here include two single bed-settees. *Half-board terms only. No dogs, except in the self-catering Hydro Chalets on a wooded hillside above the hotel (easy access for cars); a few kennels are available but require prior booking. All accommodation has free use of all the leisure facilities: young children might particularly enjoy the outdoor adventure playground and the children's swimming pool with chute, while adults may like to take a breather by using the facilities of the supervised children's nursery (for over-3s only) during meal times, relax in the hot tub by the children's pool or jog around the outdoor nature trail. Special teenage activities week in July includes free coaching. The Crieff Hydro has been family-run for over 100 years and they know that "happy children mean happy parents...". **Rooms** 199. Garden, croquet, indoor swimming pool, children's pool,*

outdoor paddling pool, whirlpool, spa bath, sauna, steam room, sunbeds,
boutique, hairdressing and beauty salon, coffee shop, tennis, squash,
badminton, basketball, volleyball, 9-hole golf course, putting, all-weather
bowling green, snooker, riding school, football pitch, cinema, playroom,
playground, dinner dancing. Access, Amex, Diners, Visa.

Cromarty	Royal Hotel		
Tel 038 17 217			Pub
Marine Terrace Cromarty Highland IV11 8YN			Map 2 C3

White harbourside hotel overlooking the Cromarty Firth and Ross-
shire mountains. The bedrooms have good views. Garden. Children's
play area. Family room.

Dirleton	Open Arms Hotel	67%	£110
Tel 0620 85241 Fax 0620 85570			Hotel
Dirleton nr North Berwick Lothian EH39 5EG			Map 3 D5

A good name for a friendly, characterful hotel ("where welcome ever
smiles and farewell goes out sighing") in a charming position
overlooking the village green and the ruins of 16th-century Dirleton
Castle. It's been in the same family for nearly half a century, and
there's a relaxed, domestic warmth to the lounge, which has
comfortable armchairs and sofas, a log fire, magazines and newspapers;
the bar is tiny but full of character. Enjoyable lunches are served in the
lounge Mon-Sat. Starters include hearty broths (£1.25), mussel and
onion stew (£2) and melon and orange cocktail with ginger-flavoured
yoghurt (£2.85). Substantial main courses range from sautéed breast
of pigeon with red wine and mushroom sauce (£5) to steamed leeks
with a mushroom and cheese sauce (£4.75). Meals in the restaurant
attract a 10% service charge. More elaborate fixed-price evening menus
include a good choice of dishes. Sunday is a favourite with families
with a traditional roast lunch (£11.50) and set afternoon tea (£3.50).
Bedrooms are mostly bright and airy, with floral curtains; each has
an easy chair and personal touches such as flowers and fruit. There's
just one cot, one high-chair and four bedrooms that might take
an extra bed; no children's menu, but it's the attitude that counts here,
along with the grace and charm. Not for tear-aways! *Rooms* 7.
Garden. Closed 5 days New Year. Access, Visa.

Dulnain Bridge	Muckrach Lodge	59%	£74
Tel 0479 85257 Fax 0479 85325			Hotel
Dulnain Bridge nr Grantown-on-Spey Highland PH26 3LY			Map 2 C3

19th-century hunting lodge set in ten acres of grounds in Dulnain
Valley. Refurbishment has recently taken place, covering the little bar,
the dining room (now with a conservatory) and the simply appointed
bedrooms. Hearty home-made soups, substantial sandwiches and
a handful of hot dishes (for 'Muckrach Minors') should satisfy hungry
families; two high-chairs are provided. The cosy panelled bar
overlooks 10 acres of grounds and tables are to be found on lawns and
terrace in fine weather. Children up to five are accommodated free
in five good-sized family rooms (cot free of charge, extra bed £5);
baby-listening is available. Straightforward family facilities, but the
willingness of hotel staff to accommodate children more than makes
up for the absence of hot and cold running clowns! No dogs.
Rooms 12. *Garden. Closed 3 weeks Nov. Access, Amex, Diners, Visa.*

Dumfries   Opus Salad Bar

Tel 0387 55752	Café
95 Queensberry Street Dumfries Dumfries & Galloway DG1 1BH	**Map 4 B2**

The Halliday family run an unpretentious salad bar that's part
of a first-floor store in a cobbled street just off the shopping square.
There's a rapid lunchtime turnover at the self-service counter, where
plenty of hot and cold dishes are on offer for both carnivores and
vegetarians. All the food is made on the premises and covers a range
of wholesome dishes like vegetable crumble (£2), chicken pancakes
(£2.20), shepherd's pie (£2.20) and a large selection of salads (60p per
portion). Lighter bites also available. Non-smoking area. Breakfast
9-10.30. *Seats 44. Open 9-4.30 (Thur to 2.15). Closed Sun, Bank
Holidays. Access, Visa.*

Edinburgh   Caledonian Hotel   79%   £192

Tel 031-225 2433 Fax 031-225 6632	Hotel
Princes Street Edinburgh Lothian EH1 2AB	**Map 3 C6**

Affectionately known as 'the Caley', the hotel stands on the site of
the old Caledonian railway station and is one mile from the current
Waverley station. The carpeted foyer leads to a grand, gracefully
proportioned and elegant lounge, furnished with plush shot-silk sofas.
Carriages Bar retains the redbrick former station entrance as an inside
wall and was recently refurbished. Bedrooms are individually styled,
featuring well-chosen furniture and luxurious drapes; 5th-floor rooms
are smaller than some of the others which can take a cot or extra bed;
the process of bedroom refurbishment is continuing. Towelling robes
are provided in all the bathrooms, which include a TV/radio speaker;
elegant antique-style fittings in Executive bathrooms. Plus factors
are the number of telephone extensions in the rooms, 24hr lounge
service, a turn-down service and chocolates at night. Families are
particularly well catered for; a children's menu is served either in
the restaurant or in your room – high tea is suggested to be served
at 6.30pm. No baby-listening, so arrange baby-sitting before arriving
should you require it. No dogs. Queens Moat Houses. *Rooms 240.
News kiosk. Access, Amex, Diners, Visa.*

Pompadour Room   £100

The Pompadour is elegant and formal; ornate plasterwork frames
large wall paintings of delicate flowers, a pianist plays soothing music
and excellent staff provide impeccable service. Chef Tony Binks
features Scottish dishes each lunchtime as *Legends of the Scottish Table*
while in the evenings the other side of the *Auld Alliance* is reflected
in a modern French menu (including a five-course *menu dégustation*).
Good French and Scottish cheeses. *Seats 50. Parties 10. L 12.30-2.30
D 7.30-10.30. Closed L Sat & Sun, also D Sun Nov-Mar.
Set L £17.95 Set D £38.50*

Carriages Restaurant   £60

The hotel's second restaurant serves familiar dishes like French onion
soup, tournedos Rossini, roast duckling and grilled Dover sole along
with a few Scottish favourites such as Musselburgh pie and haggis.
Exemplary staff. *Seats 150. L 12.30-2.30 D 6.30-10. Set L £12.95.*

Edinburgh   **Carlton Highland**   68%   £138

Tel 031-556 7277 Fax 031-556 2691   Hotel
North Bridge Edinburgh Lothian EH16 6XY   Map 3 C6

Despite its granite vastness, the Carlton is a welcome oasis for families.
Besides well-equipped bedrooms and comfortable day rooms the
Carlton Highland has a fine leisure centre (including supervised
playroom), conference facilities, two restaurants and a night club with
dancing and live entertainment Tuesday to Saturday. Children up to
14 stay free in their parents' room (15 rooms suitable for family use);
an extra bed or cot will fit in most rooms and baby-listening
is installed. Baby-sitting only requires one hour's notice, but check
when booking that this is still the case. Good children's menu in the
restaurant where you'll also find high-chairs and small portions.
*Rooms 199. Indoor swimming pool, gymnasium, spa bath, sauna, solarium,
steam room, squash, snooker, hair & beauty salon, coffee shop (10am-6pm).*
Access, Amex, Diners, Visa.

Edinburgh   **The Engine Shed Café**

Tel 031-662 0040   Café
19 St. Leonard's Lane Edinburgh Lothian EH8 9SD   Map 3 C6

A vegetarian café on the first floor of an old stone building that was
formerly an engine shed (for a standing engine that pulled other
engines up the hill), now run by Garvald Community Enterprises,
a charity employing people with special needs. The bright, airy room
has stone walls displaying up-and-coming artists' works. There's
always a home-made soup (parsnip and apple, leek and potato 50p) and
the hot dishes of the day may include spicy chick pea stew (£2.50),
nut roast with tomato sauce (£2.50). Otherwise home baking
dominates with carrot cake, chocolate brownies, scones, millionaire's
shortbread (from 40-70p) or filled rolls. Children are made
particularly welcome since access is easy, the café is spacious and they
love the tofu whips (yoghurt-style desserts); high-chairs, beakers, good
changing facilities and a lift for buggies indicate a caring attitude
towards mums and wee ones. Unlicensed. No smoking. *Seats 55.*
*Open 10.30-3. Closed Sat, Sun, 2 weeks Christmas, 1 week Easter,
2 weeks summer. No credit cards.*

Edinburgh   **Fishers**

Tel 031-554 5666   Pub
1 The Shore Leith Edinburgh Lothian EH6 6QW   Map 3 C6

Fishers is a jewel cast up from the sea, an outstanding seafood-speciality
bar which serves full meals all day, noon-10.30pm. It's taken root
in a renovated corner building at the end of The Shore, at the foot
of what looks like an ancient bell-tower or lighthouse. The bar area,
in which you can also eat, groups high stools around higher-still tables.
Up a short flight of steps, the main eating area features light-wood
panelling with night-sky blue tables and chairs, windows half
of frosted glass, half giving a view to the harbour and beyond, and all
presided over from a great height by a bejewelled mermaid figure.
The pricing structure and the variety of food on offer are admirably
suited to most appetites and pockets, whether for serious eating
or quick snacking. In addition to the photocopied-handwritten
menu, a blackboard of daily specials offers a host of starters and main
courses which should appeal to more than fish fans alone. Salads are
crunchy and fresh; choose your dressing from a piquant selection

or mix your own. Simple, home-made fruit flans, pies and crumbles (£2.50) to finish. *Bar Food & Restaurant Meals* 12-10.30 *(from 12.30 Sun). Children's portions. Free House.* **Beer** *Caledonian, Deucharn. Riverside, outdoor eating. Family room. Access, Amex, Visa.*

Edinburgh   Fruitmarket Gallery, Café Bistro

Tel 031-225 2383	Café
29 Market Street Edinburgh Lothian EH1 1DF	Map 3 C6

Housed in a warehouse built in the 1930s, the Café is on the first floor offering daily-changing hot dishes such as fillet of lamb wrapped in vine leaves with a juniper sauce (£4.30), stir-fried king prawns with ginger and mango (£5.80), chicken with honey and sesame (£4.50) or aubergine parmigiana (£3.80). Filled Italian rolls (£1.30-£1.80), scones, patisseries and puddings are also available. At the time of going to press, the Café Bistro was moving to the ground floor with more space for pushchairs and a highchair. No smoking. *Seats 40.* **Open** *11-6.* **Closed** *Sun, Mon (closures depend on exhibitions). No credit cards.*

Edinburgh   Helios Fountain

Tel 031-229 7884	Coffee House
7 Grassmarket Edinburgh Lothian EH1 2HY	Map 3 C6

Jos and Mei-Lian Bastiaensen's vegetarian and vegan coffee house at the rear of a crafts and book shop continues to draw the crowds, particularly students and academics, who appreciate the relaxed, unpretentious surroundings and very keen prices. From 10am scones (60p) and cold savouries such as lentil pie with tomato sauce (£1.20) are gradually joined by a selection of 9 or 10 cakes – Dorset apple (£1.10), banana yoghurt (£1.50) – and biscuits – tollhouse cookie (60p), date slice (50p) – and six salads such as red cabbage and tomato or curried chick-pea, priced from 60p. Lunch brings a hot quiche (£1.85), soups (spicy cauliflower £1.05) and perhaps a casserole (chestnut and Brussels sprouts £1.90). Normally closed on Sunday except during the Festival and August (open 11-6) and December (11-5). Non-smoking throughout. *Seats 35.* **Open** *10-6 (to 8 during Festival).* **Closed** *25 & 26 Dec, 1 & 2 Jan. Access, Visa.*

Edinburgh   Henderson's Salad Table

Tel 031-225 2131	Restaurant
94 Hanover Street Edinburgh Lothian EH2 1DR	Map 3 C6

Approaching their 30th anniversary, the Henderson family continue to preside over their hugely popular counter-service vegetarian restaurant, in a large basement below the family fruit shop. The day starts at 8 with organic fruit juices, yoghurt and wholemeal croissants (65p) and the counter display gradually fills up with cold savouries such as felafel, salads (from 80p) and spinach and rice balls (£1.10), and various cakes including some sugar-free items such as apricot slice and cashew nut (55p). Hot items, chalked on a blackboard (which also highlights vegan options) are available from 11.30-2.30 and again from 4.30-10.30 and could include lentil and butterbean bake (£2), broccoli and Brie crumble (£2.20) and Brava Austouri – aubergine and vegetable fritters in wine (£3.20). To finish, Scottish cheese and desserts such as trifle (£1.50), citrus cheese cake (£1.50) and dried fruits with soured cream and ginger (£1.50). *Seats 160.* **Open** *8am-10.30pm.* **Closed** *Sun (except during Festival: open 9am-10pm), Bank Holidays. Access, Amex, Visa.*

Edinburgh   **Rutland Hotel**

Tel 031-229 3402 Fax 031-228 5322	Pub
3 Rutland Street Edinburgh Lothian EH1 2AE	Map 3 C6

Overlooking the Castle from its convenient position on Princes Street,
the pub at No1 Rutland Place is a tremendously popular drinking
venue, with two floors of heavily Victorian bars and a cellar bar
offering live entertainment. Book a room on the third floor, well
away from weekend disco noise, and with the help of accommodating
staff, you will have a conveniently located base from which to explore
Edinburgh. There are five rooms particularly suitable for families, and
all the rooms have TVs and teamakers. A Z-bed or a cot can be moved
into any of the larger rooms. Baby-listening is fitted. A laundry service
is available. The hotel has a ban on under-fives in the bar, but they
are accommodated free. In general, the double-glazed bedrooms are
surprisingly quiet and peaceful, with access at the back of the building
by resident's key only. Most rooms have modern bathrooms; the
others share four public ones. *Beer McEwans.* ***Accommodation***
18 bedrooms, 10 en suite, £70. Access, Amex, Diners, Visa.

Edinburgh   **Scottish National Gallery of Modern Art, Gallery Café**

Tel 031 332 8600	Café
Belford Road Edinburgh Lothian	Map 3 C6

An attractive modern café in the basement of the National Gallery
with a beautiful terrace in the sculpture garden for eating alfresco
when the sun shines. The menu changes daily to incorporate hot
specials such as chicken and spinach noodle casserole, haddock and
prawn pie (both £3.70) or carrot and cauliflower curry (£3.60).
Soups can be tomato and leek or yellow split pea (£1.50) and among
the other savoury alternatives on the menu are salads, quiches (£3.10
with salad) and filled baked potatoes (£3). Home-made puddings
(from £1.50) and cakes include bramble fool, nutty toffee cheesecake,
ginger crunch, chocolate nut Afghan and date slice. Children's
portions; one high chair and baby cups provided; changing ledge
in the ladies. No-smoking area. *Seats 60.* ***Open*** *10.30-4.30 (Sun from
2).* ***Closed*** *25 & 26 Dec, 3 days at New Year, first Mon in May.
No credit cards.*

Elie   **Ship Inn**

Tel 0333 330246	Pub
The Toft Elie Fife KY9 1DT	Map 3 C5

Recent rebuilding of the Ship, part of a terrace of old cottages down
by the harbour, has, to the relief of the locals, left the original bar very
much as it was before, with wooden benches around the dark-painted,
boarded walls, beamed ceiling and back room with booth seating.
What has been added is a pair of restaurant rooms with old dining
tables, sturdy kitchen chairs and, on the first floor, a small balcony
with coin-operated binoculars for scanning the harbour. There
is no food served in the bar but there is no minimum charge in the
restaurant where one can have just a single dish from the printed
menu – soup of the day (£1.15), home-breaded scampi (£3.95), sirloin
steak (£7.95) plus children's dishes – or blackboard specials which
at night feature local seafood like lobster, Dover sole and monkfish

with cockles, mussels and white wine sauce (£7.50). Home-made scones feature in the daily afternoon tea. In July and August tables on the sea wall opposite the Ship are served by an open-air barbecue. When the tide is out a vast expanse of sand is revealed where, twice a year, the Ship's own cricket team plays a match against a visiting side. **Restaurant Meals** 12-2.30, 6-9 (9.30 Fri/Sat). **Afternoon Tea** 3-6. *Children's menu/portions. Free House. Beer Belhaven, Courage. Family room. Access, Visa.*

Fettercairn   Ramsay Arms Hotel

Tel 056 14 334	Pub
Fettercairn Grampian AB30 1XX	Map 3 D4

Roadside village inn, a lot older than it looks; Queen Victoria stayed here in 1861. Cheery, homely lounge. **Beer** *Theakston, Youngers. Garden. Children's play area. Family room.*

Fochabers   Gordon Arms

Tel 0343 820508	Pub
High Street Fochabers Grampian	Map 2 C3

Antlers decorate the exterior of a former coaching inn standing alongside the A96 and a short walk away from the River Spey, while the public bar sports a variety of fishing bric-a-brac – including stuffed prize catches. Simple overnight accommodation is provided by 12 well-equipped en-suite bedrooms which include both older rooms with large carpeted bathrooms and a number of smaller, quieter ones in the extension. *Free house.* **Beer** *McEwan's. Garden. Family room.* **Accommodation** *13 bedrooms, £65. Children welcome overnight, additional beds (from £10), cots supplied. Access, Amex, Visa.*

Forfar   Royal Hotel   57%   £63

Tel & Fax 0307 62691	Hotel
Castle Street Forfar Tayside DD8 3AE	Map 3 C4

A modest entrance conceals a thriving, compact, well-kept hotel complete with leisure centre, ballroom and roof garden. A cheerful welcome and real fire greet guests in the tiny tartan reception area with cosy bar and rattan-furnished lounge nearby. Bedrooms, apart from one four-poster room, are small but neat and practical. Children can eat in the informal poolside bar rather than in the more formal restaurant; nevertheless, two high-chairs are provided in the restaurant for breakfast and lunch. Baby-sitting requires 24hrs notice. Cots are free at weekends. No dogs. **Rooms** *19. Indoor swimming pool, spa bath, sauna, solarium, hair salon, coffee shop (10am-11pm). Access, Amex, Diners, Visa.*

Gairloch   The Old Inn

Tel 0445 2006	Pub
Gairloch Highland IV21 2BD	Map 2 B3

Very much a family pub, but with a bistro, lounge bar and restaurant. The large garden leads down to a river and a rope swing provides an interesting diversion for those youngsters who can sit still no longer. The no-smoking bistro and lounge bar provide simple, reliable grub (cullen skink £2.45, kipper paté £2.75, dressed local crab £5.95, char-grilled steaks £11); morning coffee from 10am until noon; high teas from 4-6pm; tea is served in the bistro from 2-6pm.

Children can choose from their own menu which currently includes cowboy's munch (Scotch mince pie £2.45) or hero turtles (cheese and ham nuggets £2.25). There is a sole high-chair, baby food will be provided free of charge and bottles warmed. Prams can be stored in the reception area and staff will find somewhere for mothers to breast feed or change a nappy if the need arises. *Seats 70.*
Open from 10am for morning coffee, Restaurant 6-9 all year, Bistro Noon-10pm (May-Sept). Closed Jan 1. Access, Amex, Visa.

Garve	Inchbae Lodge	57%	£54
Tel 099 75 269			Hotel
Inchbae by Garve Highland IV23 2PH			Map 2 B3

Les and Charlotte Mitchell welcome many regulars among the guests at their peaceful hotel, which stands six miles west of Garve on the A835 Inverness-Ullapool road. Day rooms include a lounge and tiny bar; bedrooms are divided between the lodge itself and the Red Cedar Chalet. There are no phones or TVs in the rooms. Families are welcomed, but credit cards are not. Staff are commendably indulgent of children and there's a children's menu in the restaurant, plus baby's needs (bath, potty, nappy) all provided for. *Rooms 12. Garden, clay-pigeon shooting, game fishing. No credit cards.*

Gatehouse of Fleet	Murray Arms Inn		£79
Tel 0557 814207 Fax 0557 814370			Inn
Anne Street Gatehouse of Fleet Dumfries & Galloway DG7 2HY			Map 4 B2

A warm, friendly old posting inn on the A75 Dumfries to Stranraer road whose hospitable day rooms include the Burns Room, where the poet reputedly wrote *Scots Wha Hae*. There's also a little cocktail bar. Bedrooms, all centrally heated, are by no means grand but lack nothing to provide a good night's rest. These, and the bathrooms, are kept in very good order. In the garden there's a cottage suite with its own bedroom, sitting room, bathroom and a bed settee for additional children. Children up to 16 free in parents' room, plus special family room deals during July and August. Very much part of the local community, the inn also acts as the town's pub and coffee shop; of the three dining rooms the Lunky Hole is open all day. Cardoness Castle and Castramon Wood Wildlife reserve are close by. *Rooms 13. Garden, croquet, coffee shop (10am-5pm). Access, Amex, Diners, Visa.*

Glasgow	Caffé Qui		
Tel 041-552 6099			Café
17 John Street Glasgow Strathclyde			Map 3 B6

Between Giorgio Armani and Gianni Versace in the Italian centre, this Italian café is not surprisingly rather smart. Savoury offerings include toasted focaccia with various fillings (from £2.95), open sandwiches and croissants (from £2.90), a few pizzas and *piatti grandi* like pasta carbonara (£4.65) and seafood pasta bake (£5.45). The menu becomes much shorter after about 7.30pm and from 8.45pm there are just desserts and ice creams. Pavement tables, and others in a courtyard beyond the conservatory area, add to the continental atmosphere. Three high-chairs for little ones; storage of push chairs no problem. *Seats 70. Open 10am-11.45pm (Sun from 12). Closed 25 & 26 Dec, 1 & 2 Jan. Access, Amex, Diners, Visa.*

Glasgow   Chapter House

Tel 041-221 8913	Café
26 Bothwell Street Glasgow Strathclyde	Map 3 B6

Set in the heart of of the business district, this light, airy café at the
rear of Christian bookshop *Pickering & Inglis* does a roaring trade over
its 'we-serve-you' counter, offering a simple but consistently good
selection of healthy, home-made products. Business people can browse
through the day's papers at breakfast, snacking on tray-bakes (from
65p), coffee, and bacon or scrambled egg rolls (£1), while at lunch the
choice widens to include soup with roll and butter (£1.25), salads
(£1), quiche (£2.15) and a daily casserole (£3.25). Finish with trifle,
fruit salad or perhaps rhubarb tart (£1.20). Particularly popular
with families on Saturdays – even a toy box for kids. Pavement café
during fine weather. Unlicensed. Non-smoking section. *Seats 60.*
Open *8.30-4.30 (Sat from 9).* ***Closed*** *Sun, Bank Holidays. Acccess, Visa.*

Glasgow   Janssen's Café/Restaurant

Tel 041-334 9682	Restaurant
1355 Argyle Street Glasgow Strathclyde G3 8AD	Map 3 B6

Dutchman Jan Leenhoutts and his Glaswegian wife continue to preside
over their informal café-restaurant offering a formula that allows most
items to be had as full meals or in smaller tapas-style portions. Daily
specials such as swordfish or Italian meatballs (from £7) join more
permanent items including Cajun chicken (£6.95) and grilled gambas
(£8.35), vegetarian lasagne or satay (£6.10), salads (£4.30), houmus
(£3.45) and deep-fried mussels (£3.50). Cakes and desserts all come
from an Italian pasticceria, save the apple bowl, made with cinnamon
and wrapped in puff pastry. *Seats 50.* ***Open*** *11-10.30 (Fri & Sat to 11,
Sun 12-9).* ***Closed*** *25 & 26 Dec, 1 & 2 Jan. Access, Visa.*

Glasgow   The Jenny Traditional Tea Rooms

Tel 041-204 4988	Tea Shop
18 Royal Exchange Square Glasgow Strathclyde	Map 3 B6

The Jenny is a recreation of one of the Victorian tea rooms for which
Glasgow was once as famous as Vienna was for its cafés. Cottagey
decor and waitresses in floral print dresses create a charming
atmosphere in which to enjoy one of the set teas (from £2.75),
a savoury brioche bun with various toppings, or a 2-in-1 pie (£4.25)
in which half an earthenware dish is filled with a pie, steak and
mushroom or turkey and sweetcorn perhaps, and other half with
either cauliflower cheese or sauté potatoes. A sideboard (from which
one helps oneself) is laden with all sorts of home-made cakes and
biscuits. In addition to the all day menu there is a choice of breakfasts
(till 11am) from a traditional fry-up (£4.45) to warm croissants with
preserve (£2.45). Four high-chairs and good baby facilities. *Seats 110.*
Open *7.45-6.45 (Sun 11-5.45).* ***Closed*** *25 Dec, Jan 1. Access, Amex,
Diners, Visa.*

Glasgow   Loon Fung

Tel 041-332 1240	Restaurant
417 Sauchiehall Street Glasgow Strathclyde G2 3JD	Map 3 B6

Still enormously popular with both the Chinese community who
enjoy the likes of roast piglet (£10.30), Cantonese roast duck (£7.50)

and some of the best dim sum around, and Brits who enjoy sizzling
fillets of Cantonese beef (£8.90), crunchy stuffed (with king prawns)
duck (£8.50) and honey and lemon chicken (£6.90). Good-value
business set lunch (£5.70) and set dinner menus from £10 per head.
A family favourite on Sundays. **Seats** *200.* **Open** *12-11.30. Access,
Amex, Visa.*

Glasgow   October Café
Tel 041-221 0303	Restaurant

The Rooftop, Princes Square Glasgow Strathclyde G1 3JX   **Map 3 B6**

Smart, sophisticated café/restaurant on the top level of the
architecturally stunning Princes Square – the posh place to shop
in Glasgow. An all-day bar menu includes the likes of baked
Camembert in filo pastry (£3.95), smoked salmon roulade (£4.75),
chicken liver paté with herb toast (£2.95) and caramel shortcakes
(£1.50) or one can choose from the eclectic restaurant carte
at lunchtime and in the evening. Alternatively you can have just a cup
of excellent espresso coffee or glass of wine – there's also a good range
of teas – between bouts of shopping. Plenty of high-chairs and
changing facilities within the shopping centre. **Seats** *120.* **Open** *12-11.*
Closed *Sun, 25 Dec, 1 & 2 Jan. Access, Visa.*

Glasgow   Sannino
Tel 041-332 8025	Restaurant

61 Bath Street Glasgow Strathclyde   **Map 3 B6**

The decor is darkwood panelling, Tiffany-style lamps and heavy brass
rails; the menu lists reliably good pasta (£4.45-£5.85) and pizzas.
Pizza platters offer a portion of pizza with coleslaw and potato salad
while the full 16in pizza (£8.10-£9.90) serves two – with different
toppings on each half if you so wish. Good-value, fixed-price lunch
(£4.90 Mon-Fri). Two high-chairs but no changing facilities.
Seats *160.* **Open** *12-2.30 & 5-11 (Thur/Fri to 12, Sat 12-12).*
Closed *L Sun, 25 Dec, 1 Jan. Access, Amex, Diners, Visa.*

Glasgow   Ubiquitous Chip
Tel 041-334 5007	Bar

12 Ashton Lane Glasgow Strathclyde G12 8SJ   **Map 3 B6**

Friendly staff provide exemplary service that's entirely appropriate
to the surroundings at this popular bar above the more formal
restaurant. A daily-amended menu keeps pace with current trends and
offers much to excite even the most jaded palate. Starters include
macerated Scotch beef with tapénade (£2.95), squat lobsters (£4.95)
and vegetarian haggis (£3.15), main courses range from slow-braised
duck with honey and ginger (£9.98) to Oban-landed shark marinated
in lemon and coriander (£7.95), and desserts from pear and sultana
sponge with egg custard to apple crumble (£3.15). A balcony with
seven tables overlooks the restaurant courtyard below. Children's
portions. Saturdays are particularly popular with families. Excellent
Scottish cheeses and some 16 wines by the glass on the wonderful wine
list; single malt whiskies are also outstanding. **Seats** *40.* **Open** *12-11
(Sun from 12.30).* **Closed** *25 Dec, 1 Jan. Access, Amex, Diners, Visa.*

Glasgow   Willow Tea Room

Tel 041-332 0521	Tea Room

217 Sauchiehall Street Glasgow Strathclyde G2 3EX   **Map 3 B6**

A glorious example, immaculately restored from the 1904 original,
of Charles Rennie Mackintosh art deco design. Old-fashioned cream
teas (£5.25) are served all day as are scones (50p), locally baked
cakes – millefeuille, choc fudge, carrot, lemon meringue pie (£1.20) –
and savoury items such as home-made soup (£1.20), quiche and salad
(£3.25), filled baked potatoes (from £2.25), lasagne (£3.25) and
open sandwiches, perhaps prawn (£4). Excellent selection of teas
(28 varieties) and coffee (13). *Seats 52.* **Open** *9.30-4.30.* **Closed** *Sun,
Bank Holidays. No credit cards.*

Glenrothes   Balgeddie House   65%   £87

Tel 0592 742511 Fax 0592 621702	Hotel

Balgeddie Way Glenrothes Fife KY6 3ET   **Map 3 C5**

Until recently surrounded by farmland, the hotel is now part of a
suburb of Glenrothes new town. The whole place is well kept, from
lounge and oak-panelled bar to the bedrooms; those on the first floor
are spacious (with enough room to add a cot or extra bed – for which
an extra charge is made), with fine modern bathrooms; those on the
top floor are more compact, with sloping ceilings. Baby-sitting and
listening can be arranged on request. The restaurant can also provide
high-chairs and baby food. At weekends high tea is served from 4.30-
7pm. Changing/breast feeding area. Two separate bars with juke box,
fruit machine and pool tables set the tone. *Rooms 18. Garden, croquet.
Access, Amex, Diners, Visa.*

Gollanfield   Culloden Pottery Restaurant

Tel 0667 462 749	Restaurant

Gollanfield nr Inverness Highland IV1 2QT   **Map 2 C3**

A wholefood/vegetarian restaurant above a craft and gift shop where
children, and others, will be fascinated to watch owner Bob Park
at work at his potters wheel. Half portions are available of most things
on a menu that includes the likes of houmus and nut paté (both
£1.95) with wholemeal bread, home-made cakes, filled jacket potatoes
(from £1.40) and hot dishes (from noon) such as shepherdess pie
(vegetables and tomatoes topped with potato), vegetable lasagne and
pepper and baby corn crumble (all at £4.35). The special children's
section includes fish fingers (£1.60), veggie burger (£1.60) and mini
ploughman's (£1.60). For babies there are clip-on seats and they will
happily heat up baby's bottle and food or liquidise something in the
kitchen. A small, safe play area outside has swings, a slide, scramble net
and rustic play house. Nappy changing faciliites, including wet wipes
are available in the ladies loo. For the disabled there's a special loo
on the ground floor and a stair lift up to the restaurant. On the A96
half-way between Inverness and Nairn. *Seats 42.* **Open** *9.30-7.30
(earlier out of season, to 9pm Fri & Sat all year).* **Closed** *25 & 26 Dec,
1 & 2 Jan. Access, Visa.*

Greenlaw   **Castle Inn**

Tel 03616 217 Fax 03616 500	Pub

Greenlaw Borders TD10 6UR   Map 3 D6

Greenlaw is a small town on a major road; though not far from Hume
Castle and other attractions there is not a lot of reason to stop
at Greenlaw other than to stay or eat at the handsome Georgian Castle
Inn. It is expensive for bar meals (by local standards) and falls into the
middle ground of bar meal and restaurant. The Mirror Room, where
drinking and dining take place, is large and splendid; a large mirror
on top of a marble fireplace transforming what would otherwise
be a hall into a splendid room, with a comfortable sitting area by the
fireplace, and ruffled curtains framing elegant Georgian windows,
through which there's a view to well-kept gardens. The octagonal
room is a superb feature room in which to take coffee, while a small
library also makes an excellent coffee shop, and the bar is popular with
the locals on Friday nights and weekend lunchtimes. Children are
welcome, and family facilities excellent: high-chairs, baby foods,
a Freddy Fox children's menu, books in the library and cheerful,
tolerant staff. "Where you haste to the welcome, and prolong the
goodbyes", their rather contrived catch phrase, appears with
monotonous regularity lest one forgets it. The printed menu,
supplemented by blackboard specials, is eclectic in the extreme – from
liver and bacon (£4.20) to paella (£7.00) and galette crepes. Mini-
baguettes are used for sandwiches, butter comes in pots, tables are laid
with mats rather than cloths, and puddings are displayed in a chill
cabinet. A 2-course traditional lunch (£6.50) is served on Sundays.
The local cheese is good and always features Kelsea and Stichell (cheese
platter £2.50). **Bar Food** 12-2.30, 6.30-10. Children's menu (£2.25 per
dish). Free House. **Beer** Caledonian, Greenmantle. Garden. Family room.
Accommodation 6 bedrooms, 1 en suite £40. Children welcome overnight,
additional beds (from £5), cots supplied. Access, Amex, Diners, Visa.

Innerleithen   **Traquair Arms**

Tel 0896 830229 Fax 0896 830260	Pub

Traquair Road Innerleithen Borders EH44 6PD   Map 4 C1

Hidden down a side street off the main road (well signposted) which
runs through Innerleithen and five minutes walk from the River
Tweed is the Traquair Arms Hotel, a handsome stone building on the
road leading to St Mary's Loch, which is, incidentally, a delightful
journey to one of the most picturesque parts of the Borders.
The bar leads off the hotel reception area; dine here, or in the more
comfortable dining room, or, if weather permits, in the garden – this
is typical of the admirable flexibility of the Traquair Arms, where
children are positively welcomed, even the most boisterous. Afternoon
teas and high teas are also available. Service is genuine and informal,
the atmosphere convivial. A variety of omelettes (from £2.95) and
salads (from £4.60) is served in the bar and hot dishes including
smoked haddock in cheese, onion and cream sauce (£4.20), steak pie
(£4.35), pasta with tomato and cashew balls (£3.50). One benefit
of dining in the bar is that the glass doors lead off into the garden,
which is enclosed and safe for energetic children. The formal
restaurant offers 3- and 4-course table d'hote menus (£13.50, £16).
Bed and breakfast includes a handsome Scottish morning meal,
complete with kippers. Traquair House, next door, is well worth
a visit, too – it's a romantic old house with pretty grounds and its own

ancient brewhouse; the front gates of Traquair are firmly shut, and
will never open again until a Stuart returns to the throne of Scotland.
Bar Food 12-9. Restaurant Meals 7-9. Children's portions. Free House.
Beer Traquair Bear Ale, Broughton. Garden, outdoor eating, children's play
area. Family room. Accommodation 10 bedrooms, all en suite, from £54.
Children welcome overnight, additional beds (from £5), cots supplied.
Access, Visa.

Inverness	Bunchrew House	70%	£115
Tel 0463 234917 Fax 0463 710620			Hotel
Bunchrew Inverness Highland IV3 6TA			Map 2 C3

From Inverness follow the signs to Beauly/Drywall on the A862.
A mile from the outskirts of Inverness you'll find the entrance to 16th-
century Bunchrew House, which stands in 15 acres of landscaped
gardens and woodland on the shores of Beauly Firth. Alan and Patsy
Wilson opened Bunchrew as a hotel in 1987, and summer 1991 saw
the conversion of a second wing, adding a further five luxury
bedrooms. It remains very much their home with a convivial, rather
masculine bar and a muted lounge graced by a log fire and much
reading matter. The new chef prepares local produce in a traditional
style. Staff are friendly and courteous and both mother's and baby's
needs (be it an early supper or a baby bath) are only a phone call away.
Rooms 11. Garden, fishing. Access, Amex, Visa, Diners.

Kenmore	Kenmore Hotel		
Tel 0887 830205			Pub
Kenmore by Aberfeldy Tayside PH15 2NU			Map 3 C5

The Kenmore claims to be Scotland's oldest inn, dating from 1572,
in a lovely Perthshire village at the eastern tip of Loch Tay. The Poet's
Parlour bar, devoted to Burns, is cosy, with green tartan seats; Archie's
Bar is simpler, with glorious views of the river. Excellent salmon
fishing. *Riverside garden. Children's play area. Family room.*

Kentallen of Appin	Holly Tree	65%	£122
Tel 063 174 292 Fax 063 174 345			Hotel
Kentallen of Appin Argyll Highland PA38 4BY			Map 3 B4

An old railway station which has been cleverly converted into
a civilised hotel, the Holly Tree stands on the edge of Loch Linnhe,
three miles south of Ballachulish Bridge. The little bar was once the
station tea room, and there's a delightful lounge with a central fireplace
and comfortable seating. Bedrooms are equally appealing, with floral
fabrics and pine furniture; bathrooms are up-to-date and attractively
tiled. The restaurant is non-smoking. The hotel has its own fishing
boat and creels. Children under 5 stay free in parents' room; families
are well catered for in the ten family rooms; three cots and three
high-chairs are available for the wee ones. A wee dram of Drambuie
in your breakfast porridge should set you up for exploring the West
Coast. *Rooms 11. Garden, fishing. Access, Amex, Visa, Diners.*

Kilberry	Kilberry Inn		
Tel 08803 223			Pub
Kilberry by Tarbert Strathclyde PA29 6YD			Map 3 A6

This single-storey white cottage in an isolated, pretty little hamlet
is located half a mile from a glorious coastline, and reached
by an invigorating 16-mile drive down a winding, hilly, single-track

road from the north, with superb views of Jura and other islands. John and Kath Leadbeater, English chef-proprietors, are vigorously interested in good food, and justifiably proud of their achievements here, in an out-of-the-way spot. It's very much a dining pub, though locals and others are equally welcome to drop in for a drink. The building was originally a crofting house, and the snugly comfortable little bar, with a peat fire at one end, a wood-burning stove at the other, still has an unpretentious rural style. Leading off to the left, the brighter, plainer dining and family room has good-sized pine dining tables and a genuine welcome for children; John's Donald Duck impression certainly breaks the ice. The daily blackboard-listed short menu (perhaps only four or five main courses at lunchtime) is cheerfully annotated. The house speciality is home-made meat dishes of an old-fashioned country sort, often with a modern reinterpretation: perhaps a hearty sausage pie (£6.95), roast loin of pork suffed with "locally-caught haggis" (£13.50), beef in Old Peculier casserole (£10.50), rump steak and kidney pie (£10.50); Kath has a famously light hand with pastry and the results are superb. Her salmon fish pie (£7.95), layered with sliced potato, is also wonderful. She also makes the bread, pickles, jams and chutneys – all of which are on sale at the bar. If lemon meringue pie (£2.95) is on the menu then make sure you leave room for it – it's light and delicate yet intensely tangy, with a perfect fluffy top. The Greenmantle range of beers from Broughton Brewery in the Borders is available by the bottle, and the wine list includes a few offered by the glass. Note that the pub is closed in winter and never opens on Sundays. *Bar Food 12.15-2, 6.30-9. Children's portions. Free House. Family room (no smoking). Inn closed mid October-Easter (open at New Year for 10 days). Access, Visa.*

Kilchrenan	Taychreggan Hotel	66%	£72
Tel 0866 3211			Hotel
Kilchrenan by Taynuilt Strathclyde PA35 1HQ			Map 3 B5

The hotel, reached after a drive down a single-track road, stands in a lovely position by Loch Awe, but the view from the bar is of a pretty courtyard where you can eat in fine weather. The sandwich selection includes fresh (£2.50) and smoked salmon (£3.95), roast beef (£2.25) and cheese (£1.75), there are cold cuts and salads, and hot dishes such as pot-roast breast of chicken (£6) and grilled local prawns with garlic butter (£7.50). Scottish cheeses or perhaps queen of puddings (£1.95) to finish. Children's portions. Afternoon teas are served between 2 and 6pm. *Seats 30. Open 12.30-2.15 & 7.30-9. Access, Amex, Diners, Visa.*

Kilfinan	Kilfinan Hotel		£68
Tel 070 082 201	Fax 0700 82205		Inn
Kilfinan nr Tighnabruaich Strathclyde PA21 2EP			Map 3 B5

A delightful Swiss/Scottish couple, Rolf and Lynne Mueller, now manage this remote inn, reached down a single-track road (B8000, off the A886) between Strachur and Tighnabruaich. The Dunoon ferry is less than an exhilarating hour's hell-raising drive across the moors. Purchased about ten years ago by the Laird of Kilfinan, so that it would not fall into the hands of developers, the whitewashed former coaching inn has exclusive access to beautiful Kilfinan Bay (about 20 minutes walk through the garden and the estate) as well as its own fishing, stalking and shooting. At present there are two bars, neither of them a lounge, but both cosy and characterful with log fires, and the bedrooms – some antique-furnished – offer all the usual little luxuries, including good-quality toiletries in the carpeted en-suite bathrooms. Families are well catered for, with a cot available and baby-sitting arranged. Incidentally, don't be alarmed by the brown peat-coloured water. Rolf Mueller brings Swiss precision into his cooking, exemplified in the £21 fixed-price dinner menu (in the restaurant – set with crisp table-linen, and cutlery that gleams in the candlelight); local produce naturally features: Loch Fyne oysters, Scottish salmon and mussels, fresh raspberries). The bar menu offers the likes of estate-shot venison burger (£4.50), Otter Ferry salmon fishcake (£4.50), steak and stout pie (£4.80) and chicken pancake (£4.20). The ploughman's is prepared with Scottish cheeses and the puddings are home made. For the less hungry, if such a person exists after arriving here, soup, sandwiches and paté are also avaialable. Breakfast is served from 7.30am (earlier if required), afternoon teas from 2-6, and a minimum charge of £3 applies at lunch and dinner. **Bar Food** *12-2.30, 5-8.30.* **Restaurant Meals** *12-2.30, 7.30-8.30. Set L £15 Set D £21. Children's menu/portions.* **Beer** *Theakston. Garden, outdoor eating, outdoor play area, summer barbecue. Family room.* **Accommodation** *11 bedrooms, all en suite, £68. Access, Amex, Visa.*

Killiecrankie	Killiecrankie Hotel	64%	£84
Tel 0796 473220 Fax 0796 472451			Hotel
Killiecrankie by Pitlochry Tayside PH16 5LG			Map 3 C4

Three miles north of Pitlochry, just off the A9, convenient for the Pitlochry Festival Theatre. A smart, traditional inn-like hotel with mahogany-panelled bar and beech tables in the conservatory. It's a fine white-painted old property, a former manse, in four acres of landscaped gardens at the northern end of the famous pass, overlooking the river Garry amid glorious central Scotland scenery. The reception hall and small panelled bar (which has a sun-trap extension) have displays of stuffed animals and an upstairs lounge offers various board games plus a few books as distractions. Well-equipped, pine-furnished bedrooms, all with smart modern bathrooms. Under-5s free in their parents' room. **Rooms** *11. Garden, croquet, putting, children's play area. Closed Jan & Feb. Access, Amex, Visa.*

Killin	Clachaig Hotel	
Tel 05672 270		Pub
Falls of Dochart Killin Central FK21 8SL		Map 3 B5

18th-century ex-smithy and coaching inn, once closely linked with the McNab clan, and beautifully set overlooking the spectacular Falls of Dochart with the River Tay a five-minute walk down the road; very Richard Hannay-ish. Rather basic inside, though, its bar usurped by juke box and pool table; bar food is plain and decently cooked. The clean and modest bedrooms are good value for the area; the best of them have dramatic views over the Falls. **Bar Food** *12-4, 5.30-9.30.* **Restaurant Meals** *6.30-9.30. Children's menu (£1.50 per dish). Free House.* **Beer** *McEwan. Garden, outdoor eating. Family room.* **Accommodation** *9 bedrooms, 8 en suite, £36. Children welcome overnight, additional beds (£9), cots supplied. Access, Visa.*

Kilmartin   Kilmartin Hotel

Tel 05465 250	Pub
Kilmartin by Lochgilphead Strathclyde PA31 8RQ	**Map 3 B5**

The first-floor rooms at this delightful little inn/hotel, are perfectly decent (though perhaps a little cramped) but the second-floor attic doubles are spacious and charming, and represent great value for money in a busy tourist area. One looks out over the green at the front of the inn, the other over the less inspiring rear; they share an adjacent, spruce and attractive public bathroom, and the third room is a gracious family room (one double bed, one single) with a little en-suite bathroom, freestanding furniture (including an attractive old bed) pretty fabrics, twin bedside tables and a dressing table. A cot can also be provided – but watch out on the top floor if you have toddlers or crawlers in tow – there are alarmingly wide gaps in the banister; it's very quiet up here, though. Downstairs, the cosy, rambling bar buzzes with traditional pub atmosphere, has bar stools, a lovely stone fireplace (coal fire in winter) an ochre-panelled ceiling at one end, by the bar counter, and a little square sitting area with lovely old spindle-backed and carved oak settles, a piano, and Burns memorabilia. There's fiddle music at weekends. Leading off, a comfortable little residents lounge can be used for non-resident family visits, and has piped music ranging from Simon and Garfunkel to invigorating Russian operas. The licensees are charming and personable, often coming through to the lounge to socialise. *Free House.* **Beer** *Tennents. Garden. Family room.* **Accommodation** *5 bedrooms, 3 en suite, £37. Children welcome overnight, additional beds (from £2.50), cots supplied. No credit cards.*

Kincraig   Boathouse Restaurant

Tel 0540 651 272	Restaurant
Loch Inch Kincraig Highland PH21 1NU	**Map 3 C4**

The adjacent woodland picnic area and the beach, right under the balcony, give plenty of running-about space for the children at this loch-side watersports centre. Watch the watersports on Loch Inch (or the curling when it freezes over in winter) from the balcony of this log-cabin restaurant while enjoying the home-made fare on offer. During the day it's self-service of toasted sandwiches (from £1.85), jacket potatoes (from £2.25), hamburger in a roll (£3.25), lasagne (£4.25) and steak pie plus a vegetarian section – quiche (£4.25), pizza (£3.25), vegetable lasagne (£4.25) – and home-baked scones, flapjacks and shortbread. After 6.30pm it becomes waitress service with main dishes such as fettuccine (£7.25), salmon steak with noodles and herb cream sauce (£9) and filet mignon (£10.75). A couple of high chairs, bottle-heating and children's menu (of the chicken nugget, hamburger and pizza variety) should keep the little ones happy. £3 children's meal includes a main dish, soft drink and ice cream in a cone. No special facilities for baby changing. **Seats** *30.* **Open** *10-9.* **Closed** *early Nov-Dec 26. Access, Visa.*

Kinloch Rannoch   Loch Rannoch Hotel   £74

Tel 088 2632201	Hotel
Kinloch Rannoch by Pitlochry Tayside PH16 5PS	**Map 3 C4**

This converted 19th-century mansion offers excellent leisure facilities and boasts a dry ski-slope, swimming pool, tennis and squash courts, sailing, canoeing, windsurfing and snooker all available on the

premises. Toddlers or babies are not forgotten – there is a playroom and playground and a host of supervised activities as well as baby-sitting and baby-listening services. The restaurant offers high-chairs and a children's menu or small portions. Laundry service/room.
Rooms *16. Access, Amex, Diners, Visa.*

Kinlochbervie   Kinlochbervie Hotel

Tel 0971 521 275	Hotel
Kinlochbervie by Lairg Highland IV27 4RP	**Map 2 B2**

The public bar is a favourite with local fisherman, while in the lounge and Garbet Bar visitors can enjoy a good choice of worthy snacks and more substantial dishes. Macaroni cheese (£2.50) served bubbling topped with Scottish cheddar, pizzas (£2.75), burgers and toasted sandwiches (from £1.70) are joined by blackboard specials – fish pie (£4.25), seafood lasagne (£4.25) and the day's local catch served battered or grilled (£5.75) – and own-smoked fish (mackerel £2.50), paté with oatcakes (£2.90) and a hearty soup with roll and butter (£1.75) make enjoyable starters. Gateaux (£1), sandwiches and scones (40p) are available for afternoon tea, and although advertised as closed from mid-December to the end of February, those braving the far north of Scotland in winter will always find the door open and food available. **Seats** *40.* **Open** *12-1.45 & 1.30-8.30. Access, Amex, Diners, Visa.*

Kippen   Cross Keys

Tel 0786 870293	Pub
Main Street Kippen Central FK8 3DN	**Map 3 C5**

A simple, welcoming Scottish pub with rooms, rather than an inn proper, set in a pleasant rural village not far from Stirling. The locals' public bar is large and basic; a smaller, long and narrow lounge is where most of the food is served, and a larger family room has high-chairs primed and ready for use; there's also a small, more modern restaurant. Bar food is well cooked rather than exciting: home-made lasagne (£3.75), daily specials (roast venison in raspberry and red wine sauce £8.55); meaty, home-made beefburgers (£3.40) come with good crunchy buttered cabbage and chips. Soups are thick and warming. An apple pie is made daily (£1.80). The restaurant is open in the evenings and offers more elaborate dishes such as spinach and pear soup (£1.15), fillet steak in brandy sauce (£11.95), salmon in lime and ginger sauce (£8.25). If staying the night, ask for one of the rooms under the eaves, which have sloping ceilings and fine views. Bedrooms are simple and homely, with wash handbasins. There is no residents' lounge, just the main bars downstairs, busy even midweek with diners and locals. Breakfasts, served on linen-laid tables in the restaurant, are hearty traditional fry-ups and service is pleasant and helpful. There's a beer garden at the rear with access from both the public and lounge bars. **Bar Food** *12-2 (12.30-2 Sun), 5.30-9.30.* **Restaurant Meals** *12 (12.30 Sun)-2, 5.30-9.30. Children's portions. Free House.* **Beer** *Broughton, Youngers. Garden, Outdoor eating. Family room.* **Accommodation** *3 bedrooms, sharing a bathroom, £39.50. Children welcome overnight, additional beds. Access, Visa.*

Kippford   Anchor Hotel

Tel 055 662 205	Pub
Quayside Kippford Dumfries & Galloway DG5 4LN	Map 4 B2

Prettily set, harbourside pub, with a characterful, rambling drinking
bar. Young, casual staff are friendly and tolerant of toddlers; one
high-chair. *Beer McEwans, Theakston. Family room.*

Kirkcaldy   Hoffmans

Tel 0592 204584	Pub
435 High Street Kirkcaldy Fife KW1 2SG	Map 3 C5

Hoffmans is an extraordinary place. Situated to the east of the town
centre (don't be confused by the High Street address), it's an unlikely
looking venue for a pub serving imaginative food. Owned
in partnership by Vince and Paul Hoffman, who smartened up a once-
seedy building with subtly toned wall covering, brown upholstered
bench seating, polished tables, a large central ceiling fan, angled
mirrors, and fake greenery; seascape and still life oil paintings and fine
colour photographs from a couple of regulars grace the walls. But the
food is the thing here, and it's so popular that booking is advised for
lunch as well as for dinner. Vince Hoffman is so confident in the
quality of his raw ingredients that local suppliers are listed at the front
of the hand-written, daily-changing menu. Fish is a particular interest
of Vince's, from a traditional deep-fried haddock (£3.50)
to an elaborately modern salmon and monkfish dish in lobster sauce
(£10.25). The raw materials are first class (no dye in smoked fish), the
handling first rate, and the prices at lunchtime remarkable. In the
evening, the room is partitioned, half the space reserved for drinkers,
the other run as an à la carte restaurant with candle-lit tables and
waitress service. Expect to pay around £35 for two for more complex
evening food; Vince's wife Jan makes all the puddings. *Bar Food 12-2,
5.30-7.30. Restaurant Meals 7.30-9.30 (Wed-Sat only). Children's
portions. Children allowed in bar to eat. Free House. Beer McEwan's.
No credit cards.*

Kirkcudbright   Selkirk Arms

Tel 0557 30402	Pub
Old High Street Kirkcudbright Dumfries & Galloway DG6 4JG	Map 4 B3

Modernised but characterful sleepy town hotel, its simple public bar
popular with locals. Go on a sunny day and have a drink under the
trees in the pretty little garden; they'll even carry out a high-chair
for babies. *Garden.*

Kirkton of Glenisla   Glenisla Hotel

Tel 057 582223	Pub
Glenisla nr Blairgowrie Tayside PH11 8PH	Map 3 C4

Set high up in Glenisla, one of the 'Angus Glens', this old coaching inn
dates back over 300 years to the days before the Jacobite rebellion.
A warm welcome avails today's travellers in the split-level, beamed
bar with its real fire (even in summer on chilly days) and posies
of heather and wild flowers on the tables. At lunchtime a daily-
changing menu offers the likes of haddock and chips (£4), burgers
(£3) and ploughman's (£3.95); at night main courses such as breast
of chicken poached in garlic and cream (£6.95) and lamb cutlets

grilled with rosemary (£6.15) can be preceded by Orkney herring marinated in dill (£1.95), salad of melon and prawns (£2.95) or home-made chicken liver paté (£2.50), and followed by homely 'afters'. Afternoons bring cream teas with scones fresh from the oven and home-made jam. A pretty restaurant opens for both lunch and dinner at the weekends (Friday, Saturday and Sunday) and at other times by prior arrangement. **Bar Food** *12-2.30, 6.30-9 (8.30 winter).* **Restaurant Meals** *(Fri, Sat & Sun) 12-2.30, 6.30-9. Children's portions.* **Beer** *Theakstons, S&N. Garden, outdoor eating, children's play area. Family room. Access, Visa.*

Kyle of Lochalsh	Wholefood Café & Restaurant
Tel 0599 4388	Restaurant
Plockton Road Kyle of Lochalsh Highland IV40 8DA	**Map 2 E3**

Take the Plockton Road out of town to find this wholefood/ vegetarian restaurant set in the Highland Design Works, once the village school. Counter service through the day (don't be afraid to ask staff to help, they will lend a hand to struggling parents) offers rock buns (30p), carrot cake (£1), banana bread (85p) and the like to be joined at midday by hot dishes such as aduki bean burger (£2.95), spiced chick peas and rice (£3.65) and cauliflower and courgette casserole (£3.25). Everything is prepared on the premises using local and organic produce where possible; there is always a small collection of local cheeses served with oatcakes (£1.75). Evenings bring a short, à la carte, waitress-service menu that adds seafood dishes like smoked seafood platter (£3.75) and wild Loch Duich salmon roulade with fennel and parsley sauce (£8.50) to the vegetarian choices. The café is especially busy between 5.30 and 6.30pm when children (and parents) can try breaking the burger habit. There are two high-chairs and nursing mums have a folding chair in the Ladies. Out of high season the hours may be curtailed and they might close completely on Saturday and/or Monday so it's worth checking in advance. **Seats** *50.* **Open** *10-9.* **Closed** *mid Oct-Easter. Access, Visa.*

Largs	Nardini's
Tel 0475 67455	Café
The Esplanade Largs Strathclyde KA30 8NF	**Map 3 B6**

A splendid 1930s' 'Continental lounge café', complete with gold-painted wicker chairs, glass-topped tables, parlour plants and numerous waiters and waitresses dressed in smart red waistcoats, Nardini's is a veritable institution on Scotland's west coast – and it's still run by the original Nardini family. Their own award-winning dairy ice cream comes in numerous flavours and concoctions with a special Junior Choice section on the menu 'for discerning under-12s only'. There's plenty of room for buggies, numerous high chairs and baby changing facilities are available in the Ladies loo. In the separate restaurant the children's menus for lunch and high tea are unusually extensive – not just burgers and fish fingers (although they are also on the menu) –and the special Sunday Family Lunch comes at a reduced price for under-12s and is completely free for under-fives. **Seats** *300.* **Open** *8am-10pm (in winter to 8).* **Closed** *25 Dec. Visa.*

Letham	**Fernie Castle**	60%	£68

Tel 033 781 381 Fax 033 781 422	Hotel
Letham by Cupar Fife KY7 7RU	Map 3 D4

The castle was first recorded in the mid 14th-century, and later
additions have not spoilt its charm. Best of the public rooms is the
first-floor drawing room in a Georgian extension and the most
atmospheric the medieval Keep Bar with its rough-stone vaulted
ceiling. Bedrooms vary from a very small single without desk
or dressing table to a few spacious rooms with reproduction antique
furniture; most fall somewhere between the two. Children under 12
stay free in parents' room; high-chairs, children's menu, laundry and
baby-sitting/listening can all be provided – state your requirements
when booking. No dogs. *Rooms 16. Access, Amex, Diners, Visa.*

Linlithgow	**Champany Inn Chop & Ale House**	£40

Tel 050 683 4532	Restaurant
Champany Linlithgow Lothian EH49 7LU	Map 3 C5

The same outstanding char-grilled Aberdeen Angus steaks (though less
expensive and cut a bit smaller) as at its renowned sister restaurant,
together with various burgers, deep-fried Scottish prawn tails, chargrilled grain-fed chicken and a cold buffet with help-yourself salad bar,
are amongst the offerings at this much less formal eaterie. For afters
go for the home-made, hot malted waffles or Champany's own
cheesecake served with apricot purée. A few high-chairs are provided
and extra plates happily produced for parents to share a meal with
their offspring. The pleasant courtyard is lovely in good weather but
opens on to a side road and is thus not suitable for active toddlers. The
biblical wine list here is extraordinary – 10 own-label house wines,
burgundies by the bucketful, an enormous South American selection
and a good worldwide choice at fair prices. No children under eight
in the main restaurant. *Seats 32. Parties 6. L 12-2.30 (Sat to 2.15, Sun
from 12.30) D 6.30-10. Closed 2 weeks Xmas. Access, Amex, Visa,
Diners.*

Loch Eck	**Coylet Hotel**	

Tel 036 984 322	Pub
Loch Eck nr Kilmun Strathclyde PA23 8SG	Map 3 B5

It's the setting that makes the Coylet really special: just the west coast
road to Dunoon, shrouded in trees, separates the pretty white building
from the glorious beauty of Loch Eck and the hills beyond. Not
another house can be seen in any direction; be early for a window seat
in the bar or dining room. Inside it charms in an unaffected way. The
public bar, is handsome and cosy, and friendly local ghillies and others
gather on bar stools to pass the time of day. Through the hall is an
attractively simple little dining bar, where families (even tiny babies)
are welcome. In the dining room proper are half a dozen tables (one,
large group-size, in the prize window spot), wheelback chairs and
a piano. The food is a mix of standard bar menu, from sandwiches
(even in the evening) and ploughman's to vast well-cooked platefuls
of haddock and chips, or sizzling steaks; the quality draws both locals
and tourists. But it's worth waiting for the specials board, a daily-
changing short blackboard list which applies from 7 pm. It might
typically feature home-made liver paté and Scotch broth, local game
in season (from £6.50), grilled local salmon (from £5.75) or trout,
and langoustine risotto (£8.15). Upstairs are three tiny little bedrooms

which offer simple comforts. All have sash windows with views over the loch, and pretty cottagey print paper and fabrics. The twin is a bit bigger than the two doubles. The shared bathroom, a very attractive, immaculately clean, carpeted and pine-panelled room, is bigger than any of them. Finally, a word about the service, which is genuine and friendly from both the resident owners and their few, able staff – children should be greeted with a warm welcome. *Bar Food & Restaurant Meals* 12-2 (12.30-2 Sun), 5.30-10 (7-9 Sun). *Children's portions. Free House. Beer Youngers, McEwans, Deuchars. Garden, outdoor eating. Family room. Accommodation 3 bedrooms, sharing facilities, £35. Children welcome overnight, cots supplied with advance notice. Small dogs permitted. Check-in by arrangement. No credit cards.*

Melrose	**Burts Hotel**	£64
Tel 089 682 2285 Fax 089 682 2870		Inn
Market Square Melrose Borders TD6 9PN		Map 4 C1

Graham and Anne Henderson have been the owners for more than 20 years of this 18th-century inn set on the historic town square. It's a friendly place, and the little lounge bar is a popular local meeting place. Bedrooms have pleasant matching bedcovers and curtains, padded headboards and good-quality furniture. Bathrooms, five of which have just shower/WC, feature large fluffy bath sheets. Shooting, fishing and other outdoor pursuits can be arranged for active parents; a sausage and chip supper in the TV lounge should keep the youngsters happy. Cots and extra beds provided at no charge; high-chairs in the dining room. *Rooms* 21. *Garden, snooker. Closed 26 Dec. Access, Amex, Diners, Visa.*

Moffat	**Black Bull**	
Tel 0683 20206 Fax 0683 20483		Pub
Churchgate Moffat Dumfries and Galloway DG10 9EG		Map 4 C2

Modernised 16th-century street-side local with a beer garden outside and duck pond nearby in this curiously old-fashioned, isolated little spa town, whose life blood is coach party tourism. It has been recently refurbished, but the proper local bar survives. Four of the bedrooms look out on to the courtyard and four on to the churchyard opposite. *Beer Theakstons, McEwan's. Garden, outdoor eating. Family Room. Accommodation 8 bedrooms, 6 en suite, £48. Children welcome overnight, additional beds (£6), cots available. No dogs. Access, Visa.*

Monymusk	**Grant Arms Hotel**	
Tel 046 77 226		Pub
The Square Monymusk Inverurie Grampian AB51 7HJ		Map 3 D4

18th-century coaching inn in a picturesque village. Attractively modernised inside with its comfortable lounge, and fruit-machine and space-game public bar. Excellent fishing on ten miles of the river Don. Ghillies available at reasonable rates. *Beer McEwan. Children's play area. Family room.*

Muir of Ord	**Ord House Hotel**	
Tel 0463 870492		Pub
Muir of Ord Highland IV6 7UH		Map 2 B3

Opposite a little loch, this charming country house hotel is a listed building dating from 1602 in grounds of 50 acres of parkland (with woodland trails), fields, and formal garden. Pleasant bedrooms

with garden views have antique furniture and a laundry service
if required. *Free House. Garden, children's playing area. Family room.*
*Accommodation 12 bedrooms, 10 en suite, from £54. Children welcome
overnight, additional beds (from £10), cots available. Access, Amex, Visa.*

Nairn	Golf View Hotel	64%	£125
Tel 0667 52301 Fax 0667 55267			Hotel
Seabank Road Nairn Highland IV12 4HD			Map 2 C3

Built at the very end of the last century, the hotel stands on the shores
of the Moray Firth, overlooking Black Isle. It's a great place for family
holidays, with a games room, pool, children's play area and weekend
evening entertainment indoors and a beach almost on the doorstep.
Nearly half the bedrooms are suitable for family occupation
(accommodation and food for under-4s are free). Baby-listening and
baby-sitting can be arranged. High tea at 5pm, but only one high-chair
so demand can't be inundating. *Rooms 48. Garden, outdoor swimming
pool, tennis, putting, sauna, hairdressing, games room. Access, Amex,
Diners, Visa.*

Netherley	Lairhillock Inn	
Tel 0569 30001		Pub
Netherley Grampian AB3 2QS		Map 3 D4

Standing alone surrounded by fields, the Lairhillock is easily spotted
from the B979, thanks to the large white INN daubed on its roof. The
closest major village to the inn is Peterculter, some four miles to the
north; Netherley's a mile to the south. Formerly a farmhouse, the
original building is 17th-century, with careful extensions, and the
interior is full of old rustic atmosphere. The large lounge is dominated
by a central log-burning fireplace; walls are half-panelled, and exposed
floorboards covered with numerous rugs. The public bar, in the oldest
part, is by far the most characterful room, with its exposed stone,
panelling, open fire, old settles and bench seating, every kind of horse
tack, polished brasses and numerous other bits and pieces. Bar food
is certainly taken seriously and only fresh produce is used, cooked
to order. The lunchtime menu, more limited than in the evening, still
carries a fair choice, and changes daily. The bar can get extremely
busy, especially on Friday and Saturday evenings. Across from the
main building, in the old stables, is the evening restaurant, with its
high beamed ceiling, stone walls, red-tiled flooring and solid polished
tables. There's candlelight and a pianist plays nightly. A recently built
conservatory with panoramic views and furnished with Lloyd Loom
tables and chairs provides an ideal room in which families can eat.
*Bar Food 12-2, 6-9.30 (6-10 Fri/Sat). Restaurant Meals 12-2 (Sun
only), 7.30-9.30 (7.30-10 Fri/Sat). Children's portions. Beer Courage,
McEwan's, Boddingtons. Patio/Terrace. Access, Amex, Diners, Visa.*

New Abbey	Abbey Cottage	
Tel 038 785 377		Tea Shop
26 Main Street New Abbey by Dumfries Dumfries & Galloway DG2 8BY		Map 4 B2

Next to the ruined abbey, from which the town takes its name, the
original part of this charming Victorian cottage is given over to the
sale of local arts and crafts – the tea room has moved into a new
extension to the rear. The new addition also includes a special loo for
the disabled. Mrs McKie's all-day menu ranges from home-baked

cakes (60p), fruit loaves (58p), scones (52p) and toasted teacakes (75p)
to savoury items like sandwiches (from £1.20), salads and baked jacket
potatoes (from £1.50). The ploughman's lunch (£3.40) features
an award-winning vegetarian Cheddar from the nearby Loch Arthur
Creamery (a Camphill Village Trust). Children are always welcome
and there's a high chair, books to read and toys with which to play;
toddlers can have their food heated up. For good weather there
is a neat little, brick-floored, patio garden. *Seats 46.* **Open** *10-5.*
Closed *Nov-Easter except weekends to Christmas. No credit cards.*

New Abbey   Criffel Inn

Tel 038 785 305	Pub

2 The Square New Abbey by Dumfries Dumfries & Galloway DG2 8BX **Map 4 B2**

Located five miles from the coast, an unassuming inn on the village
square, with a small garden for summer sipping and letting off juvenile
steam. The McCullochs are the most welcoming of hosts, and Jenny
keeps the customers well fed with a good variety of wholesome home
cooking using local products and vegetables from her garden.
Lunchtime brings soup – perhaps a warming vegetable broth – and
a daily special like roast pork with apple sauce (£4) or savoury mince
pie (£4), supplementing toasted sandwiches, salads, fish (fresh Solway
salmon £5) and roast beef (£4). It's worth leaving room for the day's
special sweet, which could be bread-and-butter pudding or a tart
of locally picked fruit. From 4.30pm a filling high tea is served: £5-6
including a main course of, say, salmon, home-cooked York ham and
salad, gammon steak and pineapple or sausage, bacon and eggs plus
a cake-stand featuring home-baked bread, jam, scones and meringues;
early evening menus are similar but shorter. Children are offered baby
food, fish fingers, burgers, sausages and so on (£1.75 per dish), but
palates eager to learn can be easily satisfied – particularly by the puds;
two high-chairs are provided. There is a 3-course roast lunch (£6)
on Sunday. Spotless bedrooms (TVs but no phones) share an equally
spruce tiled bathroom and residents have their own lounge. There are
two cots (under-5s free), additional beds and two family rooms. *Bar*
Food and Meals 12-2, 4.30-7. *Free house.* **Beer** *Belhaven Best Bitter,*
Broughton Bitter. Patio, outdoor eating. Family Room. **Accommodation**
5 bedrooms, shared facilities, £39. No credit cards. Access, Visa.

Newcastleton   Copshaw Kitchen

Tel 03873 75250	Coffee Shop

4 North Hermitage Street Newcastleton Borders TD9 0RB **Map 4 C2**

The charming original fittings have been left in place in this converted
grocer's shop, even the range, which still warms the restaurant/coffee
shop on cold days. The restaurant features Mrs Elliot's collection
of china washstand sets, which requires careful negotiation by toddlers.
The adjoining tea room is better suited to your little missiles, mum can
relax while they enjoy home-made beefburgers from the children's
menu. Adults can enjoy savouries like paté with oatcakes, Scotch pie
and scampi (£2-£4). Sweets and cakes on offer could be chocolate
brandy mousse, apple crumble (both £1.65), millionaire's shortbread,
almond slice and mint cake (from 40p). Full afternoon tea £2.85.
The reception area provides a convenient space for breast feeding
mothers when it's quiet; it is often busy on Sundays and Bank Hols.
Seats 18. **Open** *9.30-6 (winter 10-5).* **Closed** *Tue, 26 Dec, all Jan & Feb.*
Access, Visa.

Newton Stewart   **Creebridge House Hotel**

Tel 0671 2121	Pub

Minnigaff Newton Stewart Dumfries & Galloway DG8 6NP   **Map 4 A2**

Charming and pleasingly pubby bar with a delightful country house
setting in its own pretty grounds, just before the bridge on the
Minnigaff approach to Newton Stewart. Tolerant and helpful towards
parents with young children, too. **Beer** *Belhaven, Theakston. Garden.*
Family room.

Onich   **Onich Hotel   61%**   £70

Tel 085 53 214 Fax 085 53 484	Hotel

Onich Nr Fort William Highland PH33 6RY   **Map 3 B4**

Fine views of Loch Linnhe, well-maintained gardens and multifarious
activities for all ages make the Onich hotel a popular year-round
choice. Iain Young has put his personal stamp on the place for over 30
years, developing an atmosphere of friendly informality where guests
and locals chat together in the bars. It lies on the A82 ten miles south
of Fort William, making it a splendid base from which to explore the
West Highlands and Islands. The best front bedrooms are balconied;
all rooms have neat bathrooms and many sport new curtains and
bedspreads. None is denied a fair share of the view, but some suffer
slightly from proximity to the road. Easily sloping gardens lead down
to the pebble beach; impress the children by skimming with fool-
proof Ballachulish slates. Cook is on duty all day for nipper's nosh and
there's a coin-operated laundry for longer stays or mishaps. **Rooms** 27.
Watersports centre, ski hire shop, garden, solarium, spa bath, pool table,
coffee shop (8am-9pm). Access, Amex, Diners, Visa.

Peebles   **Kailzie Gardens**

Tel 0721 22807	Restaurant

Kailzie Gardens Peebles Borders EH45 9HT   **Map 4 C1**

A cottagey restaurant housed in converted stables in Kailzie Gardens
beside the river Tweed. Grace Innes offers good things to eat
throughout opening hours, with the widest choice at lunchtime: soup
with home-baked bread (£1.10), fresh peach with cottage cheese
(£1.75), roast gigot of pork (£4.25), beef and mushroom casserole
(£4.15), vegetarian quiche (£3.45). Afternoon tea (£3.10) features
home baking, and the bread for the open sandwiches is also home
produced. Traditional Sunday lunch (£5.20). Courtyard. **Seats** 50.
Open *11-5.30.* **Closed** *Oct-mid March. No credit cards.*

Peebles   **Kingsmuir Hotel**

Tel 0721 20151	Pub

Springhill Road Peebles Borders EH45 9EP   **Map 4 C1**

Handsome Victorian, stone-built, gabled hotel on the quiet side of this
attractive market town. Functional, spartan locals' bar; comfortable
residents' lounge with pretty views, clean simple bedrooms.
Beer *Broughton. Garden. Children's play area. Family room.*

Peebles   **Peebles Hotel Hydro   70%**   £97

Tel 0721 20602 Fax 0721 22999	Hotel

Innerleithen Road Peebles Borders EH45 8LX   **Map 4 C1**

There seem to be few facilities not provided by the energetic Pieter
van Dijk, manager for over 20 years at this majestic holiday hotel

overlooking the Tweed valley. Formally a hydropathic hotel, its extensive sports facilities in the 30 acres of grounds are a major attraction, keeping even the most active guests fully occupied. Public rooms of grand proportions are both attractive and comfortable; in the bar there's a good selection of malt whiskies. A sun room overlooks the valley, as do some of the good-size bedrooms, which are charmingly furnished and well kept. 25 rooms are designated for families and 22 have a small, separate children's bedroom. Families are well catered for with the likes of children's high tea, baby-sitting and baby-changing facilities in the Bubbles leisure centre. An outdoor adventure playground can keep older children busy and hostesses ('not nannies') organise high-season activities such as treasure hunts and painting and drawing competitions. 24 hour laundry service and an ironing room in the first-floor launderette. *Rooms 137. Garden, indoor swimming pool, sauna, solarium, spa bath, gymnasium, beautician, hairdressing, tennis, squash, badminton, pitch & putt, putting, croquet, riding, games room, snooker, coffee shop (10am-11pm), kiosk, children's playground & playroom, dinner dance (Fri & Sat). Access, Amex, Diners, Visa.*

Peebles   Sunflower

Tel 0721 22420	Coffee Shop
4 Bridgegate Peebles Borders EH45 8RZ	**Map 4 C1**

Well worth the short walk from the main street, Sunflower is friendly and intimate behind its distinctive green-and-yellow shop front. Lunches and tasty snacks are served throughout the day. For lunch you can enjoy dishes such as leek and Gruyère tart (£3.90), Ardennes ham and red pepper risotto (£4) or marinated herrings with toast and salad (£3.95). Sweets are all £2.50 and may include cardamon rice with lime cream or ice cream and maple syrup. In the evening the menu is changed and dining becomes slightly more expensive with main courses from £5.50-£7.50. There is no children's menu but portion sizes and prices will be adjusted to suit; bottles and baby food can be heated. The owners will find a quiet place for nursing mothers. The garden provides a safe place for play in clear view of parents. *Seats 30. Open 9-5.30 & 7.30-9 Tue-Sat Apr-Oct, Thur-Sat Oct-Apr. Closed Sun & Bank Holidays. No credit cards.*

Perth   Littlejohn's

Tel 0738 39888	Restaurant
65 South Methven Street Perth Tayside PH1 5NX	**Map 3 C5**

A family restaurant which is enjoyed by children and parents alike. Set on two floors, there is a café at front which looks out on to the street while at the back the restaurant divides into small sections each with its own theme from the 30s – one room is filled with sporting memorabilia including sleighs, rackets, boxing gloves and football boots while another has a musical flavour with trumpets, horns, drums and even a piano with its own life-size papier-maché pianist. In the waiting area there is an electric train which laps the bar intriguing its audience both young and old. Once seated, children are presented with a colour-in menu, crayons and a helium balloon swiftly followed by their choice of, perhaps, some fish-shaped fish fingers followed by an ice cream clown and a soft drink (£2.50). High chairs, training mugs, nappy changing and nursing area and plenty of storage space for prams and push chairs are all provided. Booking recommended. New outlets opening soon in Inverness and Aberdeen. *Seats 120.*

See over

Open *midday-11.* **Closed** *1 Jan. Access, Amex, Diners, Visa.*
Also at:
Ayr 231 High Street Ayr Strathclyde Tel 0292 288666.
Aviemore Grampian Road Aviemore Highland Tel 0479 811633.
St Andrews 73 Market Street St Andrews Fife Tel 0334 75444.
Stirling 52 Port Street Stirling Central Tel 0786 463222.
Durham Millburngate Centre Durham Co Durham (England)
Tel 091 383 1177.

Peterhead	Waterside Inn	67%	£69
Tel 0779 71121 Fax 0779 70670			Hotel
Fraserburgh Road Peterhead Grampian AB42 7BN			Map 2 D3

At Inverugie, two miles outside Peterhead on the Fraserburgh road,
surrounded by fields and the banks of the winding River Ugie.
A large, low-rise modern hotel which is comfortable and efficiently
run. There's a series of bars to suit every taste and a good leisure club
with a hot tub by the pool. 40 studio bedrooms in a separate barrack
block are compact and functional, while those in the main building
are more spacious and luxurious, thus more suitable for families (baby-
listening is offered); children up to 13 stay free in parents' room. Six
family rooms have bunk beds. Greatly reduced rates at weekends
when conference delegates are thin on the ground. A few miles away,
the Aden Park Agricultural Heritage Centre brings the rural past
of Buchan to life. **Rooms** *110. Garden, croquet, indoor swimming pool,
keep-fit equipment, spa bath, sauna, solarium, snooker, coffee shop (7am-
10pm). Access, Amex, Diners, Visa.*

Pitlochry	Luggie Restaurant	
Tel 0796 472085		Restaurant
Rie-Achen Road Pitlochry Tayside PH16 5AN		Map 3 C4

The old stone barn, which used to be a dairy, is now a roomy self-
service restaurant with rough-stone walls and a beamed ceiling. The
cold selection includes ham, beef (£3.75), fresh salmon steaks (£4),
smoked trout and a decent selection of salads, plus fruit cake, fruit pies
(from 55p), scones (80p) and shortbread. Pork and apple paté (£1.95)
and smoked venison platter (£1.95) are among the starters, and daily
hot dishes, from 11.30-2.30, include lasagne and chili (both £3.75).
Evening carvery (£7.95) with cold buffet. Traditional roast on
Sundays (£4.95 for 2 courses). Breakfasts throughout winter (from
£3.25). Children's portions. Large terrace. **Seats** *160.* **Open** *9-5 &
6-9.30.* **Closed** *Feb. Access, Visa.*

Port William	Corsemalzie House	61%	£75
Tel 098 886 254			Hotel
Port William By Newton Stewart Dumfries & Galloway DG8 9RL			Map 4 A3

Forty wooded acres make a secluded setting for a 19th-century stone
mansion which nowadays is a popular and unpretentious hotel with
many sporting attractions. Fishing is a major activity (rights
on stretches of the rivers Bladnoch and Tarff, plus nearby lochs) and
there's good rough shooting and arrangements with local golf courses.
The lounge and bar provide easy relaxation, and bedrooms are
generally of a decent size; all have private bath or shower. Children
under 13 in parents' room are charged at £3 a night. High-chairs,
children's menu, small portions and baby-listening for the wee babes.
Rooms *14. Garden, putting, croquet, game fishing, shooting. Closed 25 &
26 Dec, 14 Jan-mid Mar. Access, Visa.*

Portpatrick   Crown Hotel

Tel 077 681 261 Fax 077 681 551	Pub
Portpatrick Wigtownshire Dumfries & Galloway DG9 8SX	Map 4 A2

Right down by the harbour, the blue and white-painted Crown
is a bustling, friendly place where the several unpretentious rooms that
form the bar – with a real fire even in summer on chilly days, and
a motley collection of prints above dado panelling – contrast
with a stylishly informal restaurant and smart, appealing bedrooms.
The latter have loose rugs over polished parquet floors, a variety
of good freestanding furniture and attractive floral fabrics along with
pristine bathrooms. Restaurant and bar share the same menu (except
for the basket meals and sandwiches that are served in the bar only),
which majors on seafood. Chef Robert Campbell knows that the
lobster and crabs are fresh as he's out in his boat at 6 o'clock each
morning to collect them. Much of the other fish is bought direct from
the Fleetwood trawlers that call in at Portpatrick to unload their
catches. Grilled scallops wrapped in bacon (£4.35), moules marinière
(£4.05), herring in oatmeal (£3.45), whole plaice with almonds and
chips (£5.60), vegetable pancake (£5.40), beef hot-pot (£4.10) and
chicken and chips (£4.05) are a few examples from a longish menu.
Service is swift and efficient. *Bar Food & Restaurant Meals* 12-2.30,
*6 (6.30 Sun)-10. Children's portions. Free House. Beer S&N. Family
room. Accommodation 12 bedrooms, all en suite, £62. Children welcome
overnight, additional beds (ages 4-10 £10), cots supplied. Access, Amex,
Diners, Visa.*

Ratho   Bridge Inn

Tel 031-333 1320	Pub
27 Baird Road Ratho Lothian EH28 8RA	Map 3 C6

Part of the Edinburgh Canal Centre, which also features two canalboat
restaurants. A well-run, popular, family-orientated pub; also facilities
for disabled persons. Huge variety of children's play equipment
includes a putting green. *Beer Belhaven. Children's play area.
Family room.*

Ringford   Old School Tea Room

Tel 0557 22250	Tea Room
Ringford Dumfries & Galloway DG7 2AL	Map 4 B2

Old class photographs look down from the walls of this former
school-house on the main A75 and 'daily specials' have replaced the
alphabet on the blackboard of what is now a welcoming craft shop-
cum-tearoom. The all-day menu includes super home-made soups like
tattie and parsnip or chicken and rice (£1.20), open sandwiches such
as home-cooked ham and mayonnaise (£2.75), and lentil and
mushroom paté (£2.60) made with excellent wholemeal bread, along
with club sandwiches (from £2.95), baked tatties with various fillings
(from £1.95) and good home baking – brides tart (60p), carrot cake
(70p), shortbread, flapjacks and butterscotch fruit slice. Ask for
children's portions; high-chairs available; baby food heated on request.
*Seats 40. Open 10-6 (11-5 in winter). Closed Mon in winter.
No credit cards.*

Selkirk   Philipburn House   60%   £99

| Tel 0750 20747   Fax 0750 21690 | Hotel |

Linglie Road Selkirk Borders TD7 5LS   Map 4 C1

Set back from the A707/A708 junction, a mile from the town centre, this extended 18th-century house has been turned into a delightful family hotel with five acres of grounds and a Tyrolean-style interior. Jim and Anne Hill, owners since 1971, cater for all kinds of visitors – business people, fishermen, Border tourers, families – and friendly hospitality is their watchword. The characterful pine-panelled bar with open fire and garden outlook (sit outside in fine weather) is the place to enjoy the 'Quick Bite' menu. Lighter dishes include haggis and whisky crepe with Cheddar cheese (£2.50) and crispy crab parcels with mango coulis (£4.50), while more substantial offerings range from rösti topped with bacon, mushrooms and melted Swiss cheese (£5.45) to Tiroler Grostle – fried potato, onions and ham topped with two fried eggs (£4.85). Vegetarians have their own menu which features Pithiviers with a range of fillings (perhaps Brie and broccoli £5.95) and avocado, egg and Gruyère gratin, and desserts include banana toffee flan (£2.75) and raspberry crème brulée (£2.75). Separate high teas for toddlers and sub-teens from 5pm – if your little one wants boiled eggs and soldiers then that's what he'll get; all you have to do is ask and the Hills will provide. Bedrooms – in the house, by the pool or in the 'log cabin' – feature pine, pretty fabrics and a host of extras. Parents will appreciate the privacy provided by many separate but connecting children's rooms and rooms with bunk beds; baby-listening is offered. Organised picnics, swimming galas and barbecues in summer. Dogs by arrangement only. *Rooms 16. Garden, outdoor swimming pool, games room, children's playground with sand pit, swings & slides, woodland 'action man centre', crèche. Access, Visa.*

Sheildaigh   Tigh an Eilean

| Tel 052 05 251 | Pub |

Sheildaigh by Strathcarron Highland IV54 8XN   Map 2 B3

Beautifully set at the head of the loch, with soothing views and stunning sunsets. Spartan locals' public bar, but homely and comfortable residents' lounges. *Free House.*

Sheriffmuir   Sheriffmuir Inn

| Tel 0786 823285 | Pub |

Sheriffmuir nr Dunblane Central FK15 0LH   Map 3 C5

A real oasis in a wild moorland location, a pub more of the English than Scots sort, with plush upholstered banquettes and pretty touches. *Beer Arrols, Burton. Garden. Children's play area. Family room.*

Skeabost Bridge   Skeabost House   60%   £82

| Tel 047 032 202   Fax 047 032 454 | Hotel |

Skeabost Bridge by Portree Isle of Skye Highland IV51 9NP   Map 2 A3

Twelve acres of woodland and gardens surround a former hunting lodge on Loch Snizort, 38 miles from the unremarkable area around Broadford which is most people's first experience of the island. It's a comfortable place, with family owners, and relaxation is easy in the lounges, the flagstoned sun lounge, the cosy bar and the billiard room.

Pretty bedrooms include one with a four-poster and a few in the nearby Garden House. Four cots are available in the family bedrooms. Baby-listening installed, baby-sitting arranged; high-chairs, children's menu and small portions in the restaurant. Enquire when booking about accommodation prices for children; babies are free. The hotel owns eight miles of the river Snizort, which runs through the grounds, and has a boat on a nearby loch. **Rooms** 26. Garden, 9-hole golf course, fishing, snooker. Closed mid Oct–mid Apr. Access, Visa.

Spean Bridge	Letterfinlay Lodge	55%	£63
Tel 039 781 622			Hotel
Spean Bridge Highland PH34 4DZ			Map 3 B4

Here since 1963, the Forsyth family have created a comfortable and very Scottish atmosphere in this ruggedly beautiful setting of 12 acres on the banks of Loch Lochy. The public rooms include a cosy little bar, a homely TV lounge and a sun lounge with glorious views. Bedrooms furnished in various styles are named by colour and decorated accordingly; all have private bathrooms, three not en suite. Five rooms are considered suitable for family use. Baby-listening is provided but may not extend to the depths of the Loch which is many fathoms deep only 5 feet from the shore. **Rooms** 13. Closed Nov–mid Mar. Access, Amex, Diners, Visa.

St Andrews	Brambles	
Tel 0334 75380		Restaurant
5 College Street St Andrews Fife		Map 3 D5

A splendid little eating house that's popular with townsfolk, tourists and students. Decor is clean and simple, with plain wooden tables. A blackboard lists the daily fare, all fresh and tasty and mainly with a traditional ring: French onion soup (£1), mushroom and leek pancake (£3.85), lasagne (£3.95), salmon en croute (£5.50), chili con carne (£3.85). Good baking, too, including maple syrup cake (55p), carrot cake (65p) and fudge cake (£1.45). Tables outside in the garden. No smoking. **Seats** 45. **Open** 9-5 Mon-Sat, also 12-5 Sun Easter–mid Sep. **Closed** 2 weeks Christmas. Access, Amex, Visa.

St Fillans	Four Seasons Hotel	60%	£72
Tel & Fax 0764 85333			Hotel
St Fillans nr Crieff Tayside PH26 2NF			Map 3 C5

The setting for the Scott family's agreeable little hotel, in four acres of grounds is one of outstanding natural beauty, with Loch Earn in the foreground and the mountains beyond. Simple but comfortable public rooms take advantage of the location; there are several small lounges, the Tarken bar with a magnificent view, a restaurant and a coffee shop. Hearty food from chef Andrew Scott is served in the bar in more than generous portions; local produce, often organic, is used to good effect in dishes such as a bowl of Skye mussels (£3.95), a pastry case of wild mushrooms (£6.55), fillet of salmon with basil (£8) and breast of wild duck with a piquant sauce (£7.25). Outside eating on the terrace in good weather. Children's portions. Bedrooms are also unfussy in their appointments and include six chalets on a wooded hillside behind the main building. Children up to 11 stay free in their parents' room. **Rooms** 18. Garden, water-skiing. Closed late Nov–mid Feb. Access, Amex, Diners, Visa.

Stirling   **Birds & The Bees**

Tel 0786 73663	Pub
Easter Cornton Road Causewayhead Stirling Central FK9 5PB	Map 3 C5

Converted farmhouse with a striking interior, its open-plan bar
adorned with eccentric pieces of agricultural equipment. Pétanque
is keenly played in the garden. *Beer Broughton, Caledonian, Tetley.
Children's play area. Family room.*

Stonehaven   **Marine Hotel**

Tel 0569 62155	Pub
Shorehead Stonehaven Grampian AB3 2DY	Map 3 D4

Lively, atmospheric harbourside pub-hotel, with very much a local
pub downstairs and a dining room upstairs. Good views from most
of the bedrooms. *Beer Bass, Taylor. Children's play area. Family room.*

Stornaway   **Caberfeidh Hotel**   64%   £82

Tel 0851 702604	Hotel
Manor Park Stornaway Isle of Lewis Highland PA87 2EU	Map 2 A2

This modern (early 70s) three-storey hotel is on the edge of town,
a brisk walk from the Ullapool ferry terminal, and provides visitors
to Lewis with a high level of amenities on this truly Gaelic island.
There are four adjoining rooms suitable for families, with cots
available. Baby-sitting and baby-listening can be arranged and baby
baths, potties, nappies, high-chairs and baby food provided if you
prefer to brave the Islands unprepared! For visitors not staying at
the hotel there is an area for nappy changing and breast feeding.
The restaurant keeps children happy with their own menu (or
small portions) and parents happy with a wee dram at the Viking
Bar where a longship makes up the counter. Open all year.
Rooms 40. Garden. Access, Amex, Diners, Visa.

Strathblane   **Kirkhouse Inn**   £72

Tel 0360 70621 Fax 0360 70896	Inn
Glasgow Road Strathblane Central G63 9AA	Map 3 B5

On the A81 Stirling to Aberfoyle road, ten miles north of Glasgow,
this roadside inn is at the foot of the Campsie Fells and thus popular
with walkers. An ideal touring centre as Loch Lomond, the Trossachs,
Glasgow and Stirling are all within 30 minutes by car. Sprucely kept
public areas include a busy public bar and quieter lounge and
restaurant. Pastel colours are used in the bedrooms, which include
a honeymoon suite with a sunken bath. Children up to 12 stay free
in parents' room. Adventure weekends are a new attraction. *Rooms 15.
Garden, pool table. Access, Amex, Visa, Diners.*

Strathcarron   **Carron Restaurant**

Tel 052 02488	Restaurant
Cam-Allt Strathcarron Highland IV54 8YX	Map 2 B3

On the A890, this is an agreeable modern restaurant next to a craft
shop, with views out over Loch Carron. Open in season for 10 hours
a day it serves tea, coffees, snacks and light meals (toasted sandwiches
£1.70, quiche £3.60), plus a selection of Scottish steaks, salmon, pork
chop and venison cooked on the chargrill (sirloin steak £10.30,
salmon £8.90). *Seats 42. Open 10.30-8.45. Closed Sun & end
Oct-1 Apr. Access, Amex, Visa.*

Swinton   Wheatsheaf Hotel

Tel 089 086 257	Pub

Main Street Swinton Borders TD11 3JJ   Map 3 D6

The village of Swinton is six miles north of Coldstream, on the way
to nowhere, and is easy to miss. The Wheatsheaf, dominating this
simple Scots farming hamlet, overlooks the plain little village green
and has very limited parking; at busy periods, the main street is chock-
a-block with cars. This is very much a dining pub (drinking goes on in
the public bar at the back, so separate from the food operation that
most visitors aren't even aware it exists) with a very well-regarded
restaurant, the Four Seasons, and it's wise to book even for bar meals,
such is the reputation of the pub in the Borders. The emphasis is on
fresh food: a menu reproduced on one blackboard, daily specials listed
on another – hot baked avocado with seafood (£3.85), lamb's liver
with onions and bacon (£5.25), home-made duck terrine with
Cumberland sauce (£4.25), supreme of wild salmon Jemma Louise
(£7.95), beef in ale (£5.25), spinach pancake with cheese sauce
(£4.65) and a choice of home-made puddings (the summer pudding
(£2.50) is a house speciality). Tables are laid with cloths and place
mats; freshly baked wheaten rolls are presented as a matter of course.
Salads are imaginative and fresh. Cheeses are good, and come with
a mini-bottle of Leith port. The best bar meals in the Borders.
Bar Food (*except Monday*) *11.45-2.15, 6.30-9.30. Children's portions.
Free House.* **Beer** *Broughton, Tennents. Garden, outdoor eating, outdoor
play area. Family Room.* **Accommodation** (*closed middle two weeks Feb*)
*4 bedrooms, 2 en suite, £54. Children welcome overnight, additional beds,
cots supplied. Access, Visa.*

Tayvallich   Tayvallich Inn

Tel 05467 282	Pub

Tayvallich by Lochgilphead Strathclyde PA31 8PR   Map 3 A5

This simple white-painted dining pub is in a marvellously pretty
location at the centre of a strung-out village stretching around the top
of Loch Sween. Sit outside, on the front terrace, at one of the five
parasolled picnic tables, and enjoy the view of a dozen little boats, and
low wooded hills fringing the lochside; the word Tayvallich means
"the house in the pass". Inside, the Tayvallich is surprisingly modern –
smartly pine-clad, with a little bar and larger adjoining dining room.
The bar is tiled-floored, with raffia-backed chairs and little wood
tables, the dining room similar, but spacious and relaxing, with
a wood-burning stove, attractive dresser, and bentwood chairs around
scrubbed pine dining tables. The star of the handwritten menu is the
freshest local seafood, so local that oysters (half a dozen £5.50) come
from just yards away in Loch Sween, and clams from the Sound
of Jura (£9.50) just round the coast. Langoustines are beautifully fresh
(stir-fried £10), as are scallops (£8.75), and lobster (£15-17); salads
imaginative and crisp. Portions are generous, and the whole
atmosphere is very informal and relaxed. Holidaymakers turn up in
shorts, and babies are commendably tolerantly treated, with clip-on-
chairs and specially-rustled-up toddler food. Expect to pay about £33
for a three-course lunch for two, including half a litre of house wine.
Bar Food 12-2, 6-9. **Restaurant Meals** *7-9. Children's portions. Free
House.* **Beer** *Dryboroughs, Tetley. Patio/grassy foreshore, outdoor eating.
Inn closed 1 November to 31 March. Access, Visa.*

Troon	**Marine Highland Hotel**	67%	£132

Tel 0292 314444 Fax 0292 316922	Hotel

Crosbie Road Troon Strathclyde KA10 6HE	Map 4 A1

Not far from Prestwick and Glasgow, this handsome Victorian
sandstone structure overlooks the 18th fairway of Royal Troon
championship golf course. Accommodation options are standard,
deluxe or top-of-the-range Ambassador suites. Families are welcome,
with an occasional supervised crèche (enquire when booking), baby-
sitting and baby-listening offered; high-chairs in the brasserie and
a playpen in the ladies changing room. Some families may find the
imposing grandeur of the building and professional, adult hotel-
keeping attitudes intimidating, but, like all hotels, it's the staff that
count and the facilities are certainly suitable. *Rooms* 72. *Indoor
swimming pool, sauna, solarium, whirlpool bath, steam room, gymnasium,
beauty salon, squash, putting, snooker. Access, Amex, Visa, Diners.*

Turriff	**Towie Tavern**		

Tel 08884 201	Pub

Auchterless Turriff Grampian AB53 8EP	Map 2 D3

A favourite for its satisfying, wholesome food, this is a roadside
pebbledash pub on the A497, some four miles south of Turriff and
a short distance from the National Trust's 13th-century Fyvie Castle.
Seafood is featured at the Towie and a different daily menu assures
very fresh produce. The 'Fisherman's choice' offers whatever
is available that day: plaice, herring, mackerel or perhaps haddock
(poached or deep-fried £4.95). The food is more elaborate in the
restaurant. Smartly rustic decor and a new children's play area
equipped with swings and rope ladders. Music in the non-smoking
dining room. 50 whiskies. *Bar Food* 12-2, 6-9 (5-8.30 Sun).
Restaurant Meals 6-9. *Children's menu (£1.95-£2.50 per dish).
Children allowed in bar to eat. Free House. Beer McEwan's. Patio/Terrace,
outdoor eating. Access, Visa.*

Tweedsmuir	**Crook Inn**	59%	£52

Tel 089 97 272 Fax 089 97 294	Hotel

Tweedsmuir nr Biggar Borders ML12 6QN	Map 4 C1

Standing on the A701 and set in the ruggedly beautiful Tweed valley,
the Crook is a good base for walking, climbing and touring holidays.
A strange but winning amalgam of old stone-flagged farmers' bar and
1930s ocean liner-style lounges in the airy modern extension. Burns
wrote *Willie Wastle's Wife* in what is now the bar, and locally-born
John Buchan set many of his novels in the area. Neat bedrooms are
simple in their appointments, with no TVs or telephones; bring your
own cot for toddlers; a Z-bed will fit in the larger rooms. There
are a few Art Deco features in the lounge and some of the bathrooms.
One high-chair in the restaurant. A laundry service, storage for buggies
and the children's play area attract parents touring Scotland with
toddlers rather than tots. A craft centre has recently been created
from the old stable block. *Beer Broughton Greenmantle Ale. Garden.
Children's play area. Family room. Rooms 8. Garden, fishing. Access,
Amex, Diners, Visa.*

Ullapool   **Ceilidh Place**   £86

Tel 0854 612103   Fax 0854 612886   Inn

14 West Argyle Street Ullapool Highland IV26 2TY   Map 2 B3

Literally meaning 'Meeting Place', Ceilidh Place is much more: bookshop, arts centre, coffee shop and venue for theatre, music and poetry all housed in a cosy collection of welcoming rooms just 200 yards from Loch Broom. The pastry chef is kept busy all day providing scones, pancakes and cakes from 9.30am in the coffee shop and home-made puddings for lunch or supper. The restaurant, which opens at 8am for breakfast, also offers a smart "ally carte": fried aubergine slices in garlic mayonnaise (£3), grilled whole sole with parsley butter (£10), prawns and scallops Provençal (£13.50), dressed crab & salad (£7.50), beef stroganoff. In the bar there's a wide range of salads and stovies (£2.50) together with the likes of soup (£1.20), haggis pie (£3.25) and roulades (£4). Pretty bedrooms are comfortable and spotless; the eight rooms that are en suite also have phones; four cots (under-5s free), additional beds (from £6) and two high-chairs are provided. Eleven additional rooms in the Clubhouse (a separate building across the street) offer more spartan, budget accommodation and are not really suitable for families. *Bar Food 9.30-6 (7 in Summer). Restaurant Meals 6.30-9.30. Children's portions. Children allowed in bar to eat. Free House. Beer McEwans Export. Patio, outdoor eating. Rooms 15. Pub and accommodation closed 2 weeks Jan. Access, Amex, Diners, Visa.*

Weem   **Ailean Chraggan Hotel**

Tel 0887 820346   Pub

Weem by Aberfeldy Tayside PH15 2LD   Map 3 C4

Delightful little cottage inn, beautifully located against a steep woodland backdrop, and with two acres of gardens overlooking the Tay valley. The bright, sunny, well-kept bar has a central log-burning stove, with a dining area beside the picture windows. Simple, well-cooked food, highlighted by superb local seafood; try the Loch Etive mussels (£6.50), served in huge steaming portions with garlic bread or the Sound of Jura prawn platter (£11.95). There are special set menu seafood nights. Scottish cheeses on offer include Caboc and Tobermoray. Bedrooms are also recommended: spacious and light with fine old pieces of furniture, armchairs, and, in two rooms, small dressing areas. The front bedrooms have inspiring views. *Bar Food 12-2, 6.30-10 (8.45 winter). Children's portions. Children allowed in bar to eat. Garden, outdoor eating. Accommodation 3 bedrooms, all en suite, £52. Children welcome overnight, additional beds (£13 from 5yrs). Access, Visa.*

Owning a mobile phone is now more affordable than you think. More useful than you can imagine.

Isn't there room in your life for Cellnet?

0800

lifetime™

primetime™

Now you have the choice.

For further details call:

21 4000

Other 1993 Egon Ronay's Guides published by Pan Books Ltd

Egon Ronay's Cellnet Guide 1993

HOTELS & RESTAURANTS

3000 establishments in Great Britain and Ireland

cellnet

3000 HOTELS & RESTAURANTS

- Fully descriptive, up-to-date entries
- Comprehensive Irish section
- Unique London Serviced Apartment section
- Updated Places of Interest
- Conference and Banqueting facilities: 56-page Quick Reference section listed in county order
- Hotels individually graded
- Restaurants accurately assessed
- 46 pages of useful cross-reference lists
- 25 pages of colour maps
- Fully indexed
- **£13.99**

'...awaited as ever with a mixture of excitement and fear by the catering industry.' *The Irish Times*
'...the (1993) guide unleashed a tirade of invective against the mark-ups that some restaurants apply to the wines on their lists.' *Manchester Evening News*

1350 PUBS & INNS

The most reliable and comprehensive guide to good food and accommodation in Pubs and Inns throughout the land. An essential travelling companion.

Researched by anonymous inspections •
Fine food pubs featured •
Accommodation assessed •
Family facilities highlighted •
21 pages of colour maps •
Fully indexed •
£10.99 •

Egon Ronay's MLC Guide 1993

PUBS & INNS

The Best in Food & Accommodation

Over 1350 establishments in Great Britain

BRITISH MEAT

Also available:
Egon Ronay's Dubœuf Guide 1993 Just a Bite covering the best places nationwide in which to eat without breaking the bank – from Chinese dim sum snacks to comfortable afternoon teas, simple pizzas and bargain set meals. Completely redesigned this year. *£8.99*.

Wales

Aberaeron   Hive On The Quay

Tel 0545 570445	Café
Cadwgan Place Aberaeron Dyfed SA46 OBU	**Map 9 B4**

A bright, pleasant café situated right on the quayside, with a spacious conservatory for enjoying the views, and tables outside in the courtyard. Cakes and sandwiches are served all day, and at lunchtime and evenings in high summer there is a splendid buffet menu offering soup, quiche, pies, paté, salads and cheeses. Long-standing owners the Holgates have their own boat, hence popular seafood specials appear on the menu. Licensed only with full meals. *Seats 60.* ***Open*** *10.30-5 (Jul, Aug to 9.30).* ***Closed*** *Oct-Spring Bank Holiday. Access, Visa.*

Aberdovey   Penhelig Arms Hotel

Tel 0654 767215 Fax 0654 767690	Pub
Aberdovey Gwynedd LL35 0LT	**Map 8 C3**

'On the main road by the railway bridge' are directions which might usually strike fear into the hearts of prospective customers. But here are also unrivalled views across the Dyfi estuary to Ynyslas, making a splendid setting for Robert and Sally Hughes' smart black and white painted pub by the A493. Some disadvantages are inherent in a situation where no pavement exists 'twixt front door and double yellow lines, nor greater space, almost, between the single rail line at Penhelig halt and the hotel's gable end. Road noise and BR's occasional arrivals notwithstanding, the sea wall opposite makes a marvellous spot at any state of the tide to enjoy a leisurely al fresco lunch, while the tiny Fisherman's Bar provides a relaxing, and shady, alternative. Fan-cooled on the hottest summer days, and heated by two open fires in winter, here's an ideal place to enjoy a pint of good beer. The bar's the focal point of lunches from Monday to Saturday, and, when the weather's inclement, eaters soon overflow into the restaurant next door. Bar food features terrine of chicken (£2.65), and fresh fish vol-au-vents served with salad (£4.50), besides more substantial meals served with vegetables or chips, perhaps grilled trout (£4.95) or oxtail stew (£4.75). By night, bar meals are suspended in favour of a set-price dinner (3 courses £15.95). Sunday lunch (3 courses £9.50) has a more limited choice. Booking is advised. Plump for a room with a view: in fact, only two of the bedrooms lack a seascape. All have a cottagey feel and benefit from an individual approach to decor which makes the best of their higgledy-piggledy layout. Private bathroom, television and beverage trays are included throughout, but for a truly special occasion ask for one of the three superior rooms with balconies and sea views. *Bar Food & Restaurant Meals 12-2, 7-9. Free House.* ***Beer*** *Tetley, Marston's, Felinfoel. Patio, outdoor eating.* ***Accommodation*** *11 bedrooms, all en suite, £52. Children welcome overnight. Additional beds and cots available. Access, Visa.*

Aberdovey   Trefeddian Hotel   58%   £100*

Tel 0654 767213 Fax 0654 767777	Hotel
Aberdovey Gwynedd LL35 0SB	**Map 8 C3**

Three generations of the Cave family have run the Trefeddian, which stands a mile outside Aberdovey with fine views across Cardigan Bay, just a short walk from the sandy beach. Day rooms, which include lounge, reading room and bar, offer a choice of peace and quiet or conviviality. Neat, practical bedrooms include several with balconies; six family suites and four family rooms; cots and extra beds charged according to season. ★Half-board terms only in the hotel. Self-catering accommodation is also available. No under-5s in the dining room during dinner, but supper is arranged for children in the bedrooms between 5.45 and 6.30pm. Baby-listening is available. **Rooms** *46. Garden, indoor swimming pool & paddling pool, tennis, putting, snooker, table tennis & pool.* **Closed** *2 Jan–20 Mar. Access, Visa.*

Abergavenny Llanwenarth Arms Hotel

Tel 0873 810550	Pub
Brecon Road Abergavenny Gwent NP8 1EP	Map 9 D5

A much extended Usk-side inn with 10 acres of garden. There are two friendly bars, an attractive conservatory and a restaurant overlooking the river and valley; two stretches of good fishing are available to residents. The same menu of home-made food is available in both bar and restaurant – try the chicken and leek pie (£7.50), salmon, prawns and asparagus in cheese sauce (£7.25) followed by waffles with maple syrup (£3.80). Compact modern bedrooms in a three-storey annexe are equipped with modern facilities, and all enjoy splendid views. **Bar Food & Restaurant Meals** *12-2 (12-1.30 Sun), 6-9.45 (7-8.30 Sun). Children's menu (£3 per dish). Free House.* **Beer** *Bass, Wadworth. Garden, outdoor eating. Family room.* **Accommodation** *18 bedrooms, all en suite, £59. Children welcome overnight. Additional beds (£5), cots supplied. No dogs. Access, Amex, Diners, Visa.*

Abersoch Porth Tocyn Hotel 69% £88

Tel 0758 713303 Fax 0758 713538	Hotel
Bwlchtocyn Abersoch Gwynedd LL53 7BU	Map 8 B2

Check directions to find Porth Tocyn, once a row of lead-miners' cottages, high above Cardigan Bay. The Fletcher-Brewer family have guarded their reputation for attentive hospitality for more than 40 years, and the chintzy lounges, with their bright floral decor, fresh flowers and family antiques, contribute just the right degree of homeliness. A sitting room is now set aside for children with TV, videos, toys and games; children's high tea is also served there. Bedrooms, though generally small, are individually furnished in a similar style, many with restful sea views, all with private bathrooms and showers. Baby-sitting and baby-listening are provided by arrangement. Children can also let off steam in the 25 acres of grounds. Riding stables are just outside the hotel grounds. **Rooms** *17. Garden, outdoor swimming pool, tennis. Closed Nov–week before Easter. Access.*

Restaurant £60

The focal point of Louise Fletcher-Brewer's culinary output is her short-choice two- or five-course dinner menu, changed daily. Lobster and mango salad and almond roulade with avocado filling to start; pan-fried turbot with pepper butter or roast Welsh lamb with rosemary sauce are flanked by interesting herby soups and homely crumbles, syllabub or cheesecake. Lunch is casual, maybe alfresco by the pool, with a hot and cold buffet on Sundays. Improving, diverse wine list. A huge picture window in the dining room takes advantage of the views of Cardigan Bay. **Seats** *50. Parties 8. L 12.30-2 D 7.30-9.30. Set L (Sun) £14 Set D £17.50/£23.*

Barry   **Mount Sorrel Hotel**   59%   £85

Tel 0446 740069 Fax 0446 746600	Hotel

Porthkerry Road Barry South Glamorgan CF6 8AY   Map 9 C6

Converted from two Victorian houses 30 years ago, with more recent
additions for extra accommodation, meeting rooms and leisure
facilities. Comfortable day rooms, very acceptable bedrooms (children
up to 12 stay free when sharing with parents); two family suites with
interconecting rooms and six other family rooms. High-chairs and
a children's menu in the restaurant. Baby-listening available. *Rooms 50.*
Indoor swimming pool, keep-fit equipment, sauna, coffee shop (7am-8pm),
dinner dance (monthly). Access, Amex, Visa, Diners.

Brecon   **Wellington Hotel**

Tel 0874 625225 Fax 0874 623223	Pub

The Bulwark Brecon Powys LD3 7AD   Map 9 C5

Converted from a well-heeled merchant's town house, a Georgian-
fronted hotel standing opposite the Iron Duke's statue in the market
square. Recent modernisation has brought up-to-date hotel facilities
but kept the informality of a popular local; the former courtyard and
stables are now a shopping arcade, with a coffee shop and pub access.
Diverse food choices: chicken and ham pie (£4.20), steak and kidney
pie (£4.55), spinach and cheese crunch (£3.15), and 'house-special'
jumbo-sized vol-au-vents (£4.05). The residents' breakfast room
is coffee-shop by day, candle-lit restaurant by night, with strong
showings for both traditional Welsh and modern vegetarian cooking.
Guests can choose from a weekly-changing table d'hote menu
(3 courses £15.95) or à la carte. There's also Bacchus, an intimate wine
bar, which offers charcoal grills and self-served salads. Neatly-kept,
plainly-furnished bedrooms; first-floor residents' lounge. *Bar Food*
11-11 (12-10 Sun). Restaurant Meals 6.30-10. Children's menu
(£4.99). Children allowed in bar to eat. Free House. Beer Bass.
Accommodation 21 bedrooms, all en suite, £59. Children welcome
overnight, additional beds (£12 over 12 years), cots supplied.
Access, Amex, Visa.

Cenarth   **White Hart**

Tel 0239 710305	Pub

Cenarth nr Newcastle Emlyn Dyfed SA38 9JP   Map 9 B5

Unpretentious, homely but recommendable food – Anglesey eggs
(£2), steak and kidney pie (£4.25), home-cooked ham (£4.25)
at a characterful old village pub with low, beamed ceilings, carved
wooden pews and a wood-burning stove. *Bar Food 12-2.30, 6.30-9.30.*
Children's menu (£2.50 per dish). Free House. Beer Bass, Buckleys Bitter,
Worthington. Garden, outdoor eating, children's play area. Family room.
No credit cards.

Chepstow   **Castle View Hotel**   £65

Tel 0291 620349 Fax 0291 627397	Inn

16 Bridge Street Chepstow Gwent NP6 5EZ   Map 9 D6

This friendly little white-painted pub/hotel was built in the 17th
century as a private residence, perhaps with stones from neighbouring
Chepstow Castle, which was by then already in ruins; there are also
old art works and wooden winding staircase. Original walls and
timbers may still be seen, both in the public area and in some

bedrooms. One room, with its own lounge, is in a small cottage next door. Children are welcome overnight; additional beds and cots available. There's a secluded walled garden that children will enjoy, along with standard children's dishes (fish fingers, chipolatas with beans and chips); one high-chair is available. Good variety of snacks in the bar; simple but more substantial dishes served in the restaurant. Lovely garden. No-smoking area. **Rooms** *11. Garden. Access, Amex, Diners, Visa.*

Chepstow	St Pierre Hotel, Golf & Country Club	66%	£95
Tel 0291 625261 Fax 0291 629975			Hotel
St Pierre Park Chepstow Gwent NP6 6YA			Map 9 D6

Three miles from the Severn Bridge, take exit 22 off the M4, then A48 away from Chepstow. The heart of the hotel is a much-extended 14th-century mansion standing in 400 acres complete with an 11-acre lake. An extensive leisure club, two golf courses and a conference area make it a fine base for work or leisure. Among the day rooms are spacious lounges, three restaurants and a poolside bar. Bedrooms, many with splendid views, include 30 of Executive standard and 43 in the Lakeside village, where there are also multi-roomed lodges. Children up to 16 stay free in their parents' room. No dogs. Country Club Hotels. **Rooms** *147. Garden, croquet, tennis, bowling, badminton, indoor swimming pool, sauna, spa bath, solarium, beauty salon, squash, clay-pigeon shooting, children's playground, coffee shop (10am-10pm). Access, Amex, Visa, Diners.*

Crickhowell	Bear Hotel		£48
Tel 0873 810408 Fax 0873 811696			Inn
Brecon Road (A40) Crickhowell Powys NP8 1BW			Map 9 D5

As late as the year 1852 there were a dozen daily coach departures from the Bear, the London coach heading for Gloucester at 4.50pm and the North Mail leaving for Brecon at midnight. Vehicular access today is through the same cobbled archway, and the probable former waiting rooms. The bars of today are still evocative of those romantic days, with open fires, blackened oak beams, ponderous Welsh dressers and Victorian farmhouse furniture. Further inside in a maze of rooms and recesses, the original layout, with its various levels, has been mercifully preserved in three tiers of restaurant and function rooms which share the tranquillity of rear views across the garden. Where the old now meets the new is virtually impossible to detect. Eating arrangements are similarly two-tiered. Aged-looking bar menus offer starters and light snacks like soups, Welsh filo of Pencarreg cheese with redcurrants (£2.75), roll of smoked salmon with cream of salmon filling (£3.50), and wild local rabbit and hazelnut terrine (£3.95). Attractive main-house bedrooms are approached overlooking the Bear's wondrous interior on stairs with antique gnarled oak balustrades; the curve of the main road, less enchantingly, brings modern traffic within inches of the windows, a disadvantage of the front rooms. The inn's extension successfully echoes the balconied theme, with access to the neatly appointed new bedrooms looking inwards over the brick paving and flower beds of the courtyard. There is also a splendid honeymoon suite with four-poster bed and whirlpool bath. **Bar Food** *12-2, 6-10 (7-9.30 Sun).* **Restaurant Meals** *7-9.30 (except Sun). Children's portions. Free House.* **Beer** *Bass, Ruddles, Webster. Garden, outdoor eating. Family room.*

See over

Accommodation 29 bedrooms, all en suite, £48. Children welcome
overnight, additional beds (from £5), cots supplied. Access, Amex, Visa.

East Aberthaw   **Blue Anchor**

Tel 0446 750329	Pub

East Aberthaw nr Barry South Glamorgan CF6 9DD   Map 9 C6

There's a full six centuries of history to the splendid Blue Anchor, and
the old cliché about stepping back in time is truer here than is usual.
Entering this quaint thatched cottage through the black oak door,
under hanging ivy that appears to be holding the old stone walls
together, visitors are taken by way of nooks and crannies into
a smugglers' den which includes an internal doorway little more than
four feet high. Fifty years now in ownership of the Coleman family,
and administered day-to-day by the urbane Jeremy, the pub has gone
from strength to strength since the opening last year of its new
restaurant. A nearly hidden, almost cavernous stairway leads
to a dining room of surprising spaciousness, presided over by brilliant
young chef, Andrew Lawrence. The output of his young team
producing bar lunches daily (except Sunday), a six-night restaurant
menu (not Sunday), and comprehensive Sunday lunch (3-courses
£8.95), is little short of prodigious. From a regularly changing
restaurant menu choose the smoked Wye salmon, asparagus and
mango salad (£5.25), leek, laverbread and crab cocottes (£3.95), roast
Aylesbury duck (£11.20), fillets of Welsh beef (£11.95) or Wye
salmon (£10.35) and fishy specials from a blackboard. *Bar Food* 12-2
(not Sun). *Restaurant Meals* 12-2 (Sun only), 7.30-9.30 (except Sun)
(7-9.30 Sat). *Vegetarian dishes. Children's menu (lunch in bar – £1.50 per
dish). Free House*. *Beer* Buckley, Marston, Theakston, Wadworth. Patio,
outdoor eating. Family room. Access, Visa.

Felindre Farchog   **Salutation Inn**

Tel 0239 820564	Pub

On A487 Felindre Farchog Dyfed SA41 3UY   Map 9 B5

Modernised, well-kept old inn (the original building goes back to the
16th century) at the centre of the Preseli National Park. Olde worlde
lounge, games room-cum public bar, and overflow Garden Room
leading off, with patio doors to riverside garden. Good bedrooms
in modern wing are well-equipped and maintained; bright, good-sized
residents' lounge. *Free House. Beer* Burton. *Riverside garden, outdoor
eating, children's play area. Family room. Accommodation 9 bedrooms,
all en suite, £52. Children welcome overnight, additional beds (from £5),
cots supplied. Access, Visa.*

Harlech   **Llew Glas**

Tel 0766 780700	Bistro

Plas-y-Goits High Street Harlech   Map 8 B2

Having closed their village bakehouse and tearoom in early 1992, the
Pharaoh family now concentrate their efforts on this health-conscious
upstairs Bistro. Substantial starters and light main dishes are
interchangeable here: Mermeester (£3.95), tagliatelle carbonara
(£5.60) and avocado and prawn thermidor (£4.40) are typical
choices. Clearly indicated vegetarian and vegan dishes include
ratatouille crumble (£5.60) and tiene of rice and stir-fried vegetables
(£5.40); meat-eaters can choose from pies of game (£6.50), lamb,
mint and cranberry (£5.45) and duck and orange (£6.10). Children

are offered their own recommended menu and welcomed until
7.30pm. Watch out for the minimum charge, £10.50 as we went
to press. No smoking. *Seats 40. Open Dinner only 7-10. Closed Sun.*
Access, Visa.

Hay-on-Wye   Kilvert Country Hotel

Tel 0497 821042 Fax 0497 821004	Pub

Bull Ring Hay-on-Wye Powys HR3 5AG   **Map 9 D5**

A town-centre inn dating from the late 17th century, named after the
diarist Reverend Francis Kilvert. The characterful single bar also
doubles as reception, and behind a stained-glass partition is the intimate
residents' lounge. Splendid brass bedsteads are a feature of the
bedrooms, many of which are beamed. All have en-suite shower
rooms as well as modern hotel conveniences; cots, baths, changing
mats and potties can all be provided. The baby-listening is reliable and
baby-sitting can be arranged. Extremely busy during May Bank
Holiday when the world-famous festival of literature takes place.
*Garden. Free House. Beer Bass, Flowers. Accommodation 11 bedrooms,
all en suite, £57.50. Children welcome overnight, additional beds and cots
available. Check-in by arrangement. Access, Amex, Visa.*

Hay-on-Wye   Old Black Lion

Tel 0497 820841	Pub

26 Lion Street Hay-on-Wye Powys HR3 5AD   **Map 9 D5**

Tucked away from the bustling centre of this Welsh Marches town
(renowned for its book shops), the Lion has established an enviable
reputation for its food: what it lacks is room. Residents have priority
in the restaurant (open evenings only) where booking is essential:
as diners study their menus in the single bar there can be a scramble
for seats and bar menus, and thus a log-jam of orders. From a very
long menu choices range from a simple ploughman's (£3.20) through
to seafood pancakes with spicy tomato sauce (£5.25) and aubergines
in chili and garlic sauce (£4.75) and there's a 'simply steaks' menu
in the £8-£12 range. The pub's blackened beams and bowers, though
not all original, are nonetheless full of character. Accommodation
is divided between the main house and a purpose-built extension
adjoining the car park. All rooms except one are en suite and all are
neatly kept: what the older rooms may lack in space and modern-day
comforts is now compensated by some smart new fabrics and carpets
alongside the evocative character of little-changed 17th-century inn.
*Bar Food 12-2, 7-9. Restaurant Meals 12-2, 7-9 (Sun only). Children's
portions. Free House. Beer Bass, Flowers. Outdoor eating. Accommodation
10 bedrooms, 9 en suite, £40. Children welcome overnight, additional beds
(£10), cots supplied. Check-in by arrangement. Access, Visa.*

Letterston   Something's Cooking

Tel 0348 840621	Café

The Square Letterston Dyfed   **Map 9 A5**

Recent additions here of a bright, airy conservatory and full restaurant
licence have helped develop Trevor Rand's roadside fish-and-chip take-
away (by the A40 at its junction with the B4331) into the area's
premier chippy. A warm family welcome is the added bonus, while
senior citizens benefit from keenly-priced mid-week lunches.
In addition to a plethora of lightly battered fresh fish, specials add

perhaps shrimps and herrings marinated with dill, with Southern fried chicken, BBQ spare ribs and vegetarian spring rolls for those of less aquatic persuasion. No dogs. No smoking. *Seats 44. Open 11-2 &* *5.30-10.30 (Sun 6-10, Sat 11-10.30). Closed L Sun (all Sun in winter). Access, Visa.*

Llanarmon Dyffryn Ceiriog	West Arms Hotel	£78
Tel 069 176 665 Fax 069 176 622		Inn
Llanarmon Dyffryn Ceiriog nr Llangollen Clwyd LL20 7LD		Map 8 D2

In a picturesque hamlet at the head of the Ceiriog Valley, this 16th-century former farmhouse stands to the front of well-manicured gardens which run down to the river bridge. Black and white painted outside and bedecked with creeper and summer flowers, it's a haven of cosy comfort within, the tone set by open log fires, flagstone floors, blackened beams and rustic furniture. Tucked around the back, the Wayfarers' Bar serves a modest selection of well-prepared snacks in chintzy surroundings with an adjacent family lounge and patio. Following soup (£2.40), smoked mackerel paté (£3) and Stilton mushrooms (£3.50), local Ceiriog trout (£5.75) heads a list of main meals that might include turkey, ham and mushroom pie (£4.75), tagliatelle with peppers, mushrooms and cream (£4.50) or a cauliflower, peanut and cream cheese bake (£2.50). Bedrooms retain the period comfort afforded by handsome antique furnishings alongside modern fitted bathrooms; homely extras include pot pourri and quality toiletries. Five rooms are reserved for non-smokers and two suites have plenty of space for family use. Up for sale as we went to press, but the management hoped to build on their recent success. *Bar Food 12-2.30, 6.30-9.30 (Sun from 7). Restaurant Meals 12-2.30 (Sun only), 7.30-9.30. Free House. Beer Boddington. Garden. Outdoor eating. Children's play area. Family Room. Accommodation 13 rooms, all en suite, £78. Children welcome overnight, additional beds £21.50. Cots supplied £10. Access, Amex, Diners, Visa.*

Llanddarog	Butchers Arms	
Tel 026 727 5330		Pub
Llanddarog nr Carmarthen Dyfed SE32 8NS		Map 9 B5

This tiny pub stands by the 19th-century stone-built St Tarog's church, and the old village street runs down to where the A40 once thundered by. We say hooray today for the new by-pass which makes this such a sleepy spot, and say another as the low, flower-bedecked exterior of the pub gives way to a splendidly atmospheric interior. Felinfoel ales take their rightful place at the bar, as Welsh is widely spoken here and there's a warm welcome plus friendly service. If you have decided to eat, then book ahead and side-step the queue. Take time, however, to admire the Toby jug collection hanging in the bar, and the shining collection of miniature brass lamps and candleholders on the mantel, under which the dog-grate glows in winter and flower vases add a blaze of summer colour. In addition to the regular menu, on which the prime steaks offer particularly good value, look for the specials board, which is strong on fresh fish and seafood. *Bar Food & Restaurant Meals 11-2.45 (except Sun), 6-10. Children's menu (from £1.20). Free House. Beer Felinfoel. Children allowed in bar to eat. Patio, outdoor eating. Family room. Access, Visa.*

Llandissilio   Bush Inn

Tel 043756 3626	Pub

Llandissilio nr Clynderwen Dyfed SA66 7TS   Map 9 B5

Tiny, characterful little bar in a cosy old pub offering good food.
Open fires, polished tables, plants and dressers crammed with plates
and ornaments provide a cosy background in the bright dining room,
where help-yourself salads are laid out for choosing; try them with
home-cooked local turkey (£4.95), cheese and onion tart (£3.95),
or go for a simple hot dish like lasagne (£3.95), followed by good
local cheese and apple crumble or treacle tart (£1.60). One high-chair
in the dining room. *Bar Food & Restaurant Meals 12-2.30, 6.30-9.30.
Free House.* **Beer** *Bass, Worthington. Garden, outdoor eating.
No credit cards.*

Llandudno   St Tudno Hotel   69%   £90

Tel 0492 874411 Fax 0492 860407	Hotel

The Promenade Llandudno Gwynedd LL30 2LP   Map 8 C1

Effusive and attentive owners Martin and Janette Bland unexpectedly
reveal a wealth of Edwardian charm behind the terraced facade of their
delightful seafront hotel. Guests are made truly welcome in the stylish
bar/lounge and in a reading room reserved for non-smokers.
Bedrooms, though modestly sized, achieve a feeling of space through
sympathetic use of bright fabrics and natural daylight; two family
suites and five particularly spacious bedrooms that will take an extra
bed or cot. Bathrooms are thoughtfully kitted out with top-class
towelling and toiletries. High tea is served in the coffee lounge where
high-chairs are provided. No dogs. *Rooms 24. Indoor swimming pool,
patio. Access, Amex, Visa.*

Garden Room   £65

While conservatory-style furniture, potted plants and painted
trelliswork and trees on the walls create the garden-room illusion,
David Harding's modern British menus are altogether more authentic.
At fixed prices, lunch and dinner start with the likes of grilled goat's
cheese with leaf salad and bacon, and crab tart with butter sauce.
Following a soup or sorbet come salmon, venison, free-range chicken,
Welsh lamb and a daily vegetarian main dish. Lavish desserts, savoury
and organically produced Welsh cheeses all follow. Lighter lunches
are served in the coffee lounge. Fair prices on the thoughtfully-put-
together and helpfully descriptive wine list. No under-5s; no smoking.
Seats 60. L 12.30-2 D 6.45-9.30. Set L £11.50 Set D £23.50.

Llanfrynach   White Swan

Tel 0874 86276	Pub

Llanfrynach Powys LD3 7BZ   Map 9 C5

Flagstone floors, rough stone walls, beams and a vast inglenook create
a simple rustic setting for the Bells' hearty, carefully prepared food
at this pretty village pub. French onion soup (£2.15), smoked
mackerel paté (£3.90) and tasty meat (beef and mushroom £7.20)
and fish pies are popular dishes. Vegetarians are catered for (macaroni
and broccoli cheese £4.30) and a children's menu is available in the
bar. *Bar Food (except Mon) 12-2 (12-1.30 Sun), 5-10 (7-9 Sun).
Children's menu (£3.50). Children allowed to eat in bar. Free House.*
Beer *Brains, Whitbread. Garden. Family room. No credit cards.*

Llangammarch Wells Lake Country House Hotel 68%

£90

Tel 059 12 202   Fax 059 12 457   Hotel

Llangammarch Wells Powys LD4 4BS   Map 9 C4

Standing in 50 acres of parkland and enjoying genuine tranquillity,
a mainly Edwardian building run along personable lines by Jean-Pierre
and Jan Mifsud. Grandly proportioned day rooms include a handsome
parlour lounge that retains much of the period character by using
traditional furnishings and fabrics. Elegant bedrooms have fine views
and are individually styled with a combination of antiques and restful
colour schemes; four family rooms share two cots (under-5s free
of charge) and baby-sitting can be easily arranged. Smart, efficient staff
mirror the owners' enthusiasm. Popular with fishermen as the river
Irfon runs through the grounds; the lake is well stocked with trout.
94 species of birds are claimed to have been spotted around
the grounds. Children have their own high tea at 6pm. *Rooms 19.*
Garden, pitch & putt, tennis, fishing, clay-pigeon shooting, snooker.
Closed Jan. Access, Amex, Visa.

Restaurant

£65

Fixed-price, four-course dinners are typified by cream of winter
vegetable soup with hazelnut dumplings, timbale of salmon, smoked
salmon and crab with a cucumber and mint yoghurt sauce, followed
by fillet of Welsh venison with mustard and horseradish sauces and
finishing with a langue de chat basket of plum and almond mousse
with plum and orange sauce. Table d'hote lunches are served in
the restaurant or lighter lunches in the lounge. No children under
12 in the dining room. Plenty of choice on the varied wine list.
Seats 50. Parties 8. L 1-2 (non-residents by arrangement only)
D 7-8.45. Set L £14.50 Set D £24.50.

Llangorse   Red Lion

Tel 0874 84238   Pub

Llangorse nr Brecon Powys LD3 7TY   Map 9 D5

Nestling in a lovely valley between the Brecon Beacons and the Black
Mountains is a pleasant 180-year-old village pub offering
accommodation in ten homely, comfortable and unfussy bedrooms.
Half have simple but immaculately kept en-suite bathrooms, the
remainder showers and washbasins only; baby-listening is fitted and
baby-sitting can be arranged. There is a tiny residents lounge, and
downstairs there are two cosy, stone-walled bars. There is a sand pit,
but children too young for hill-walking will need supervision, as the
garden is precipitous. Mealtimes bring high-chairs, baby food,
a children's menu or small portions of the equally unfussy food.
Free House. **Beer** *Flowers, Marston's, Brains, Boddingtons. Riverside*
terrace/patio. Family room. **Accommodation** *10 bedrooms, 5 en suite.*
Children welcome overnight. Additional beds (no charge under 12 yrs)
and cots supplied. No credit cards.

Llanrwst   Meadowsweet   63%

£45

Tel 0492 640732   Hotel

Station Road Llanrwst Gwynedd LL26 0DS   Map 8 C2

Overlooking the Conwy Valley towards Snowdonia, Meadowsweet's
attractions include nearby fishing and riding, home comforts and fine
food. An intimate hotel with individually designed bedrooms
featuring antique pine furniture; all have en-suite shower rooms,

though there's also a separate bathroom on each floor. Under-10s accommodated free in their parents' room; baby-listening available. Parents should formalise meal times in advance for very junior residents; two high-chairs are provided. ***Rooms** 10. Access, Visa.*

Restaurant £60

John Evans is a self-taught cook whose dedication is an integral part of the Meadowsweet philosophy. The five-course fixed-price dinner might comprise hot spiced wild mushrooms, home-cured gravad lax with soured cream sauce, boned quail on chicken liver risotto with wine and olive sauce, fine Welsh farmhouse cheeses and chocolate marquise with orange custard. A spendid, classic wine list. No smoking. ***Seats** 36. Parties 12. L 12-1.30 D 6.30-9.30 (Sun to 9). Closed L in winter. Set L £8.95. Set D £26.*

Llanwrtyd Wells	Drover's Rest	
Tel 059 13 264		Café
The Square Llanwrtyd Wells Powys		Map 9 C4

Nestling by the Irfon river bridge at the heart of Wales's smallest town (population 600) is Peter James's delectable café. He cares about his customers and his catering: local suppliers provide the produce, his sister is the proud patissière. Start the day with a substantial Welsh breakfast (£3.80), or choose at lunchtime between fresh filled sandwiches and baked potatoes, local trout (£6.95) and lamb cutlets (£5.95) or vegetarian-friendly baked cauliflower cheese (£3.20) and pasta with vegetable cream sauce (£5.20). The popular Welsh Afternoon Tea (£3.65) includes buttered *bara brith* and Welsh cakes. Book for family Sunday lunches (£6.95) and gourmet Friday and Saturday dinners, which are more expensive. ***Seats** 34. **Open** 10-4.30 (Sun from 12), also Fri & Sat 7-10.30. **Closed** Mon, 25 Dec. No credit cards.*

Llyswen	Griffin Inn	£50
Tel 0874 754241 Fax 0874 754592		Inn
Llyswen Brecon Powys LD3 0OU		Map 9 D5

Mythically speaking, the griffin is a creature of vast proportions, half lion, half dragon, its whole being considerably less awesome than its constituent parts. No such problems exist for Richard and Di Stockton, for their Griffin is nothing short of splendid in all departments and so conspicuously well-run as to have been voted the most welcoming pub in Britain. That locally-caught salmon and brook trout feature so regularly on the menu is scarcely surprising as the Griffin employs its own ghillie, and fishing stories abound in the bar – the centre of village life. It's hung with framed displays of fishing flies and maps of the upper and lower reaches of the Wye valley (there's fine walking country all around), and is dominated by a splendid inglenook fire. In the adjacent lounge, low tables, high-backed Windsor chairs, two high-chairs and window seats make a comfortable setting for either a light snack or one of the daily-changing hot dishes, perhaps home-made soup (£2.50), hot chicken liver and bacon salad (£3.35), ratatouille pasta (£5.95) or jugged venison (£7.50). Evening meals provide a wider choice of more substantial fare either in the no-smoking restaurant or the bars, as space allows. Plenty of space in the ladies for non-resident mums to change a nipper's nappy. Bedrooms, all but one with en-suite facilities, are named with fishing themes. To say

that they are cottagey is not to decry the pretty floral curtains and
bed-covers; they are also wonderfully tranquil, and though there are
telephones, television is considered superfluous. The splendid new
residents' lounge on the upper floor of the inn's oldest part
is dramatically set under original rafters dating, it is thought, from
1467. *Bar Food 12-2, 7-9.* *Restaurant Meals 1-3 (Sun only), 7-9.*
Children's portions. Children allowed in bar to eat. Free House.
Beer Boddingtons, Flowers. Enclosed garden, patio, outdoor eating.
Accommodation 8 bedrooms, 7 en suite, £50. Children welcome
overnight. Additional beds and cots available. Access, Amex,
Diners, Visa.

Lydart   Gockett Inn

Tel 0600 860486	Pub
Lydart nr Monmouth Gwent NP5 4AD	Map 9 D5

This former staging post on the St David's to London route stands atop
an escarpment (now the B4293) three miles outside Monmouth;
'Gockett' was the local name for the black grouse which inhabited
these heathlands until their extinction a century or so ago. Central
to the inn's modern attractions are Hazel Short's daily-selected menus.
Beef pie may be cooked with Guinness and mushrooms or smoked
oysters. Equally popular pies are rabbit with mustard and rosemary,
or chicken and asparagus (£4.95). Home-made soups (£2.25) are
thick, flavourful, and popular, along with the likes of garlic
mushrooms, duck liver paté, local salmon mayonnaise (£3.95)
or tagliatelle Alfredo. Though all are officially starters, a light lunch
of two of them is equally acceptable, except on Sundays, when
bookings should be made for the fixed-price lunch (3 courses £8.95).
Leather banquettes, silk flowers and gathered drapes lend a bright,
cottagey feel to the original dining room, where tables are neatly
spaced in front of a smoky, stone fireplace hung with horse brasses and
copper bed-warmers. A recent extension to the bar leads to an enclosed
rear patio and a neat garden for al fresco eating in fine weather. *Bar*
Food & Restaurant Meals 12-2, 7-10 (7-9 Sun). Children's portions
(£2.25 per dish). Children allowed in bar to eat. Free House. Beer Bass,
Felinfoel. Garden, outdoor eating, children's play area.
Access, Visa.

Machynlleth   Centre for Alternative Technology

Tel 0654 702400	Restaurant
Pantperthog Machynlleth Powys	Map 8 C3

A co-operative-run vegetarian restaurant and coffee house that forms
part of a fascinating complex, 3 miles north of Machynlleth, just off
the A487, at the forefront of alternative technology. The counter
service selection is slightly restricted and winter months, but in the
busy summer season offers tempting cakes – carrot or bara brith (70p),
a salad bar (£1.10 per portion), vegetarian pasties (85p) and sausage
rolls (75p), and, from midday onwards, hot foods ranging from soup
(carrot and red lentil £1.75) and baked potatoes with cheese (£1.80),
to homity pie (£1.95) and lasagne (£2.50). Try the trifle (£1.50)
to finish. Always a vegan soup and main course, and plenty of organic
produce from local sources. Picnic area in fine weather. No smoking.
Good children's facilities. *Seats 80. Open 10-5 (summer to 6),*
11-3 Nov-Mar. Closed 1 week Christmas, 2 weeks Jan.
No credit cards.

Machynlleth   **Quarry Shop**

Tel 0654 702624	Café
13 Maengwyn Street Machynlleth Powys	**Map 8 C3**

Part of the same co-operative that runs the Centre of Alternative
Technology, a friendly counter-service café with pine furniture, and
wholefood shop. Various cakes – carrot and coconut, carob, ginger and
date ripple, apricot slice – are 65p, salads are 90p per portion,
or there's a daily soup (£1.10), pizza (£1.75) and hot daily specials,
perhaps sweet and sour vegetables and tofu, strudel parcels
or moussaka (all £3.20). Breakfast, from 9-11am, includes muesli,
toast, yoghurt and fruit. Pavement tables. Good children's facilities.
No-smoking area. **Seats** 35. **Open** 9-5 (*winter to 4.30 and Thur to 2*).
Closed *Sun & Bank Holidays* (*except during school holidays*).
No credit cards.

Miskin   **Miskin Manor**   **70%**   £107

Tel 0443 224204 Fax 0443 237606	Hotel
Penddylan Road Pontyclun Miskin Mid-Glamorgan CF7 8ND	**Map 9 C6**

Built in 1858, Miskin Manor is a handsome stone mansion set
in 20 acres of garden and woodland close to the river Ely, 8 miles
from the centre of Cardiff. Day rooms are very comfortable and deep
sofas in floral fabrics invite guests to relax and gaze out over the
gardens. Bedrooms are vast – even singles have sofas – and are
luxurious without being ostentatious; some have four-posters and
there are two suites. The Fredericks sports and leisure complex (open
10am-11pm) offers informal eating and relaxing areas; conference
facilities handle up to 180 delegates. Parents with children may feel
engulfed by mid-week conference delegates or even by weekend
weddings; nevertheless, the Manor can be a haven of tranquillity –
enquire when booking about large gatherings. A supervised crèche
(from 9am-3pm) operates Monday to Friday for children up to the
age of five. **Rooms** 32. *Garden, indoor swimming pool, gymnasium, spa
bath, steam room, sauna, solarium, beauty salon, badminton, coffee shop
(10am-11pm). Access, Amex, Visa, Diners.*

Newport   **Cnapan**

Tel 0239 820575	Restaurant
East Street Newport Dyfed	**Map 9 D6**

The charming Lloyd and Cooper families are well known by other
families for having created a lovely country-house setting with pretty
garden in which to enjoy inventive, vegetarian-biased food. The day
starts for coffee at 10.30, but at 12.15 the main interest arrives with
the light lunch menu which offers thick vegetable soup with soda
bread and Llanboidy cheese (£1.95), the Cnapan cheese platter with
home-made chutney (£3.25) and oat-based flans, the boozy carrot,
cashew nut and cream cheese or flaked smoked fish, horseradish,
mustard seed and mango versions, served with jacket potato and salad
(both £3.75) the most popular. A blackboard lists puddings, perhaps
treacle tart, fruit crumble or old favourite piggy's delight (all £2.25).
Special children's burgers. Popular family Sunday lunch. Smoking
in the bar area only. More elaborate evening meals and five letting
bedrooms. **Seats** 48. **Open** 10.30-2.30. **Closed** *Tue, all Feb and
Nov-Easter (except L Sun). Access, Visa.*

Penmaenpool   George III Hotel   £63

Tel 0341 422525   Fax 0341 423565   Inn

Penmaenpool nr Dolgellau Gwynedd LL40 1YD   Map 8 C3

In a memorable location hedged between the road (A493) and former
railway line, the George III, which hugs the bank of the tidal
Mawddach estuary, was once an integral part of Penmaenpool railway
station. Today's inn was created in the 1890s from two 17th-century
buildings, one the original pub and the other a ship chandler's which
serviced the adjacent boat-builder's yards. As an alternative to sharing
with locals and visitors the stone-flagged cellar bar, residents might
prefer the rather dated air of the Welsh Dresser bar and its cosy
lounge with striking copper-hooded inglenook. Main-house bedrooms
echo the period feel with creaky floors and some fine exposed roof
timbers. The Victorian Lodge, which, prior to the railway's closure
by Dr Beeching in 1964, housed the station waiting room and ticket
office, was converted latterly into six quite stylish bedrooms, all
en suite, which enjoy the pick of the views. New owners took over
at the end of last year and, hopefully, some of the more obvious signs
of neglect will speedily be rectified. *Free House.* **Beer** *Marston's,
Felinfoel.* **Accommodation** *12 rooms, 10 en suite, £63. Children welcome
overnight, additional beds £5. Cots supplied. Access, Amex, Visa.*

Pont ar Gothi   Cresselly Arms

Tel 0267 290221   Pub

Pont ar Gothi nr Nantgaredig Dyfed   Map 9 B5

A good pub for family expeditions; fun play equipment for children
in the garden. **Beer** *Whitbread, Marston's. Riverside garden. Children's
play area. Family room.*

Raglan   Beaufort Arms Hotel

Tel and Fax 0291 690412   Pub

High Street Raglan Gwent NP5 2DY   Map 9 D5

Spotlessly maintained both inside and out, a whitewashed village inn,
built in the 15th century; exposed stonework and Tudor timbers
survive in the Castle Country Bar. Bar food is wholesome and home-
made: soup (£1.50), mussels Provençal (£2.95), fresh sardines
(£2.50). A 3-course £12.50 table d'hote menu is available in the
restaurant. Bedrooms are bright, comfortable and attractively
decorated. **Bar Food** *12-2, 6-10.* **Restaurant Meals** *7-9.30. Children's
menu (£3.99). Children allowed in bar to eat. Free House.* **Beer** *Courage.
Patio, outdoor eating.* **Accommodation** *15 bedrooms, all en suite, £45.
Children welcome overnight. Additional beds and cots available. Access,
Amex, Diners, Visa.*

Red Wharf Bay   Old Boathouse Café

Tel 0248 852731   Café

Red Wharf Bay Anglesey   Map 8 B1

Typical seaside fare at the Griffiths' summer café remains
commendable more for freshness than originality. To great advantage
are the home cooked steak and kidney (£3.95) and cottage pies,
chicken tikka masala (£4.95) and lasagnes piled with chips which
make for substantial inexpensive eating, with children's portions
of almost anything. Start of the day with an all-morning Welsh
breakfast (£3.50) or snack or sandwiches and baked potatoes (from

£1.50) through the day, or scones with jam and cream (£1.25) and dependable home baking. The tiled floor and pine tables are neat and tidy within and there's a spacious front patio. Unlicensed, so bring your own. **Seats** 30. **Open** 10-7. **Closed** Nov-Easter. No credit cards.

Red Wharf Bay   Ship Inn

Tel 0248 852568	Pub

Red Wharf Bay Anglesey LO75 4RJ   Map 8 B1

Right on the shore at Traeth Coch and overlooking the sweep of the bay, the low white-painted limestone Ship Inn is fronted by hanging baskets and sports a fine pair of Lloyd and Trouncer cast iron street lamps at its entrance. A depiction of SS Royal Charter is inlaid in the upper wall, and a Silver Jubilee replica of the royal yacht Britannia's wheel is mounted in the bar. Customers come early at mealtimes, so at busy summer peak times delays are unavoidable, yet the menu remains sensibly short and with it comes a guarantee of freshness. Stick around a while and you'll see the local fishermen delivering their catch. The menu includes a selection of light meals, described as snacks: paté and toast (£3.50), smoked salmon trout, stuffed mushrooms (£3.90) and Stilton and apple in filo pastry (£3.95), all of which come with salad. Main meals, accompanied by chips or baked potato, start with beef and garlic sausage in burgundy wine sauce (£5.30), spicy monkfish casserole (£5.20), chicken stuffed with Stilton and wrapped in bacon (£5.40) or the grilled catch of the day in the £7-£9 range. Quarry-tiled floors, genuine exposed beams and stonework, plus a mish-mash of maritime memorabilia and chiming clocks all make for an interesting interior; look too for the Tom Browne snooker cartoons and the fine Toby jug collection, whose rarest specimens are glass-encased. Children can enjoy their own menu (£2.25-2.65 per dish) in the little back family room, or, while parents keep a constant eye on the treacherous tide, they can romp in the garden on the shore line. **Bar Food** 12-2.15 (Jul-Sep 12-9.15), 7-9.15. **Restaurant Meals** 12-2.15 (only Sun in winter), 7-9.15 (only Fri/Sat in winter). Children's menu (£2.25-£2.65). Free House. **Beer** Marston's, Tetley. Garden, outdoor eating, children's playing area. Family room. Access, Visa.

St David's   St Non's Hotel   56%   £73

Tel 0437-720239 Fax 0437 721839	Hotel

St David's Dyfed SA62 6RJ   Map 9 A5

A friendly family hotel just outside the town which offers some of the best children's terms around: under-6s sharing their parents' room both stay *and* eat free (breakfast and high-tea); over-6s are charged £12 half board. Other bonuses include five ground-floor bedrooms for the less mobile, and free golf at the picturesque St David's 9-hole course. **Rooms** 24. Garden. Access, Amex, Visa, Diners.

Tintern Abbey   Royal George   59%   £64

Tel 0291 689205 Fax 0291 689448	Hotel

Tintern Abbey nr Chepstow Gwent NP6 6SF   Map 9 D5

A friendly hotel set at the foot of a lovely wooded hillside; a trout stream runs alongside, and the ruins of Tintern Abbey are just a short walk away. There's ample bar and lounge space (one lounge is stocked with board games) and a function room. Some of the bedrooms have balconies overlooking the gardens. One child under 14 free when

sharing with two adults; each additional child £6. Ten rooms are
suitable for family occupation; three cots, baby-sitting and baby-
listening are available. 'Good grub for mini tots' includes mermaid's
favourite fish fingers and cowboy's allnighter. **Rooms** 19. *Garden,
fishing. Access, Amex, Visa, Diners.*

Trecastle   Castle Hotel

Tel 0874 636354 Fax 0874 638000	Pub
Trecastle Powys LD3 8UH	Map 9 C5

Imposing Georgian hotel, a former coaching halt, with lots
of character surviving. Bar meals in the cosy hotel bar with its open
fire, long wooden tables, benches and window seats; there's also
an elegantly proportioned restaurant. Individually decorated bedrooms
vary in size from small to spacious. *Free House.* **Beer** *Courage.
Patio/terrace, outdoor eating.* **Accommodation** *9 bedrooms, 5 en suite, £48.
Children welcome overnight. Additional beds and cots available.
Access, Visa.*

Trellech   The Village Green

Tel 0600 860119	Pub
Trellech nr Monmouth Gwent NP5 4PA	Map 9 D5

Saved from dereliction five years ago by Bob and Jane Evans,
the 450-year-old, creeper-clad Village Green comprises restaurant
(recommended in our 1993 *Hotels and Restaurants Guide*) and bistro
as well as pub, and there are even a couple of small bedroom suites
with kitchenette-cum-lounge and bedroom with en-suite shower room
(they are let either on a self-catering or a bed and breakfast basis).
The two small, carpeted bars display rugby paintings by local artist
Richard Wills, one of Wales's best-known artists, and the stone-walled
bistro is festooned with bunches of dried flowers hanging from the
rafters. In the bistro, a long, wide-ranging blackboard menu changes
frequently and might include whole grilled lobster (£11.50), beef
teriyaki (£7.75), loin of pork in cider (£7.75), beef bourguignon
(£8), chicken niçoise (£7.50) and deep-fried potato skins. A separate
bar menu offers more traditional pub fare with sandwiches (from
£1.50), jacket potatoes and various ploughman's lunches (from £3.50)
with home-made bread. **Bar Food** *11.45-2, 6.30-9.45. Children's
portions. Free House.* **Beer** *Bass. Outdoor eating. Family room.*
Accommodation *2 bedrooms, both en suite, £45 inc. Continental breakfast
only. Children welcome overnight. Check-in by arrangement. Access, Visa.*

Welshpool   Powis Castle Tea Rooms

Tel 0938 555499	Tea Room
Powis Castle Welshpool Powys	Map 8 D3

You needn't pay admission to the famous gardens to enjoy a snack
at this National Trust restaurant, and the drive past ponds and
peacocks is draw enough. A spacious hall, refectory-style, adjoins the
castle keep; from morning coffee through light lunches to afternoon
teas it's a bustling place. Most notable are the assorted Welsh cheeses
of the Coachman's Choice (£4.95), a Powis Welsh Cream Tea (£2.75)
and imaginative alternatives for youngsters (£1.60). There are daily
hot lunches and salads; licensed also with main meals. No smoking.
The tea rooms are open Wed to Sun April to end June and
September/October; Tue to Sun July and August; also Bank Holiday
Mondays. **Seats** *80.* **Open** *11-5.30. Access, Visa.*

Whitebrook   **Crown at Whitebrook**

Tel 0600 860254 Fax 0600 860607	Pub

Whitebrook Monmouth Gwent NP5 4TX   **Map 9 D5**

Scarcely the archetypal Welsh pub, scarcely, in fact, a pub at all, the
Crown's uniqueness lies in the successful re-creation of a French-style
auberge deep in the Wye valley. Don't be deterred by the road:
Whitebrook may be signposted as a mile from the A466 at the river
bridge, but the inn is at least two, through a doubt-inducing farmyard
crossing; keep going. Once safely within, a welcoming lounge, mixing
deep sofas and coffee tables leads to an almost rustic dining room and
a gingham-clothed extension which serves as a breakfast room. For
lunch or dinner (the latter menu also optional at lunchtime), the accent
of Sandra Bates's menu is set firmly in France, yet remains in harmony
with the rural Welsh setting. Dinner is *prix fixe* (£24.50); the £14
lunch menu is a little simpler. Bar meals are somewhat secondary
by comparison, though equal in quality and imagination. Pancakes
filled with melted Gruyère, mushroom and ham (£4.95), or home-
made venison sausage rolls with chutney (£4.95) are typical dishes.
100-bottle wine list with 30 half bottles and a fine selection of mostly
Welsh cheeses. Residents are particularly rewarded by their journey
up the valley; this is a delightful refuge from the world. A dozen
pastel-coloured bedrooms feature up-to-date fittings, cosy, carpeted
bathrooms, and peace undisturbed by anything other than whispering
trees and the dawn chorus. Morning brings a commendably un-Gallic
tradition: full English (or is it Welsh?) breakfast in bed.
Bar Food 12-2 *(except Mon).* ***Restaurant*** *12-2, 7-9.30. Children's
portions. Free House.* **Beer** *Samuel Smith, Whitbread Best. Patio,
outdoor eating. Family room.* ***Accommodation*** *(closed first 2 weeks Jan).
12 bedrooms, all en suite, £80. Children welcome overnight. Additional
beds and cots available. Access, Amex, Diners, Visa.*

Channel Islands
& Isle of Man

Guernsey

Le Bourg Forest   Deerhound Inn

Tel 0481 38585	Pub
Le Bourg Forest Guernsey	Map 13 E4

Cosy, friendly country inn, popular bar meals. **Bar Meals** *12-1.45
7-9.30, bar snacks both sessions. Children's menus/portions* **Beer** *Guernsey
Brewery Bitter. Family Room. Outdoor play area. Garden. Outdoor eating.*
Accommodation *10 Bedrooms, 2 en suite from £32. Children welcome
overnight. Cot available. Diners, Visa.*

Pleinmont   Imperial Hotel

Tel 0481 64044 Fax 0481 66139	Inn
Pleinmont Torteval Guernsey	Map 13 E4

This turn-of-the-century inn is situated on the beach overlooking
Rocquaine Bay and Portelet Harbour and boasts fine sea-views. The
new owners, Patrick and Diana Lindley, have renovated extensively
including upgrading all bedrooms to en suite. Sepia-tinted photographs
of the original dining room (circa 1900) adorn the walls downstairs.
Children are especially welcome "if well behaved". *Garden.* **Beer** *Triple
X, Randalls, Worthingtons.* **Accommodation** *17 bedrooms, all en suite,
£52. Children welcome overnight, additional beds and cots available,
children under 2 £5, over 2-11 50% reduction. Access, Visa.*

St Martin   La Trelade Hotel   61%   £70

Tel 0481 35454 Fax 0481 37855	Hotel
Forest Road St Martin Guernsey	Map 13 E4

A holiday hotel in its own grounds off the main airport road. Two
split-level lounge areas have modern brown leather-look seating, and
the bar has smart and comfortable salmon-pink upholstery. Bedrooms
are decent-sized and are equipped with simple white built-in units and
clean bathrooms, some with shower and bath, others with shower
only. Friendly staff. Families are well catered for with a children's play
area and both baby-sitting and baby-listening available. **Rooms 45.**
*Garden, outdoor swimming pool, putting, croquet, games room, dinner dance
(Friday). Access, Amex, Diners, Visa.*

St Peter Port	**St Pierre Park**	**70%**	**£125**
Tel 0481 728282 Fax 0481 712041			Hotel

Rohais St Peter Port Guernsey   Map 13 E4

A short drive from St Peter Port, set in 45 acres of parkland that include a 9-hole golf course designed by Tony Jacklin and extensive leisure facilities with three tennis courts. Bedrooms, most of them with balconies, are furnished with built-in units and offer plenty of writing space and up-to-date accessories. Bright day rooms running off the foyer include a terrace lounge/bar that overlooks a large ornamental lake. Families are well catered for with a children's playground, a children's menu served in Café Renoir up to 7pm and both baby-sitting and baby-listening available. *Rooms 135. Garden, indoor swimming pool, spa bath, sauna, solarium, beauty & hair salons, snooker, gymnasium, tennis, 9-hole golf course, coffee shop (10am-10pm), dinner dance (Saturday in summer). Access, Amex, Diners, Visa.*

Jersey

Gorey	**Jersey Pottery Restaurant**	
Tel 0534 51119		Restaurant

Gorey Village Gorey Jersey   Map 13 F4

Pottery plant holders hanging from the domed glass ceiling and on the tables as well as display cabinets around the dining room give the visitor a preview of the wares from the pottery next door. There's a conservatory-type atmosphere in this self-service café where in summer, people spill out on to the patio in the garden. The reputation is built on the freshest of seafood served generously – cold dishes only in summer, seafood salad (£8.95), crab salad (£10.75) and hot dishes such as mussels and chips (£5.50) or grilled king prawn sandwich (£5.95) in winter. For non-fish-eaters, there's a choice of filled granary rolls with mixed salad (from £1.95) or grilled steak sandwich with béarnaise sauce (£4.95). Home baking extends to scones, tartlets and cream cakes. A fuller à la carte menu is served in the adjacent restaurant. A walk around the pottery factory and gift shop may aid digestion but not the wallet. Children's portions. No-smoking area. *Seats 300. Open 9-5.30. Closed Sat, Sun, 10 days Christmas. Access, Amex, Diners, Visa.*

Havre des Pas	**Hotel de la Plage**	**66%**	**£100**
Tel 0534 23474 Fax 0534 68642			Hotel

Havre des Pas St Helier Jersey JE2 4UQ   Map 13 F4

A well-run modern hotel on the seafront, with picture windows to enhance the views. Day rooms are in various styles: subdued and modern in the split-level lounge-bar, tropical in the Caribbean bar, bamboo in the sun lounge. Sea-facing bedrooms have balconies; inland-view rooms are cheaper. Baby-sitting by arrangement. No dogs. *Rooms 78. Keep-fit facilities, solarium, games room. Closed end Oct-early Apr. Access, Amex, Visa, Diners*

St Aubin — Old Court House Inn — £80

Tel 0534 46433 Fax 0534 45103	Inn
St Aubin Jersey	Map 13 F4

Modern comforts and old-world charm in a tall, handsome house
dating back to 1450 and overlooking the harbour. It's a family-run
hotel/restaurant/inn with a young outlook and a popular alfresco
eating trade – bar snacks on the front patio and à la carte in the rear
courtyard. Children are offered their own menu or smaller portions
and charged accordingly. The beamed cellar bars and upstairs Mizzen
Bar (well-known to *Bergerac* fans as the *Royal Barge* pub) are favourite
rendezvous. Bedrooms, the best with harbour views, are furnished
with old pine; extra beds and cot provided. No dogs. *Rooms 9. Closed
25 & 26 Dec. Access, Visa.*

St Brelade — La Place Hotel — 67% — £110

Tel 0534 44261 Fax 0534 45164	Hotel
Route du Coin La Haule St Brelade Jersey JE3 8BF	Map 13 F4

Once a farmhouse but now much enlarged by modern extensions,
La Place is for those who like rural surroundings. The main public
rooms are part of the original, 400-year-old building. There's
a delightful open-air seating area in a south-facing courtyard, a bright
bar with green bamboo furniture and two lounges, one of which has
a black-beamed ceiling, a pink granite fireplace, antique furniture and
polished brass ornaments. Many of the bedrooms have been recently
refurbished, including seven around the pool. Children up to seven
stay free in parents' room; children's high tea is offered. *Rooms 40.
Outdoor swimming pool, sauna. Access, Amex, Diners, Visa.*

St Brelade — La Pulente Hotel

Tel 0534 41760	Pub
St Brelade Jersey	Map 13 F4

Dramatically set above rocky cove; cleanly modernised inside, pretty
terrace. *Beer Bass. Family room.*

St Brelade — Smugglers Inn

Tel 0534 41510	Pub
Quaisne Bay St Brelade Jersey	Map 13 F4

Good traditional atmosphere in the stone and timber bars, close
to beach; routine food. *Beer Bass. Family room.*

St Brelade's Bay — St Brelade's Bay Hotel — 70% — £134

Tel 0534 46141 Fax 0534 47278	Hotel
St Brelade's Bay Jersey	Map 13 F4

This smartly whitewashed, low-level hotel bears evidence of the long-
term care and pride heaped upon it by the Colley family. Behind
it is a lovely garden set with sun-loungers where parents can relax
while a lifeguard teaches their children to swim; inside, an airy,
spacious foyer leads you to the elegant and comfortable lounge, with
antiques, chesterfields, parquet floors and beautiful rugs. There's live
music in the cocktail bar, and a club room and games room for
younger guests. First- and second-floor rooms are traditional, while
those on the third floor are more modern; all are attractively and
tastefully decorated and furnished. Families are well catered for.
*Rooms 82. Garden, croquet, outdoor swimming pool, sauna, solarium,
games room, tennis, putting. Closed 12 Oct-29 Apr. Access, Visa.*

St Helier	**Apollo Hotel**	63%	**£84**
Tel 0534 25441 Fax 0534 22120			Hotel
9 St Saviour's Road St Helier Jersey JE2 4LA			Map 13 F4

A modern two-storey hotel built round a courtyard. Public areas
provide plenty of space to relax: there are two bars (one in pub
style), a coffee shop serving snacks throughout the day, an indoor
leisure centre and a sun-trap terrace. Bedrooms, some with balconies,
include many suitable for family occupation. *Rooms 85. Indoor
swimming pool, spa bath, sauna, solarium, gymnasium, coffee shop (10am-
9pm). Access, Amex, Diners, Visa.*

St Helier	**Grand Hotel**	68%	**£117**
Tel 0534 22301 Fax 0534 37815			Hotel
The Esplanade St Helier Jersey JE4 8WD			Map 13 F4

The long, gabled frontage of the Grand is a distinctive feature on the
seafront and the entrance is appropriately impressive, with ornate,
coloured pillars and a marble floor. The smart period-style bar and
lounge have fine views and so do balconied front bedrooms, which
attract a hefty surcharge. It's a busy hotel catering for both holiday and
business visitors. Families are well catered for with free
accommodation for under-14s in their parents' room, plus baby-sitting
and special children's meals also available. De Vere Hotels. *Rooms 115.
Indoor swimming pool, sauna, solarium, spa bath, keep-fit equipment, beauty
salon, hairdressing, snooker, news kiosk, garage. Access, Amex, Diners,
Visa.*

Victoria's   £70

Polished service, elegant appointments, and a traditional French/British
à la carte menu (plus a limited choice, fixed-price menu) that features
fresh fish and shellfish – typically, moules marseillaise, paupiette of sole,
prawn consommé, crab soup with seaweed and daily specials.
Vegetarian main dishes are available, often featuring mushrooms
as a favoured ingredient. Dancing to live music every evening;
gentlemen should wear jackets and ties. Breakfast and dinner are also
served in the Regency restaurant. 10% service is automatically added
to the fixed-price menus. *Seats 250. L 12.15-2.15 D 7-10 (Sun to 9.30).
Set L £14 Set D £19.50.*

St Helier	**Pizza Express**	
Tel 0534 33291		Pizzeria
59 Halkett Place St Helier Jersey		Map 13 F4

Two shops knocked into one created this, the second busiest of the
chain of pizza restaurants. It stands near the market, a light and
spacious place with white tiles and walls. The exception to the rule
on the otherwise standard menu is spaghetti bolognese. The pizza bases
are crisp and thin, with fresh ingredients used for the toppings.
Cappuccino coffee available. No-smoking area. *Seats 120.
Open 11.30-midnight. Closed 25-28 Dec. Access, Amex, Visa.*

Sark

Sark	Aval Du Creux	57%	£63
Tel 0481 832036 Fax 0481 832368			Hotel
Sark Channel Islands			Map 13 E4

Peter and Cheryl Tonks's friendly little hotel started life
as a farmhouse. Public rooms consist of two simply furnished lounges
with a homely appeal and a small bar hung with local pictures. There
are six bedrooms in the main house, six smaller ones in the annexe.
Four are suitable for family use. Modest shower rooms are clean and
tidy. **Rooms 12.** *Garden, outdoor swimming pool, children's splash pool,
boules. Closed Oct-Apr. Access, Visa.*

Restaurant   £52

Seafood plays the leading role here, with local crab served hot
in a shell with cheese glaze, plus oysters, lobster (surf'n'turf) and
monkfish. Fresh asparagus from Guernsey (in season) and pan-fried
pigeon breast with gingerbread sauce, and guinea fowl in filo pastry
with sweet red peppers show that care is taken not only in preparation
but also in attaining quality ingredients. **Seats 40.** *Parties 32. Private
Room. L 12-2 D 7-8. Set D £15.95.*

Sark	Stocks Hotel	61%	£90*
Tel 0481 832001 Fax 0481 832130			Hotel
Sark Channel Islands			Map 3 E4

Following four years of uncertainty, the Armorgie family have now
purchased the hotel and restaurants outright, demonstrating their long-
term commitment to their business. Peace and relaxation come
without too much trouble, with a homely atmosphere in the lounge,
and comfortable, unfussy bedrooms decorated with darkwood
furniture and floral fabrics. No TVs in the rooms. *Half-board terms
only. **Rooms 25.** *Garden, outdoor swimming pool, coffee shop (10am-
10pm). Closed mid Oct-Easter. Access, Visa, Diners*

Cider Press Restaurant   £50

Both table d'hote and à la carte menus are offered, with local fish and
shellfish always featuring on both. Moules marinière, mackerel,
oysters, Sark rabbit, lobster and crab, plus regular pasta dishes are all
typical offerings. Traditional roast lunch every Sunday; "all-weather
barbecue lunch" served on the front lawn or inside. Coffee, lunch,
cream teas and light evening meals served in the *Courtyard Bistro*, with
alfresco tables in summer adjacent to the swimming pool; children's
supper menu served here from 5.30-7pm. **Seats 60.** *Parties 12. Private
Room. L 12-2.30 D 7.30-9 (Sun to 9). Set L £9.50 Set D £16.50.*

Isle of Man

Peel Creek Inn
Tel 0624 842216	Pub
The Quayside Peel Isle of Man	Map 4 B4

A bustling pub right by the quayside of Peel harbour, out of which
working boats ply their trade. The industrious and friendly landlords
Robert and Jean McAleer offer seafood specialities from the fish yard
in their large, bright and unpretentious bar. Easy parking. *Bar Food
11-10.45 (Sun 12-1.30, 8-10). Children's menu (£1.50-2.00 per dish).
Beer Bass, Okells. Outdoor eating on the quayside. Children welcome in bar
12-1.30 if eating. No credit cards.*

Ramsey Harbour Bistro
Tel 0624 814182	£45
5 East Street Ramsey Isle of Man	Restaurant · Map 4 B4

Fish and shellfish, much of it landed on the nearby quay, is the chief
attraction of this friendly, informal bistro. Available as starter or main
course, the choice ranges from queenies (succulent little scallops,
a Manx speciality) to crisp-fried fillets of plaice, a sauté of giant prawns
and the ever-popular fisherman's pie. Plenty of meat options, too, and
some naughty desserts ("To hell with the calorie count – let's enjoy
ourselves" says the menu). *Seats 46. Parties 20. L 12.15-2.30
D 6.30-10.30. Closed Xmas, Good Friday, 2 weeks Oct. Set L £9.95.
Access, Visa.*

Tynwald Mill Tynwald Mill Patisserie
Tel 0624 801600	Café
St John's Isle of Man	Map 4 B4

Plans are afoot to move the café downstairs in this complex of craft
shops near the Seat of the Manx Parliament. Staff are helpful and
children are bound to find something tasty on the adult menu, from
which half portions are offered; if not, fish fingers are bound to please.
High-chairs, crayons and colouring sheets are all provided. Outside
there's a picnic area and a playground with slides, swings and tunnels.
*Seats 90. Open 10-5.30. Closed 25 & 26 Dec, 1 Jan, Good Friday.
Access, Visa.*

260 Group Hotels

LONDON GROUP HOTELS

Key: QMH (Queens Moat Houses), MtCT (Mount Charlotte Thistle).
Note: Lodges (Forte Travelodge, Travel Inn, Granada, Campanile) and Inns are ungraded.
We recommend that you call to confirm family facilities before staying at the hotels listed.

Location	Establishment	Group	Grade	Price	Tel	Rooms	Pool	Address
E1	Tower Thistle	MtCT	66%	£155	071-481 2575	808		St Katharine's Way E1 9LD
EC1	New Barbican Hotel	MtCT	51%	£100	071-251 1565	470		Central Street Clerkenwell EC1V 8DS
N1	Great Northern Hotel	Compass	62%	£93	071-837 5454	89		King's Cross N1 9AN
NW1	Kennedy Hotel	MtCT	63%	£102	071-387 4400	360		Cardington Street NW1 2LP
NW1	White House	Rank	71%	£127	071-387 1200	576		Albany Street Regent's Park NW1 3UP
NW3	Clive Hotel	Hilton	64%	£64	071-586 2233	96		Primrose Hill Road NW3 3NA
NW3	Forte Posthouse	Forte	65%	£64	071-794 8121	138		215 Haverstock Hill NW3 4RB
NW3	Regent's Park Marriott	Marriott	73%	£178	071-722 7711	303	yes	128 King Henry's Road NW3 3ST
NW4	Hendon Hall	MtCT	63%	£105	081-203 3341	52		Ashley Lane NW4 1HE
NW8	Hilton International Regent's Park	Hilton	73%	£148	071-722 7722	377		18 Lodge Road St John's Wood NW8 7JT
SW1	The Berkeley	Savoy Group	86%	£277	071-235 6000	160	yes	Wilton Place SW1X 7RL
SW1	Forte Crest St James's	Forte	68%	£116	071-930 2111	256		80 Jermyn Street SW1Y 6JF
SW1	Grosvenor Hotel	MtCT	64%	£138	071-834 9494	366		101 Buckingham Palace Road SW1W 0SJ
SW1	Hyde Park Hotel	Forte	82%	£253	071-235 2000	185		66 Knightsbridge SW1Y 7LA
SW1	Royal Court Hotel	QMH	68%	£164	071-730 9191	102		Sloane Square SW1W 8EG
SW1	Royal Horseguards Thistle	MtCT	71%	£140	071-839 3400	376		2 Whitehall Court SW1A 2EJ
SW1	Royal Westminster Thistle	MtCT	71%	£150	071-834 1821	134		Buckingham Palace Road SW1W 0QT
SW1	Stakis St Ermin's	Stakis	71%	£159	071-222 7888	290		Caxton Street SW1H 0QW
SW5	Swallow International Hotel	Swallow	64%	£121	071-370 4200	417	yes	Cromwell Road SW5 0TH
SW7	Embassy House Hotel	Jarvis	59%	£106	071-584 7222	69		31 Queen's Gate SW7 5JA
SW7	The Gloucester	Rank	74%	£170	071-373 6030	550		4 Harrington Gardens SW7 4LH
SW7	Holiday Inn Kensington	Holiday Inns	68%	£160	071-373 2222	162		94-106 Cromwell Road SW7 4ER
SW7	Norfolk Hotel	QMH	69%	£164	071-589 8191	96		2 Harrington Road SW7 3ER
SW19	Cannizaro House	MtCT	76%	£138	081-879 1464	45		West Side Wimbledon Common SW19 4UF
W1	The Athenaeum	Rank	78%	£222	071-499 3464	144		116 Piccadilly W1V 0BJ

	Hotel	Group	%	Price	Phone	No.		Address
W1	Berkshire Hotel	Edwardian	72%	£230	071-629 7474	147		350 Oxford Street W1N 0BY
W1	Britannia Inter-Continental	Inter-Continental	77%	£233	071-629 9400	317		Grosvenor Square W1A 3AN
W1	Brown's Hotel	Forte	74%	£218	071-493 6020	133		Albemarle Street W1A 4SW
W1	Claridge's	Savoy Group	88%	£289	071-629 8860	190		Brook Street W1Y 9JQ
W1	The Connaught	Savoy Group	91%	£270	071-499 7070	90		Carlos Place W1Y 6AL
W1	Cumberland Hotel	Forte	69%	£150	071-262 1234	894		Marble Arch W1A 4RF
W1	Forte Crest Regent's Park	Forte	64%	£116	071-388 2300	320		Carburton Street W1P 8EE
W1	Grafton Hotel	Edwardian	63%	£160	071-388 4131	323		130 Tottenham Court Road W1P 9HP
W1	Grosvenor House	Forte	83%	£219	071-499 6363	454		90 Park Lane W1A 3AA
W1	Marble Arch Marriott	Holiday Inns	65%	£183	071-723 1277	241	yes	134 George Street W1H 6DN
W1	Holiday Inn Mayfair	Holiday Inns	72%	£185	071-493 8282	185	yes	3 Berkeley Street W1X 6NE
W1	Hospitality Inn Piccadilly	MtCT	64%	£138	071-930 4033	92		39 Coventry Street W1M 8EZ
W1	Inter-Continental Hotel	Inter-Continental	84%	£212	071-409 3131	467		1 Hamilton Place Hyde Park Corner W1V 1QY
W1	The Langham	Hilton	75%	£243	071-636 1000	411		Portland Place W1N 3AA
W1	London Hilton on Park Lane	Hilton	75%	£246	071-493 8000	448		22 Park Lane W1A 2HH
W1	London Marriott Hotel	Marriott	77%	£236	071-493 1232	223		Grosvenor Square W1A 4AW
W1	London Mews Hilton on Park Lane	Hilton	67%	£155	071-493 7222	72		2 Stanhope Row Park Lane W1Y 7HE
W1	May Fair Inter-Continental	Inter-Continental	79%	£252	071-629 7777	293	yes	Stratton Street W1A 2AN
W1	St George's Hotel	Forte	65%	£142	071-580 0111	86		Langham Place W1N 8QS
W1	The Selfridge	MtCT	75%	£220	071-408 2080	296		Orchard Street W1H 0JS
W1	Sherlock Holmes Hotel	Hilton	61%	£149	071-486 6161	126		108 Baker Street W1M 1LB
W1	The Westbury	Forte	75%	£193	071-629 7755	243		Conduit Street W1A 4UH
W2	Coburg Resort Hotel	Resort	53%	£129	071-221 2217	132		129 Bayswater Road W2 4RJ
W2	Hospitality Inn Bayswater	MtCT	60%	£102	071-262 4461	175		104 Bayswater Road W2 3HL
W2	London Embassy	Jarvis	68%	£132	071-229 1212	193		150 Bayswater Road W2 4RT
W2	Royal Lancaster Hotel	Rank	75%	£156	071-262 6737	418		Lancaster Terrace W2 2TY
W2	Whites Hotel	MtCT	77%	£190	071-262 2711	54		90 Lancaster Gate W2 3NR
W6	Novotel	Novotel	65%	£105	081-741 1555	640		1 Shortlands W6 8DR
W8	Copthorne Tara	Copthorne	69%	£132	071-937 7211	829		Scarsdale Place Wrights Lane W8 5SR
W8	Kensington Palace Thistle	MtCT	67%	£130	071-937 8121	298		De Vere Gardens W8 5AP
W8	Kensington Park Hotel	MtCT	67%	£165	071-937 8080	323		16-32 De Vere Gardens W8 5AG
W8	Royal Garden Hotel	Rank	80%	£224	071-937 8000	398		Kensington High Street W8 4PT
W11	Hilton International Kensington	Hilton	67%	£180	071-603 3355	603		179 Holland Park Avenue W11 4UL
W14	Hilton International Olympia	Hilton	66%	£157	071-603 3333	406		380 Kensington High Street W14 8NL
WC1	Forte Crest Bloomsbury	Forte	65%	£119	071-837 1200	284		Coram Street WC1N 1HT
WC1	Holiday Inn Kings Cross	Holiday Inns	69%	£130	071-833 3900	405	yes	1 Kings Cross Road WC1X 9DF

Location	Establishment	Group	Grade	Price	Tel	Rooms	Pool	Address
WC1	Kenilworth Hotel	Edwardian	63%	£172	071-637 3477	192		97 Great Russell Street WC1B 3LB
WC1	The Marlborough	Edwardian	69%	£184	071-636 5601	169		9-14 Bloomsbury Street WC1B 3QD
WC1	Hotel Russell	Forte	68%	£140	071-837 6470	326		Russell Square WC1B 5BE
WC2	Hampshire Hotel	Edwardian	77%	£230	071-839 9399	124		31 Leicester Square WC2 7LH
WC2	Moat House	QMH	65%	£177	071-836 6666	153		10 Drury Lane WC2B 5RE
WC2	Mountbatten Hotel	Edwardian	70%	£205	071-836 4300	127		20 Monmouth Street Covent Garden WC2H 9HD
WC2	Royal Trafalgar Thistle	MtCT	64%	£145	071-930 4477	108		Whitcomb Street WC2 7HG
WC2	The Savoy	Savoy Group	90%	£242	071-836 4343	202		Strand WC2R 0EU
WC2	The Waldorf	Forte	72%	£192	071-836 2400	292		Aldwych WC2B 4DD

London Airport Heathrow

Location	Establishment	Group	Grade	Price	Tel	Rooms	Pool	Address
Heathrow Airport	Berkeley Arms Hotel	Jarvis	67%	£110	081-897 2121	56		Bath Road Cranford TW5 9QF
Heathrow Airport	Edwardian International	Edwardian	76%	£206	081-759 6311	462	yes	Bath Road Hayes UB3 5AW
Heathrow Airport	Excelsior Hotel	Forte	71%	£118	081-759 6611	839	yes	Bath Road West Drayton UB7 0DU
Heathrow Airport	Forte Crest	Forte	68%	£99	081-759 2323	572		Sipson Road West Drayton UB7 0JU
Heathrow Airport	Forte Posthouse Ariel Hotel	Forte	65%	£64	081-759 2552	180		Bath Road Hayes UB3 5AJ
Heathrow Airport	Granada Lodge	Granada		£52	081-574 5875	46		M4 Junction 2/3 Heston TW5 9NA
Heathrow Airport	Heathrow Hilton Hotel	Hilton	76%	£160	081-759 7755	400	yes	Terminal 4 Heathrow Airport Hounslow TW6 3AF
Heathrow Airport	Holiday Inn Heathrow	Holiday Inns	69%	£135	0895 445555	384	yes	Stockley Road West Drayton UB7 9NA
Heathrow Airport	Park Hotel	MtCT	61%	£111	081-759 2400	306		Bath Road Longford West Drayton UB7 0EQ

London Airport Gatwick

Location	Establishment	Group	Grade	Price	Tel	Rooms	Pool	Address
Gatwick Airport	Chequers Thistle	MtCT	66%	£106	0293 786992	78		Brighton Road Horley RH16 8PH
Gatwick Airport	Copthorne Effingham Park	Copthorne	72%	£126	0342 714994	122		West Park Road Copthorne RH10 3EU
Gatwick Airport	Copthorne London Gatwick	Copthorne	69%	£127	0342 714971	227		Copthorne nr Crawley RH10 3PG
Gatwick Airport	Forte Crest Gatwick	Forte	74%	£99	0293 567070	474	yes	North Terminal Gatwick Airport RH6 0PH
Gatwick Airport	Forte Posthouse	Forte	63%	£64	0293 771621	216		Povey Cross Road Horley RH6 0BA
Gatwick Airport	Gatwick Concorde Hotel	QMH	61%	£104	0293 533441	116		Church Road Lowfield Heath Crawley RH11 0PQ
Gatwick Airport	Gatwick Hilton International	Hilton	72%	£150	0293 518080	550	yes	Gatwick RH11 0PD
Gatwick Airport	Holiday Inn Gatwick	Holiday Inns	68%	£131	0293 529991	223	yes	Langley Drive Crawley RH11 7SX
Gatwick Airport	Moat House	QMH	62%	£104	0293 785599	121		Longbridge Roundabout Horley RH6 0AB

ENGLAND GROUP HOTELS

Key: QMH (Queens Moat Houses), MtCT (Mount Charlotte Thistle). Pool = indoor swimming pool.
Note: Lodges (Forte Travelodge, Travel Inn, Granada, Campanile) and Inns are ungraded.
We recommend that you call to confirm family facilities before staying at the hotels listed.

Location	Establishment	Group	Grade	Price	Tel	Rooms	Pool	Address
Avon								
Alveston	Forte Posthouse	Forte	62%	£64	0454 412521	74		Thornbury Road Alveston nr Bristol BS12 2LL
Bath	Bath Spa Hotel	Forte	87%	£171	0225 444424	100	yes	Sydney Road Bath BA2 6JF
Bath	Francis Hotel	THF	70%	£116	0225 324257	94		Queen Square Bath BA1 2HH
Bath	Hilton National	Hilton	67%	£116	0225 463411	150	yes	Walcot Street Bath BA1 5BJ
Bath	Priory Hotel	Select	81%	£161	0225 331922	21		Weston Road Bath BA1 2XT
Bath	Royal Crescent Hotel	QMH	83%	£162	0225 319090	42		16 Royal Crescent Bath BA1 2LS
Bristol	Aztec Hotel	Shire Inns	74%	£100	0454 301090	88	yes	Aztec West Business Park Almondsbury Bristol BS12 4TS
Bristol	Bristol Marriott Hotel	Marriott	New	£129	0272 294281	284	yes	Lower Castle Street Bristol BS1 3AD
Bristol	Forte Crest	Forte	67%	£97	0272 564242	197	yes	Filton Road Hambrook Bristol BS16 1QX
Bristol	Grand Hotel	MtCT	64%	£96	0272 291645	178		Broad Street Bristol BS1 2EL
Bristol	Hilton Hotel	Hilton	72%	£132	0272 260041	201	yes	Redcliffe Way Bristol BS1 6NJ
Bristol	Moat House	QMH	72%	£100	0272 255010	132		Victoria Street Bristol BS1 6HY
Bristol	Redwood Lodge	Country Club	64%	£85	0275 393901	112	yes	Beggar Bush Lane Failand Bristol BS8 3TG
Bristol	Stakis Bristol Hotel	Stakis	64%	£106	0454 201144	111	yes	Woodlands Way Patchway Bristol BS12 4JF
Bristol	Swallow Royal Hotel	Swallow	77%	£110	0272 255100	242	yes	College Green Bristol BS1 5TE
Bristol	Unicorn Hotel	Rank	62%	£75	0272 230333	245		Prince Street Bristol BS1 4QF
Gordano	Forte Travelodge	Forte		£40	0275 373709	40		Gordano Service Area, M5 Gordano nr Portbury BS20 9XG
Hunstrete	Hunstrete House	Clipper	75%	£150	0761 490578	24		Hunstrete Chelwood nr Bath BS18 4NS
Sedgemoor	Forte Travelodge	Forte		£40	0934 750831	40		M5 N'bound Sedgemoor Weston-super-Mare BS24 0JL
Weston-super-Mare	Grand Atlantic	Forte	64%	£96	0934 626543	76		Beach Road Weston-super-Mare BS23 1BA
Winterbourne	Grange Resort Hotel	Resort	68%	£95	0454 777333	52	yes	Northwoods nr Winterbourne BS17 1RP

Location	Establishment	Group	Grade	Price	Tel	Rooms	Pool	Address
Bedfordshire								
Bedford	Moat House	QMH	65%	£85	0234 355131	100		2 St Mary's Street Bedford MK42 0AR
Dunstable	Forte Travelodge	Forte		£40	0525 211177	28		A5 Watling Street Hockliffe Dunstable LU7 9LZ
Leighton Buzzard	The Swan	Resort	64%	£80	0525 372148	38		High Street Leighton Buzzard LU7 7EA
Luton	Forte Crest	Forte	60%	£87	0582 575911	93		Waller Avenue Luton LU4 9RU
Luton	Forte Posthouse	Forte	57%	£62	0582 575955	117		641 Dunstable Road Luton LU4 8RQ
Luton	Strathmore Thistle	MtCT	63%	£102	0582 34199	150		Arndale Centre Luton LU1 2TR
Marston	Forte Travelodge	Forte		£43	0234 766755	32		Junction 13 M1/A421 Beancroft Road Marston Moretaine
Toddington	Granada Lodge	Granada		£43	052 587 3881	43		Service Area M1 Southbnd Toddington nr Dunstable LU5 6HR
Woburn	Bedford Arms	MtCT	63%	£96	0525 290441	55		George Street Woburn nr Milton Keynes MK17 9PX
Berkshire								
Ascot	Berystede Hotel	Forte	67%	£122	0344 23311	91		Bagshot Road Sunninghill Ascot SL5 9JH
Ascot	Royal Berkshire	Hilton	76%	£168	0344 23322	81	yes	London Road Sunninghill Ascot SL5 0PP
Bracknell	Hilton National	Hilton	69%	£129	0344 424801	167		Bagshot Road Bracknell RG12 3QJ
Elcot	Elcot Park Resort Hotel	Resort	67%	£105	0488 58100	75	yes	Elcot nr Newbury RG16 8NJ
Hungerford	Bear Hotel	Resort	63%	£90	0488 682512	41		Charnham Street Hungerford RG17 0EL
Hurley	Ye Olde Bell	Resort	65%	£105	0628 825881	36		High Street Hurley nr Maidenhead SL6 5LX
Maidenhead	Holiday Inn	Holiday Inns	66%	£136	0628 23444	189	yes	Manor Lane Maidenhead SL6 2RA
Newbury	Chequers Hotel	Forte	66%	£106	0635 38000	56		Oxford Street Newbury RG13 1JB
Newbury	Hilton National	Hilton	69%	£127	0635 529000	104	yes	Pinchington Lane Newbury RG14 7HL
Newbury	Stakis Newbury Hotel	Stakis	67%	£109	0635 247010	112	yes	Oxford Road Newbury RG16 8XY
Reading	Caversham Hotel	QMH	71%	£119	0734 391818	114	yes	Richfield Avenue Caversham Bridge Reading RG1 8BD
Reading	Forte Posthouse	Forte	64%	£64	0734 875485	138	yes	500 Basingstoke Road Reading RG2 0SL
Reading	Forte Travelodge	Forte		£40	0734 750618	36		Basingstoke Road Reading RG2 0JE
Sindlesham	Reading Moat House	QMH	70%	£132	0734 351035	96		Mill Lane Sindlesham nr Wokingham RG11 5DF
Slough	Copthorne Hotel	Copthorne	71%	£127	0753 516222	219	yes	Cippenham Lane Slough SL1 2YE
Slough	Heathrow/Slough Marriott	Marriott	73%	£157	0753 544244	352	yes	Ditton Road Langley Slough SL3 8PT

Windsor	Castle Hotel	Forte	67%	£137	0753 851011	104		High Street Windsor SL4 1LJ
Windsor	Oakley Court	QMH	78%	£166	0628 74141	92		Windsor Road Water Oakley nr Windsor SL4 5UR
Wokingham	Stakis St Anne's Manor	Stakis	68%	£135	0734 772550	130	yes	London Road Wokingham RG11 1ST

Buckinghamshire

Aylesbury	Forte Crest	Forte	69%	£87	0296 393388	94	yes	Aston Clinton Road Aylesbury HP22 5AA
Beaconsfield	Bellhouse Hotel	De Vere	67%	£140	0753 887211	136	yes	Oxford Road Beaconsfield HP9 2XE
Burnham	Burnham Beeches Moat House	QMH	68%	£95	0628 603333	75	yes	Burnham SL1 8DP
Chenies	Bedford Arms Thistle	MtCT	64%	£108	0923 283301	10		Chenies nr Rickmansworth WD3 6EQ
Gerrards Cross	Bull Hotel	De Vere	63%	£125	0753 885995	95		Gerrards Cross SL9 7PA
High Wycombe	Forte Posthouse	Forte	65%	£62	0494 442100	106		Crest Road High Wycombe HP11 1TL
Marlow	Compleat Angler Hotel	Forte	73%	£161	0628 484444	64		Marlow Bridge Marlow SL7 1RG
Milton Keynes	Forte Crest	Forte	68%	£98	0908 667722	163	yes	500 Saxon Gate Milton Keynes MK9 2HQ

Cambridgeshire

Cambridge	Cambridgeshire Moat House	QMH	63%	£78	0954 780555	100	yes	Bar Hill Cambridge CB3 8EU
Cambridge	Forte Posthouse	Forte	67%	£84	0223 237000	118	yes	Lakeview Bridge Road Cambridge CB4 4PH
Cambridge	Garden House	QMH	69%	£130	0223 63421	118		Granta Place Mill Lane Cambridge CB2 1RT
Cambridge	Holiday Inn	Holiday Inns	68%	£119	0223 464466	199	yes	Downing Street Cambridge CB2 3DT
Cambridge	University Arms	De Vere	65%	£110	0223 351241	117		Regent Street Cambridge CB2 1AD
Ely	Forte Travelodge	Forte		£40	0353 668499	39		A10/A142 Roundabout Ely
Ely	Lamb Hotel	QMH	62%	£75	0353 663574	32		2 Lynn Road Ely CB7 4EJ
Fenstanton	Forte Travelodge	Forte		£40	0954 30919	40		A604 Eastbound Fenstanton nr Cambridge
Huntingdon	Old Bridge Hotel	Poste Hotels	68%	£92	0480 52681	26	yes	1 High Street Huntingdon PE18 6TQ
Lolworth	Forte Travelodge	Forte		£40	0954 781335	20		A604 Huntingdon Road Lolworth Bar Hill CB3 8DR
Peterborough	Forte Posthouse	Forte	60%	£61	0733 240209	93	yes	Great North Road Norman Cross Peterborough PE7 3TB
Peterborough	Forte Travelodge	Forte		£40	0733 231109	32		A1 Great North Road Alwalton Village nr Peterborough
Peterborough	Moat House	QMH	64%	£91	0733 260000	129	yes	Thorpe Wood Peterborough PE3 6SG
Peterborough	Swallow Hotel	Swallow	69%	£99	0733 371111	163	yes	Lynch Road Peterborough PE2 0GB

Location	Establishment	Group	Grade	Price	Tel	Rooms	Pool	Address
Swavesey	Forte Travelodge	Forte		£40	0954 789113	36		A604 Cambridge Road Swavesey nr Cambridge
Wansford-in-England	Haycock Hotel	Poste Hotels	70%	£90	0780 782223	51		Wansford-in-England Peterborough PE8 6JA

Cheshire

Location	Establishment	Group	Grade	Price	Tel	Rooms	Pool	Address
Alsager	Manor House	Compass	65%	£85	0270 884000	57		Audley Road Alsager ST7 2QQ
Bramhall	Moat House	QMH	63%	£85	061-439 8116	65		Bramhall Lane South Bramhall SK7 2EB
Bucklow Hill	The Swan	De Vere	62%	£75	0565 830295	70		Bucklow Hill Knutsford WA16 6RD
Burtonwood	Forte Travelodge	Forte		£40	0925 710376	40		M62 Service Area Burtonwood Warrington WA5 3AX
Chester	Abbots Well	Jarvis	62%	£90	0244 332121	127	yes	Whitchurch Road Christleton Chester CH3 5QL
Chester	Blossoms Hotel	Forte	63%	£101	0244 323186	64		St John Street Chester CH1 1HL
Chester	Chester International	QMH	69%	£150	0244 322330	152		Trinity Street Chester CH1 2BD
Chester	Chester Resort Hotel	Resort	62%	£75	0244 851551	113		Backford Cross Chester CH1 6PE
Chester	Forte Posthouse	Forte	62%	£64	0244 680111	107	yes	Wrexham Road Chester CH4 9DL
Crewe	Forte Travelodge	Forte		£40	0270 883157	42		Junction 16 M6/A500 Alsager Road Barthomley nr Crewe
Knutsford	Cottons Hotel	Shire Inns	65%	£112	0565 650333	86	yes	Manchester Road Knutsford WA16 0SU
Knutsford	Forte Travelodge	Forte		£40	0565 652187	32		A556 Chester Road Tabley Knutsford WA16 0PP
Mottram St Andrew	Mottram Hall	De Vere	70%	£140	0625 828135	133	yes	Mottram St Andrew Prestbury SK10 4QT
Nantwich	Rookery Hall	Select	79%	£118	0270 610016	45		Worleston nr Nantwich CW5 6DQ
Parkgate	Ship Hotel	Forte	58%	£76	051-336 3931	26		The Parade Parkgate The Wirral L64 6SA
Runcorn	Campanile Hotel	Campanile		£36	0928 581771	53		Lowlands Road Runcorn WA7 5TP
Runcorn	Forte Crest	Forte	62%	£88	0928 714000	134	yes	Wood Lane Beechwood Runcorn WA7 3HA
Sandbach	Chimney House	Lansbury	61%	£85	0270 764141	48		Congleton Road Sandbach CW11 0ST
Stockport	Forte Travelodge	Forte		£40	0625 875292	32		A253 London Road South Adlington Stockport SK12 4NA
Stockport	Travel Inn	Travel Inns		£42	061-499 1944	41		Finney Lane Heald Green Stockport SK8 2QH
Warrington	Holiday Inn Garden Court	Holiday Inns	0%	£73	0925 838779	100		Woolston Grange Avenue Woolston Warrington
Warrington	Lord Daresbury Hotel	De Vere	67%	£115	0925 267331	141	yes	Chester Road Daresbury Warrington WA4 4BB
Warrington	Travel Inn	Travel Inns		£42	0582 482224	40		Winwick Road Warrington
Wilmslow	Moat House	QMH	58%	£103	0625 529201	125	yes	Altrincham Road Wilmslow SK9 4LR

Cleveland

Location	Hotel	Group	%	£	Phone	Rooms		Address
Stockton-on-Tees	Swallow Hotel	Swallow	67%	£92	0642 679721	124	yes	10 John Walker Square Stockton-on-Tees TS18 1AQ
Thornaby-on-Tees	Forte Posthouse	Forte	59%	£65	0642 591213	135		Low Lane By Stainton Village nr Thornaby-on-Tees TS17 9LW

Cornwall

Location	Hotel	Group	%	£	Phone	Rooms		Address
Saltash	Granada Lodge	Granada		£43	0752 848408	31		A38 by-pass Saltash PL12 6LF

Cumbria

Location	Hotel	Group	%	£	Phone	Rooms		Address
Borrowdale	Stakis Lodore Swiss Hotel	Stakis	71%	£160	076 87 77285	70	yes	Borrowdale Keswick CA12 5UX
Bowness-on-Windermere	Belsfield Hotel	Forte	62%	£105	053 94 42448	66	yes	Kendal Road Bowness-on-Windermere LA23 3EL
Bowness-on-Windermere	Old England Hotel	Forte	65%	£115	053 94 42444	79		Church Street Bowness-on-Windermere LA23 3DF
Carlisle	Granada Lodge	Granada		£43	069 74 73131	39		M6 Junction 41/42 Southwaite Carlisle CA4 0NT
Carlisle	Swallow Hilltop	Swallow	58%	£80	0228 29255	92	yes	London Road Carlisle CA1 2PQ
Grasmere	The Swan	Forte	65%	£109	053 94 35551	36		Grasmere nr Ambleside LA22 9RF
Keswick	Keswick Hotel	Principal	60%	£75	076 87 72020	66		Station Road Keswick CA12 4NQ
Penrith	Forte Travelodge	Forte		£40	0768 66958	32		A66 Redhills Penrith CA11 0DT
Penrith	North Lakes Gateway Hotel	Shire Inns	71%	£100	0768 68111	85	yes	Ullswater Road Penrith CA11 8QT
Ullswater	Leeming House	Forte	77%	£139	076 84 86622	40		Watermillock Ullswater CA11 0JJ
Wetheral	The Crown	Shire Inns	70%	£106	0228 561888	49	yes	Wetheral nr Carlisle CA4 8ES

Derbyshire

Location	Hotel	Group	%	£	Phone	Rooms		Address
Castle Donington	Donington Thistle	MtCT	70%	£113	0332 850700	110	yes	East Midlands Airport Castle Donington DE7 2SH
Chesterfield	Forte Travelodge	Forte		£40	0246 455411	20		A61 Brimington Road North Wittington Moor Chesterfield
Derby	Forte Posthouse	Forte	61%	£64	0332 514933	62		Pastures Hill Littleover Derby DE3 7BA
Dovedale	Peveril of the Peak	Forte	60%	£96	033 529 333	47		Thorpe Dovedale nr Ashbourne DE6 2AW
Matlock Bath	New Bath Hotel	Forte	63%	£111	0629 583275	55	yes	New Bath Road Matlock Bath DE4 3PX

Location	Establishment	Group	Grade	Price	Tel	Rooms	Pool	Address
Morley	Breadsall Priory	Country Club	69%	£102	0332 832235	91	yes	Moor Road Morley nr Derby DE7 6DL
Newton Solney	Newton Park	Jarvis	67%	£116	0283 703568	51		Newton Solney Burton-on-Trent DE15 0SS
Rowsley	Peacock Hotel	Jarvis	64%	£75	0629 733518	14		Rowsley Matlock DE4 2EB
South Normanton	Swallow Hotel	Swallow	69%	£92	0773 812000	161	yes	Carter Lane East South Normanton DE55 2EH

Devon

Location	Establishment	Group	Grade	Price	Tel	Rooms	Pool	Address
Barnstaple	Imperial Hotel	Forte	60%	£81	0271 45861	56		Taw Vale Parade Barnstaple EX32 8NB
Exeter	Forte Crest	Forte	69%	£91	0392 412812	110	yes	Southern Hay East Exeter EX1 1QF
Exeter	Rougemont Hotel	MtCT	63%	£79	0392 54982	90		Queen Street Exeter EX4 3SP
Exeter	Royal Clarence	QMH	71%	£95	0392 58464	56		Cathedral Yard Exeter EX1 1HD
Exmouth	Imperial Hotel	Forte	60%	£101	0395 274761	57		The Esplanade Exmouth EX8 2SW
Okehampton	Forte Travelodge	Forte		£40	0837 52124	32		A30 Sourton Cross nr Okehampton EX20 4LY
Paignton	Palace Hotel	Forte	60%	£96	0803 555121	52		Esplanade Road Paignton TQ4 6BJ
Plymouth	Astor Hotel	MtCT	58%	£69	0752 225511	56		14 Elliott Street The Hoe Plymouth PL1 2PS
Plymouth	Campanile Hotel	Campanile		£36	0752 601087	50		Marsh Mills Longbridge Road Plymouth PL6 8LD
Plymouth	Copthorne Hotel	Copthorne	70%	£106	0752 224161	135	yes	Armada Way Plymouth PL1 1AR
Plymouth	Moat House	QMH	70%	£98	0752 662866	217	yes	Armada Way Plymouth PL1 2HJ
Plymouth	Novotel	Novotel	62%	£68	0752 221422	101		Marsh Mills Roundabout Plymouth PL6 8HN
Tiverton	Forte Travelodge	Forte		£40	0884 821087	40		Sampford Peverell Service Area M5 J27 nr Tiverton EX16 4LY
Torquay	Imperial Hotel	Forte	81%	£150	0803 294301	167	yes	Parkhill Road Torquay TQ1 2DG

Dorset

Location	Establishment	Group	Grade	Price	Tel	Rooms	Pool	Address
Bournemouth	Forte Posthouse	Forte	59%	£64	0202 553262	98		The Lansdowne Bournemouth BH1 2PR
Bournemouth	Royal Bath Hotel	De Vere	73%	£140	0202 555555	131	yes	Bath Road Bournemouth BH1 2EW
Bournemouth	Swallow Highcliff Hotel	Swallow	70%	£115	0202 557702	157		St Michael's Road West Cliff Bournemouth BH2 5DU
Christchurch	Travel Inn	Travel Inns		£42	0202 485376	38		Somerford Road Christchurch Bournemouth BH23 3QG
Ferndown	Dormy Hotel	De Vere	71%	£115	0202 872121	128	yes	New Road Ferndown BH22 8ES

Location	Hotel	Chain	%	£	Phone	Rooms		Address
Mudeford	Avonmouth Hotel	Forte	59%	£101	0202 483434	41		95 Mudeford Christchurch BH23 3NT
Poole	Hospitality Inn	MtCT	63%	£101	0202 666800	68		The Quay Poole BH15 1HD
Shaftesbury	Grosvenor Hotel	Forte	62%	£86	0747 52282	41		The Commons Shaftesbury SP7 8JA
Sherborne	Eastbury Hotel	Clipper	67%	£98	0935 813131	15		Long Street Sherborne DT9 3BY
Sherborne	Forte Posthouse	Forte	58%	£64	0935 813191	59		Horsecastles Lane Sherborne DT9 6BB

Durham

Location	Hotel	Chain	%	£	Phone	Rooms		Address
Darlington	Blackwell Grange Moat House	QMH	62%	£96	0325 380888	99		Blackwell Grange Darlington DL3 8QH
Darlington	St George Thistle	MtCT	56%	£79	0325 332631	59		Teesside Airport nr Darlington DL2 1RH
Darlington	Swallow King's Head	Swallow	57%	£80	0325 380222	85		Priestgate Darlington DL1 1LW
Durham	Royal County Hotel	Swallow	67%	£98	091-386 6821	150	yes	Old Elvet Durham DH1 3JN

Essex

Location	Hotel	Chain	%	£	Phone	Rooms		Address
Basildon	Campanile Hotel	Campanile		£36	0268 530810	98		Southend Arterial Road Pipps Hill Basildon SS14 3AE
Basildon	Forte Crest	Forte	59%	£97	0268 533955	110		Cranes Farm Road Basildon SS14 3DG
Basildon	Travel Inn	Travel Inns		£42	0268 522227	42		Felmores East Mayne Basildon SS13 1BW
Brentwood	Forte Posthouse	Forte	61%	£61	0277 260260	150	yes	Brook Street Brentwood CM14 5NF
Brentwood	Forte Travelodge	Forte		£40	0277 810819	22		A127 East Horndon nr Brentwood CM13 3LL
Brentwood	Moat House	QMH	67%	£113	0277 225252	33		London Road Brentwood CM14 4NR
Epping	Forte Posthouse	Forte	63%	£63	0992 573137	79		High Road Bell Common Epping CM16 4DG
Great Dunmow	Saracen's Head	Forte	58%	£91	0371 873821	24		High Street Great Dunmow CM6 1AG
Harlow	Green Man	Forte	60%	£91	0279 442521	55		Mulberry Green Old Town Harlow CM17 0ET
Harlow	Moat House	QMH	68%	£72	0279 422441	120		Southern Way Harlow CM18 7BA
Ingatestone	Heybridge Moat House	QMH	68%	£101	0277 355355	22		Roman Road Ingatestone CM4 9AB
Maldon	Blue Boar	Forte	59%	£82	0621 852681	28		3 Silver Street Maldon CM9 7QE
North Stifford	Moat House	QMH	61%	£103	0375 390909	126		High Street North Stifford nr Grays RM16 1UE
Old Harlow	Travel Inn	Travel Inns		£42	0279 442545	38		Cambridge Road Old Harlow CM20 2EP
Thurrock	Granada Lodge	Granada		£52	0708 891111	35		M25 J 30/31 Dartford Crossing Thurrock RM16 3BG

Gloucestershire

Location	Establishment	Group	Grade Price	Tel	Rooms	Pool	Address
Cheltenham	Cheltenham Park	Park Hotels	69% £106	0242 222021	154	yes	Cirencester Road Charlton Kings Cheltenham GL53 8EA
Cheltenham	Golden Valley Thistle	MtCT	69% £108	0242 232691	124	yes	Gloucester Road Cheltenham GL51 0TS
Cheltenham	Hotel de la Bere	Forte	64% £96	0242 237771	57		Southam Cheltenham GL52 3NH
Cheltenham	Queen's Hotel	Forte	69% £119	0242 514724	77		The Promenade Cheltenham GL50 1NN
Cheltenham	Travel Inn	Travel Inns	£42	0242 233847	40		Tewkesbury Road Uckington Cheltenham GL51 9SL
Cirencester	Fleece Hotel	Resort	64% £92	0285 658507	25		Market Square Cirencester GL7 4NZ
Gloucester	Travel Inn	Travel Inns	£42	0452 862521	40		Witcombe nr Gloucester GL3 4SS
Gloucester	Travel Inn	Travel Inns	£42	0452 523519	40		Tewkesbury Road Longford Gloucester GL2 9BE
Moreton-in-Marsh	Redesdale Arms	De Vere	£50	0608 50308	17		High Street Moreton-in-Marsh GL56 0AW
Stonehouse	Stonehouse Court	Clipper	68% £98	0453 825155	37		Bristol Road Stonehouse GL10 3RA
Stow-on-the-Wold	Unicorn Hotel	Forte	59% £95	0451 30257	20		Sheep Street Stow-on-the-Wold GL54 1HQ
Tewkesbury	Royal Hop Pole	Forte	66% £101	0684 293236	29		Church Street Tewkesbury GL20 5RT
Tewkesbury	Tewkesbury Park	Country Club	62% £89	0684 295405	78	yes	Lincoln Green Lane Tewkesbury GL20 7DN

Greater Manchester

Location	Establishment	Group	Grade Price	Tel	Rooms	Pool	Address
Bolton	Forte Posthouse	Forte	58% £63	0204 651511	96		Beaumont Road Bolton BL3 4TA
Bolton	Pack Horse Hotel	De Vere	62% £74	0204 27261	73		Nelson Square Bradshawgate Bolton BL1 1DP
Manchester	Copthorne Hotel	Copthorne	70% £115	061-873 7321	166	yes	Clippers Quay Salford Quays Manchester M5 3DL
Manchester	Forte Posthouse	Forte	60% £64	061-998 7090	190		Palatine Road Northenden Manchester M22 4EH
Manchester	Granada Lodge	Granada	£43	061-410 0076	37		M62 Junction 18/19 Birch Manchester OL10 2QH
Manchester	Holiday Inn Crowne Plaza	Holiday Inns	73% £147	061-236 3333	303	yes	Peter Street Manchester M60 2DS
Manchester	Novotel	Novotel	62% £82	061-799 3535	119		Worsley Brow Worsley Manchester M28 4YA
Manchester	Hotel Piccadilly	Jarvis	73% £138	061-236 8414	271	yes	Piccadilly Plaza Manchester M60 1QR
Manchester	Portland Thistle	MtCT	69% £130	061-228 3400	205	yes	Portland Street Manchester M1 6DP
Manchester Airport	Forte Crest	Forte	65% £97	061-437 5811	297	yes	Ringway Road Wythenshawe M22 5NS
Manchester Airport	Hilton International	Hilton	71% £162	061-436 4404	223	yes	Outwood Lane Ringway Manchester Airport M22 5WP

Standish	Almond Brook Moat House	QMH	63%	£90	0257 425588	126	yes	Almond Brook Road Standish nr Wigan WN6 0SR
Stockport	Alma Lodge	Jarvis	61%	£98	061-483 4431	56		149 Buxton Road Stockport SK2 6EL

Hampshire

Alton	Forte Travelodge	Forte		£40	0420 62659	31		A31 Four Marks Winchester Road Alton GU34 5HZ
Alton	The Swan	Forte	58%	£91	0420 83777	36		High Street Alton GU34 1AT
Ampfield	Potters Heron Hotel	Lansbury	60%	£87	0703 266611	54		Ampfield nr Romsey SO51 9ZF
Andover	White Hart Inn	Forte		£86	0264 352266	20		Bridge Street Andover SP10 1BH
Barton Stacey	Forte Travelodge	Forte		£40	0264 72260	20		A303 Barton Stacey nr Andover SO21 3NP
Basingstoke	Audleys Wood	MtCT	75%	£123	0256 817555	71		Alton Road Basingstoke RG25 2JT
Basingstoke	Forte Posthouse	Forte	64%	£63	0256 468181	85		Grove Road Basingstoke RG21 3EE
Basingstoke	Forte Travelodge	Forte		£40	0256 843566	32		Winchester Road Basingstoke RG22 6HN
Basingstoke	Hilton Lodge	Hilton	66%	£116	0256 460460	144	yes	Old Common Road Black Dam Basingstoke RG21 3PR
Basingstoke	Hilton National	Hilton	65%	£121	0256 20212	134		Aldermaston Roundabout Ringway North Basingstoke
Basingstoke	Travel Inn	Travel Inns		£42	0256 811477	49		Worting Road Basingstoke RG22 6PG
Eastleigh	Forte Crest Southampton	Forte	66%	£87	0703 619700	120		Leigh Road Pasfield Avenue Eastleigh SO5 5PG
Eastleigh	Forte Travelodge	Forte		£40	0703 616813	32		Twyford Road Eastleigh nr Southampton
Fareham	Red Lion	Lansbury	57%	£81	0329 822640	44		East Street Fareham PO16 0BP
Fareham	Solent Hotel	Shire Inns	75%	£101	0489 880000	90	yes	Solent Business Park Whiteley Fareham PO15 7AJ
Farnborough	Forte Crest	Forte	66%	£97	0252 545051	110	yes	Lynchford Road Farnborough GU14 6AZ
Fleet	Forte Travelodge	Forte		£40	0252 815578	40		M3 Fleet Service Area Hartley Wintney Basingstoke
Havant	Bear Hotel	Lansbury	59%	£81	0705 486501	42		East Street Havant PO9 1AA
Havant	Forte Posthouse	Forte	62%	£62	0705 465011	92	yes	Northney Road Hayling Island Havant PO11 0NQ
Lymington	Stanwell House	Clipper	65%	£98	0590 677123	35		High Street Lymington SO41 9AA
Portsmouth	Forte Crest	Forte	65%	£87	0705 827651	163	yes	Pembroke Road Southsea Portsmouth PO1 2TA
Portsmouth	Hilton National	Hilton	66%	£121	0705 219111	122		Eastern Road Farlington Portsmouth PO6 1UN
Portsmouth	Hospitality Inn	MtCT	61%	£79	0705 731281	115		South Parade Southsea Portsmouth PO4 0RN
Portsmouth	Pendragon Hotel	Forte	59%	£81	0705 823201	49		Clarence Parade Southsea Portsmouth PO5 2HY
Portsmouth	Portsmouth Marriott Hotel	Marriott	74%	£127	0705 383151	170		North Harbour Cosham Portsmouth PO6 4SH
Romsey	White Horse Hotel	Forte	63%	£96	0794 512431	33	yes	Market Place Romsey SO5 8ZJ
Southampton	Dolphin Hotel	Forte	60%	£86	0703 339955	73		High Street Southampton SO9 2DS

Location	Establishment	Group	Grade	Price	Tel	Rooms	Pool	Address
Southampton	Forte Posthouse	Forte	58%	£63	0703 330777	128	yes	Herbert Walker Avenue Southampton SO1 0HJ
Southampton	Hilton National	Hilton	68%	£127	0703 702700	135		Bracken Place Chilworth Southampton SO2 4HB
Southampton	Novotel	Novotel	62%	£74	0703 330550	121		1 West Key Road Southampton SO1 0RA
Southampton	Polygon Hotel	Forte	65%	£72	0703 330055	119		Cumberland Place Southampton SO9 4DG
Stockbridge	Grosvenor Hotel	Lansbury	57%	£80	0264 810606	25		High Street Stockbridge SO20 6EU
Sutton Scotney North	Forte Travelodge	Forte		£40	0962 761016	31		A34 North S/Area nr Winchester SO21 3JY
Sutton Scotney South	Forte Travelodge	Forte		£40	0962 760779	40		A34 South S/Area nr Winchester SO21 3JY
Winchester	Forte Crest	Forte	69%	£97	0962 861611	94		Paternoster Row Winchester SO23 9LQ

Hereford & Worcester

Location	Establishment	Group	Grade	Price	Tel	Rooms	Pool	Address
Abberley	Elms Hotel	QMH	71%	£97	0299 896666	25		Stockton Road Abberley nr Worcester WR6 6AT
Broadway	Lygon Arms	Savoy Group	78%	£172	0386 852255	66	yes	High Street Broadway WR12 7DU
Bromsgrove	Perry Hall	Jarvis	56%	£93	0527 579976	58		Kidderminster Road Bromsgrove B61 7JN
Bromsgrove	Stakis Country Court	Stakis	69%	£112	021-447 7888	141	yes	Birmingham Road Bromsgrove B61 0JB
Droitwich	Forte Travelodge	Forte		£40	0527 86545	32		A38 Rashwood Hill Droitwich WR9 8DA
Hartlebury	Forte Travelodge	Forte		£40	0299 250553	32		A449 S'bound Shorthill Nurseries nr Kidderminster DY11 6DR
Hereford	Moat House	QMH	63%	£78	0432 354301	60		Belmont Road Hereford HR2 7BF
Hereford	Travel Inn	Travel Inns		£42	0432 274853	40		Holmer Road Holmer nr Hereford HR4 9RS
Malvern	Abbey Hotel	De Vere	62%	£85	0684 892332	107		Abbey Road Malvern WR14 3ET
Redditch	Campanile Hotel	Campanile		£36	0527 510710	50		Far Moor Lane Winyates Green Redditch B98 0SD
Stourport-on-Severn	Moat House	QMH	62%	£69	0299 827733	68		Hartlebury Road Stourport-on-Severn DY13 9LT
Worcester	Fownes Resort Hotel	Resort	70%	£96	0905 613151	61		City Walls Road Worcester WR1 2AP
Worcester	Giffard Hotel	Forte	61%	£75	0905 726262	103		High Street Worcester WR1 2QR

Hertfordshire

Location	Establishment	Group	Grade	Price	Tel	Rooms	Pool	Address
Baldock	Forte Travelodge	Forte		£40	0462 835329	40		A1 Great North Road Hinxworth nr Baldock SG7 5EX
Harpenden	Moat House	QMH	68%	£109	0582 764111	53		Southdown Road Harpenden AL5 1PE

Location	Hotel	Group	%	Price	Phone	Rooms		Address
Hertingfordbury	White Horse Hotel	Forte	63%	£101	0992 586791	42		Hertingfordbury Road Hertingfordbury SG14 2LB
Rushden	Forte Travelodge	Forte		£40	0933 57008	40		A45 Saunders Lodge Rushden
South Mimms	Forte Posthouse	Forte	60%	£62	0707 43311	123	yes	Bignells Corner South Mimms nr Potters Bar EN6 3NH
South Mimms	Forte Travelodge	Forte		£40	0707 665440	52		M25 Service Area Bignells Corner South Mimms EN6 3QQ
St Albans	Noke Thistle	MtCT	68%	£102	0727 54252	111		Watford Road St Albans AL2 3DS
Stanstead Abbots	Briggens House	QMH	70%	£102	0279 792416	54		Stanstead Abbots nr Ware SG12 8LD
Stevenage	Novotel	Novotel	60%	£80	0438 742299	100		Knebworth Park Stevenage SG1 2AX
Tring	Travel Inn	Travel Inns		£42	0442 824819	30		Tring Hill Tring HP23 4LD
Watford	Hilton National	Hilton	64%	£109	0923 35881	198	yes	Elton Way Watford WD2 8HA

Humberside

Location	Hotel	Group	%	Price	Phone	Rooms		Address
Beverley	Beverley Arms	Forte	62%	£101	0482 869241	57		North Bar Within Beverley HU17 8DD
Grimsby	Forte Crest	Forte	64%	£87	0472 350295	52		Littlecoates Road Grimsby DN34 4LX
Hull	Campanile Hotel	Campanile		£36	0482 25530	50		Beverley Road Freetown Way Hull HU2 9AN
Hull	Forte Posthouse	Forte	69%	£96	0482 225221	99	yes	Castle Street Hull HU1 2BX
Hull	Forte Travelodge	Forte	62%	£62	0482 645212	97		Ferriby High Road Hull HU14 3LG
South Cave	Forte Travelodge	Forte		£40	0430 424455	40		A63 Eastbound Beacon Service Area South Cave Hull

Isle of Wight

Location	Hotel	Group	%	Price	Phone	Rooms		Address
Ventnor	Royal Hotel	Forte	60%	£76	0983 852186	54		Belgrave Road Ventnor PO38 1JJ

Kent

Location	Hotel	Group	%	Price	Phone	Rooms		Address
Ashford	Ashford International	QMH	71%	£107	0233 611444	200	yes	Simone Weil Avenue Ashford TN24 8UX
Ashford	Eastwell Manor	QMH	82%	£113	0233 635751	23		Eastwell Park Boughton Aluph Ashford TN25 4HR
Ashford	Forte Posthouse	Forte	66%	£65	0233 625790	60		Canterbury Road Ashford TN24 8QQ
Ashford	Holiday Inn Garden Court	Holiday Inns	65%	£70	0233 713333	104		Maidstone Road Hothfield Ashford TN26 1AR
Ashford	Travel Inn	Travel Inns		£42	0223 712571	40		Maidstone Road A20 Hothfield Common Ashford TN26 1AP
Bearsted	Tudor Park	Country Club	67%	£109	0622 34334	120	yes	Ashford Road Bearsted nr Maidstone ME14 4NQ

Location	Establishment	Group	Grade	Price	Tel	Rooms	Pool	Address
Brands Hatch	Brands Hatch Thistle	MtCT	70%	£97	0474 854900	137	yes	Brands Hatch nr Dartford DA3 8PE
Canterbury	Chaucer Hotel	Forte	61%	£90	0227 464427	42		63 Ivy Lane Canterbury CT1 1TT
Canterbury	Falstaff Hotel	Lansbury	57%	£80	0227 462138	25		8 St Dunstan's Street Canterbury CT2 8AF
Canterbury	Slatters Hotel	QMH	63%	£74	0227 463271	31		St Margarets Street Canterbury CT1 2DR
Dover	Forte Posthouse	Forte	63%	£64	0304 821222	67		Singledge Lane Whitfield Dover CT16 3LF
Dover	Moat House	QMH	66%	£100	0304 203270	79	yes	Townwall Street Dover CT16 1SZ
Dover	Travel Inn	Travel Inns		£42	0304 213339	30		Folkestone Road Dover CT15 7AB
Fawkham	Brandshatch Place	Hidden	67%	£106	0474 872239	29		Ash Green Fawkham DA3 8NQ
Hollingbourne	Great Danes	Jarvis	63%	£78	0622 30022	126	yes	Ashford Road Hollingbourne ME17 1RE
Maidstone	Larkfield Priory	Forte	62%	£96	0732 846858	52		812 London Road Maidstone ME20 6HJ
Maidstone	Stakis Country Court Hotel	Stakis	69%	£109	0622 34322	139	yes	Bearsted Weavering Maidstone ME14 5AA
Rochester	Forte Crest	Forte	62%	£87	0634 687111	105	yes	Maidstone Road Rochester Airport Rochester ME5 9SF
Tonbridge	Rose & Crown	Forte	59%	£91	0732 357966	50		125 High Street Tonbridge TN9 1DD
Wrotham Heath	Forte Posthouse	Forte	67%	£64	0732 883311	118	yes	London Road Wrotham Heath nr Sevenoaks TN15 7RS
Wrotham Heath	Travel Inn	Travel Inns		£42	0732 884214	40		London Road Wrotham Heath nr Sevenoaks TN15 7RX

Lancashire

Location	Establishment	Group	Grade	Price	Tel	Rooms	Pool	Address
Blackburn	Moat House	QMH	58%	£83	0254 264441	98		Preston New Road Blackburn BB2 7BE
Blackpool	Imperial Hotel	Forte	64%	£109	0253 23971	183	yes	North Promenade Blackpool FY1 2HB
Bolton	Egerton House	Rank	63%	£85	0204 307171	32		off Blackburn Road Egerton Bolton BL7 9PL
Bolton	Last Drop Village Hotel	Rank	68%	£85	0204 591131	83	yes	Hospital Road Bromley Cross Bolton BL7 9PZ
Broughton	Broughton Park	Country Club	64%	£89	0772 864087	98	yes	418 Garstang Road Broughton nr Preston PR3 5JB
Burnley	Forte Travelodge	Forte		£40	0282 416039	32		Cavalry Barracks Barracks Road Burnley BB11 4AS
Lancaster	Forte Posthouse	Forte	69%	£64	0524 65999	110		Waterside Park Caton Road Lancaster LA1 3RA
Leyland	Leyland Resort Hotel	Resort	65%	£80	0772 422922	93		Leyland Way Leyland PR5 2JX
Lytham	Clifton Arms	Lansbury	63%	£87	0253 739898	41		West Beach Lytham FY8 5QJ
Mellor	Millstone Hotel	Shire Inns		£74	0254 813333	20		Church Lane Mellor nr Blackburn BB2 7JR
Preston	Forte Crest	Forte	63%	£87	0772 59411	126		The Ringway Preston PR1 3AU
Preston	Novotel	Novotel	62%	£64	0772 313331	100		Reedfield Place Walton Summit Preston PR5 6AB

Location	Hotel	Group	%	£	Phone	Rooms		Address
Preston	Travel Inn			£42	0772 720476	40		Blackpool Road Lea Preston PR4 0XL
Samlesbury	Swallow Trafalgar	Swallow	64%	£82	0772 877351	78	yes	Preston New Road Samlesbury PR5 0UL

Leicestershire

Location	Hotel	Group	%	£	Phone	Rooms		Address
Leicester	Forte Posthouse	Forte	62%	£64	0533 630500	172		Braunston Lane East Leicester LE3 2FW
Leicester	Granada Lodge	Granada		£43	0530 244237	39		M1/A50 Junction 22 Markfield Leicester LE6 0PP
Leicester	Grand Hotel	Jarvis	66%	£106	0533 555599	92		Granby Street Leicester LE1 6ES
Leicester	Holiday Inn	Holiday Inns	72%	£113	0533 531161	188	yes	129 St Nicholas Circle Leicester LE1 5LX
Leicester	Leicester Forest Moat House	QMH	58%	£73	0533 394661	34		Hinckley Road Leicester LE3 3GH
Leicester	Park International	Park Hotels	61%	£82	0533 620471	209		Humberstone Road Leicester LE5 3AT
Leicester	Stakis Country Court	Stakis	69%	£107	0533 630066	141	yes	Braunstone Leicester LE3 2WQ
Lockington	Hilton National E Midlands	Hilton	69%	£118	0509 674000	151	yes	Derby Road Lockington DE7 2RH
Loughborough	King's Head	Jarvis	58%	£94	0509 233222	78		High Street Loughborough LE11 2QL
Lutterworth	Denbigh Arms	Resort	66%	£79	0455 553537	34		High Street Lutterworth LE17 5AD
Rothley	Rothley Court	Forte	67%	£101	0533 374141	36		Westfield Lane Rothley LE7 7LG
Thrussington	Forte Travelodge	Forte		£40	0664 424525	32		A46 Thrussington Green Acres Thrussington LE7 8TF
Uppingham	Forte Travelodge	Forte		£40	0572 87719	40		A47 Glaston Road Morcott nr Uppingham LE15 8SA

Lincolnshire

Location	Hotel	Group	%	£	Phone	Rooms		Address
Boston	New England Hotel	Forte	56%	£76	0205 365255	25		49 Wide Bargate Boston PE21 6SH
Colsterworth	Forte Travelodge	Forte		£40	0476 861181	32		A1 Southbound Colsterworth nr Grantham NG33 5JJ
Grantham	Forte Travelodge	Forte		£40	0476 77500	40		A1 Grantham Service Area Gonerby Moor Grantham
Grantham	Granada Lodge	Granada		£43	0476 860686	38		A1/A151 Colsterworth Grantham NG33 5JR
Lincoln	Forte Crest	Forte	63%	£88	0522 520341	70		Eastgate Lincoln LN2 1PN
Lincoln	White Hart	Forte	69%	£116	0522 526222	50		Bailgate Lincoln LN1 3AR
Sleaford	Forte Travelodge	Forte		£40	0529 414752	40		A17/A15 Holdingham Sleaford NG34 8PN
South Witham	Forte Travelodge	Forte		£40	057 283 586	32		A1 New Fox South Witham Colsterworth LE15 8AU
Stamford	The George of Stamford	Poste Hotels	72%	£90	0780 55171	47		71 St Martins Stamford PE9 2LB

Location	Establishment	Group	Grade	Price	Tel	Rooms	Pool	Address
Merseyside								
Bebington	Forte Travelodge	Forte		£40	051-327 2489	31		A41 N'bound New Chester Rd Eastham Wirral L62 9AQ
Gayton	Travel Inn	Travel Inns		£42	051-342 1982	37		Chester Road Gayton Wirral L60 3FD
Haydock	Forte Posthouse	Forte	65%	£64	0942 717878	136	yes	Lodge Lane Newton-le-Willows Haydock WA12 0JG
Haydock	Forte Travelodge	Forte		£40	0942 272055	40		A580 Piele Road Haydock St Helens WA11 9TL
Haydock	Haydock Thistle	MtCT	67%	£107	0942 272000	139	yes	Penny Lane Haydock St Helens WA11 9SG
Liverpool	Atlantic Tower	MtCT	65%	£102	051-227 4444	226		Chapel Street Liverpool L3 9RE
Liverpool	Campanile Hotel	Campanile		£36	051-709 8104	82		Chaloner Street Queen's Dock Liverpool L3 4AJ
Liverpool	Forte Crest	Forte	58%	£87	051-709 7050	154		Lord Nelson Street Liverpool L3 5QB
Liverpool	Moat House	QMH	67%	£112	051-709 0181	251		Paradise Street Liverpool L1 8JD
Liverpool	St George's Hotel	Forte	60%	£91	051-709 7090	155	yes	St John's Precinct Lime Street Liverpool L1 1NQ
Southport	Prince of Wales Hotel	Forte	65%	£65	0704 536688	104		Lord Street Southport PR8 1JS
Middlesex								
Hayes	Travel Inn	Travel Inns		£42	081-573 7479	40		362 Uxbridge Road Hayes UB4 0HE
Heathrow Airport - see under London Airport Heathrow								
Kenton	Travel Inn	Travel Inns		£42	081-907 1671	43		Kenton Road Kenton HA3 8AT
Shepperton	Moat House	QMH	61%	£98	0932 241404	180		Felix Lane Shepperton TW17 8NP
Wembley	Hilton National	Hilton	65%	£163	081-902 8839	300		Empire Way Wembley HA9 8DS
Norfolk								
Acle	Forte Travelodge	Forte		£40	0493 751970	40		A47 Acle Bypass Acle nr Norwich NR13 3BE
East Dereham	Phoenix Hotel	Forte	59%	£76	0362 692276	23		Church Street East Dereham NR19 1DL
Great Yarmouth	Carlton Hotel	Waveney	67%	£79	0493 855234	90		Marine Parade Great Yarmouth NR30 3JE
King's Lynn	Duke's Head	Forte	60%	£91	0553 774996	71		Tuesday Market Place King's Lynn PE30 1JS
King's Lynn	Forte Travelodge	Forte		£40	0406 362230	40		A17 Wisbech Road Long Sutton King's Lynn PE12 9AG

Location	Hotel	Group	%	Price	Phone	Rooms		Address
Norwich	Forte Posthouse	Forte	63%	£64	0603 56431	113	yes	Ipswich Road Norwich NR4 6EP
Thetford	The Bell	Forte	62%	£91	0842 754455	47		King Street Thetford IP24 2AZ

Northamptonshire

Location	Hotel	Group	%	Price	Phone	Rooms		Address
Crick	Forte Posthouse Northampton	Forte	64%	£64	0788 822101	88	yes	Crick NN6 7XR
Desborough	Forte Travelodge	Forte		£40	0536 762034	32		A6 Southbound Harborough Road Desborough
Northampton	Forte Travelodge	Forte		£40	0604 758395	40		A45 Upton Way Northampton NN5 6EG
Northampton	Holiday Inn Garden Court	Holiday Inns	65%	£75	0604 22777	104		Bedford Road Northampton NN4 0YF
Northampton	Moat House	QMH	63%	£93	0604 22441	138		Silver Street Northampton NN1 2TA
Northampton	Stakis Country Court	Stakis	68%	£111	0604 700666	144	yes	100 Watering Lane Collingtree Northampton NN4 0XW
Northampton	Swallow Hotel	Swallow	72%	£99	0604 768700	122	yes	Eagle Drive Northampton NN4 0HN
Northampton	Travel Inn	Travel Inns		£42	0604 832340	51		Harpole Turn Weedon Road Northampton NN7 4DD
Northampton	Westone Moat House	QMH	59%	£77	0604 406262	66		Ashley Way Weston Favell Northampton NN3 3EA
Oundle	Talbot Hotel	Forte	62%	£91	0832 273621	40		New Street Oundle PE8 4EA
Thrapston	Forte Travelodge	Forte		£40	0801 25199	40		A14 Link Road Thrapston By-Pass Thrapston
Towcester	Forte Travelodge	Forte		£40	0327 359105	33		A43 East Towcester By-Pass Towcester NN12 0DD

Northumberland

Location	Hotel	Group	%	Price	Phone	Rooms		Address
Alnwick	White Swan	Williamson	58%	£75	0665 602109	43		Bondgate Within Alnwick NE66 1TD
Chollerford	George Hotel	Swallow	59%	£98	0434 681611	50	yes	Chollerford nr Hexham NE46 4EW

Nottinghamshire

Location	Hotel	Group	%	Price	Phone	Rooms		Address
Barnby Moor	Ye Olde Bell	Principal	60%	£90	0777 705121	55		Barnby Moor nr Retford DN22 8QS
Blyth	Forte Travelodge	Forte		£40	0909 591775	32		A1 Blyth Worksop
Blyth	Granada Lodge	Granada		£43	0909 591836	39		A1M/A614 Blyth S82 8HG
Newark	Forte Travelodge	Forte		£40	0636 703635	30		A1 North Muskham Newark NG23 6HT
Nottingham	Forte Crest	Forte	70%	£87	0602 470131	130		St James's Street Nottingham NG1 6BN
Nottingham	Forte Posthouse	Forte	61%	£64	0602 397800	91		Bostocks Lane Sandiacre Nottingham NG10 5NJ

Location	Establishment	Group	Grade Price	Tel	Rooms	Pool	Address
Nottingham	Holiday Inn Garden Court	Holiday Inns	65% £70	0602 500600	100		Castle Marina Park Nottingham NG7 1GX
Nottingham	Moat House	QMH	59% £82	0602 602621	172		Mansfield Road Nottingham NG5 2BT
Nottingham	Novotel	Novotel	62% £70	0602 720106	112		Bostocks Lane Long Eaton Nottingham NG10 4EP
Nottingham	Royal Moat House	QMH	70% £100	0602 414444	201		Wollaton Street Nottingham NG1 5RH
Nottingham	Stakis Victoria Hotel	Stakis	62% £69	0602 419561	166		Milton Street Nottingham NG1 3PZ
Nottingham	Strathdon Thistle	MtCT	66% £102	0602 418501	69		44 Derby Road Nottingham NG1 5FT
Retford	Forte Travelodge	Forte	£40	0777 838091	40		A1 Northbound Markham Moor nr Retford DN22 0QU
Southwell	Saracen's Head	Forte	62% £86	0636 812701	27		Market Place Southwell NG25 0HE
Worksop	Forte Travelodge	Forte	£40	0909 501528	40		A47 St Anne's Drive Dunkeries Mill Worksop S80 3QD

Oxfordshire

Location	Establishment	Group	Grade Price	Tel	Rooms	Pool	Address
Abingdon	Upper Reaches	Forte	62% £101	0235 522311	25		Thames Street Abingdon OX14 3TA
Banbury	Moat House	QMH	62% £79	0295 259361	48		27-29 Oxford Road Banbury OX16 9AH
Banbury	Whately Hall	Forte	65% £100	0295 263451	74		Banbury Cross Banbury OX16 0AN
Burford	Bay Tree	Select	67% £97	099 382 279	23		Sheep Street Burford OX8 4LW
Oxford	Eastgate Hotel	Forte	61% £120	0865 248244	43		Merton Street The High Oxford OX1 4BE
Oxford	Forte Travelodge	Forte	£40	0867 75705	24		London Road Wheatley nr Oxford OX9 1JH
Oxford	Moat House	QMH	62% £105	0865 59993	155		Wolvercote Roundabout Oxford OX2 8AL
Oxford	Randolph Hotel	Forte	68% £148	0865 247481	109		Beaumont Street Oxford OX1 2LN
Wallingford	George Hotel	MtCT	62% £106	0491 36665	39		High Street Wallingford OX10 0BS
Weston-on-the-Green	Weston Manor	Hidden	61% £100	0869 50621	37		Weston-on-the-Green OX6 8QL
Woodstock	Bear Hotel	Forte	66% £116	0993 811511	45	yes	Park Street Woodstock OX7 1SZ

Shropshire

Location	Establishment	Group	Grade Price	Tel	Rooms	Pool	Address
Ludlow	Forte Travelodge	Forte	£40	058 472 695	32		A49 Woofferton Ludlow SY8 4AL
Oswestry	Forte Travelodge	Forte	£40	0691 658178	40		A5/A483 Mile End Service Area Oswestry SY11 4JA

Town	Hotel	Group	%	Price	Phone	Rooms		Address
Shifnal	Park House	Rank	71%	£85	0952 460128	54		Park Street Shifnal nr Telford TF11 9BA
Shrewsbury	Lion Hotel	Forte	62%	£91	0743 353107	59		Wyle Cop Shrewsbury SY1 1UY
Shrewsbury	Prince Rupert Hotel	QMH	64%	£83	0743 236000	65		Butcher Row Shrewsbury SY1 1UQ
Telford	Forte Travelodge	Forte		£40	0952 251244	40		Admaston Road Shawbirch Telford TF1 3QA
Telford	Holiday Inn	Holiday Inns	68%	£104	0952 292500	100	yes	St Quentin Gate Telford TF3 4EH
Telford	Moat House	QMH	67%	£95	0952 291291	148	yes	Foregate Telford TF3 4NA

Somerset

Town	Hotel	Group	%	Price	Phone	Rooms		Address
Dunster	Luttrell Arms	Forte	64%	£106	0643 821555	27		High Street Dunster nr Minehead TA24 8SG
Ilminster	Forte Travelodge	Forte		£40	0460 53748	32		A303 Southfield Roundabout Horton Cross Ilminster
Podimore	Forte Travelodge	Forte		£40	0935 840074	31		A303 Podimore nr Yeovil BA22 8JG
Taunton	County Hotel	Forte	61%	£86	0823 337651	66		East Street Taunton TA1 3LT
Taunton	Forte Posthouse	Forte	66%	£64	0823 332222	97		Deane Gate Avenue Taunton TA1 2UA
Taunton	Travel Inn	Travel Inns		£42	0823 321112	40		81 Bridgwater Road Taunton TA1 2DU
Yeovil	The Manor	Forte	63%	£91	0935 231161	41		Hendford Yeovil BA20 1TG

Staffordshire

Town	Hotel	Group	%	Price	Phone	Rooms		Address
Barton-under-Needwood	Forte Travelodge N	Forte		£40	0283 716343	20		A38 N'bound Barton-under-Needwood Burton-on-Trent
Barton-under-Needwood	Forte Travelodge S	Forte		£40	0283 716784	40		A38 S'bound Barton-under-Needwood Burton-on-Trent
Cannock	Travel Inn	Travel Inns		£42	0543 572721	38		Watling Street Cannock WS11 1SJ
Lichfield	George Hotel	Jarvis	59%	£88	0543 414822	38		Bird Street Lichfield WS13 6PR
Newcastle-under-Lyme	Clayton Lodge	Jarvis	60%	£97	0782 613093	50		Clayton Road Newcastle-under-Lyme ST5 4AF
Newcastle-under-Lyme	Forte Posthouse	Forte	60%	£64	0782 717171	126		Clayton Road Newcastle-under-Lyme ST5 4DL
Rugeley	Forte Travelodge	Forte		£40	0889 570096	32	yes	A51/B5013 Western Springs Road Rugeley WS15 2AS
Stafford	Tillington Hall	De Vere	63%	£95	0785 53531	90	yes	Eccleshall Road Stafford ST16 1JJ
Stoke-on-Trent	North Stafford Hotel	Principal	61%	£86	0782 744477	69		Station Road Stoke-on-Trent ST4 2AE
Stoke-on-Trent	Stakis Grand Hotel	Stakis	68%	£96	0782 202361	128	yes	Trinity Hall Hanley Stoke-on-Trent ST1 5NB
Stoke-on-Trent	Stoke-on-Trent Moat House	QMH	70%	£99	0782 219000	147	yes	Etruria Hall Festival Way, Etruria Stoke-on-Trent ST1 5BQ
Tamworth	Granada Lodge	Granada		£43	0827 260123	63		M42/A5 Junction 10 Tamworth B77 5PH
Uttoxeter	Forte Travelodge	Forte		£40	0889 562043	32		A50/A5030 Ashbourne Road Uttoxeter ST14 5AA

Location	Establishment	Group	Grade Price	Tel	Rooms	Pool	Address
Suffolk							
Aldeburgh	Brudenell Hotel	Forte	60% £91	0728 452071	47		The Parade Aldeburgh IP15 5BU
Barton Mills	Forte Travelodge	Forte	£40	0638 717675	32		A11 Barton Mills Mildenhall IP28 6AE
Bury St Edmunds	Suffolk Hotel	Forte	59% £86	0284 753995	33		38 Buttermarket Bury St Edmunds IP33 1DL
Copdock	Ipswich Moat House	QMH	64% £84	0473 86444	74	yes	London Road Copdock nr Ipswich IP8 3JD
Felixstowe	Orwell Moat House	QMH	69% £90	0394 285511	58		Hamilton Road Felixstowe IP11 7DX
Framlingham	The Crown	Forte	62% £96	0728 723521	14		Market Hill Framlingham IP13 9AN
Ipswich	Forte Posthouse	Forte	63% £54	0473 690313	112		London Road Ipswich IP2 0UA
Ipswich	Novotel	Novotel	61% £78	0473 232400	101		Greyfriars Road Ipswich IP1 1UP
Lavenham	The Swan	Forte	71% £121	0787 247477	47		High Street Lavenham nr Sudbury CO10 9QA
Long Melford	Bull Hotel	Forte	65% £96	0787 78494	25		Hall Street Long Melford CO10 9JG
Newmarket	Moat House	QMH	62% £78	0638 667171	47		Moulton Road Newmarket CB8 8DY
Stowmarket	Forte Travelodge	Forte	£40	0449 615347	40		A45 Stowmarket IP14 3PY
Surrey							
Camberley	Frimley Hall	Forte	68% £111	0276 28321	67		Portsmouth Road Camberley GU15 2BG
Chessington	Travel Inn	Travel Inns	£42	0372 744060	42		Leatherhead Road Chessington KT9 2NE
Cobham	Hilton National	Hilton	65% £129	0932 864471	152	yes	Seven Hills Road South Cobham KT11 1EW
Cobham	Woodlands Park	Select	69% £137	0372 843933	58		Woodlands Lane Stoke d'Abernon Cobham KT11 3QB
Croydon	Forte Posthouse	Forte	61% £64	081-688 5185	83		Purley Way Croydon CR9 4LT
Croydon	Travel Inn	Travel Inns	£42	081-686 2030	40		Coombe Road Croydon CR0 5RB
Dorking	Forte Travelodge	Forte	£40	0306 740361	29		A25 Reigate Road Dorking RH4 1QB
Dorking	White Horse	Forte	62% £96	0306 881138	68		High Street Dorking RH14 1BE
East Horsley	Thatchers Resort Hotel	Resort	63% £95	048 65 4291	59		Epsom Road East Horsley KT24 6TB
Farnham	Bush Hotel	Forte	62% £101	0252 715237	68		The Borough Farnham GU9 7NN
Guildford	Forte Crest	Forte	68% £97	0483 574444	111	yes	Egerton Road Guildford GU2 5XZ

Horley, Gatwick Airport - *see under* **London Airport Gatwick**

Town	Hotel	Group	Disc.	Price	Phone	Rooms		Address
Morden	Forte Travelodge	Forte	70%	£40	081-640 8227	32		A24 Epsom Road Morden SM4 5PH
Nutfield	Nutfield Priory	Hidden		£114	0737 822072	52		Nutfield Redhill RH1 4EN
Scale	Hog's Back Hotel	Jarvis	64%	£106	025 18 2345	75	yes	Scale nr Farnham GU10 1EX
Weybridge	Ship Thistle	MtCT	63%	£116	0932 848364	39	yes	5 Monument Green Weybridge KT13 8BQ

Sussex, East

Town	Hotel	Group	Disc.	Price	Phone	Rooms		Address
Brighton	Grand Hotel	De Vere	74%	£158	0273 21188	200	yes	King's Road Brighton BN1 2FW
Brighton	Hospitality Inn	MtCT	79%	£155	0273 206700	204	yes	King's Road Brighton BN1 2GS
Cooden	Cooden Resort Hotel	Resort	60%	£75	042 43 2281	41	yes	Cooden Sea Road Bexhill-on-Sea TN39 4TT
Eastbourne	Cavendish Hotel	De Vere	68%	£124	0323 410222	112		Grand Parade Eastbourne BN21 4DH
Eastbourne	Grand Hotel	De Vere	75%	£150	0323 412345	164	yes	King Edward's Parade Eastbourne BN21 4EQ
Eastbourne	Queen's Hotel	De Vere	67%	£93	0323 22822	108		Marine Parade Eastbourne BN21 3DY
Eastbourne	Wish Tower Hotel	Principal	66%	£90	0323 22676	65		King Edward's Parade Eastbourne BN21 4EB
Hailsham	Forte Travelodge	Forte		£40	0323 844556	40		A22 Boship Roundabout Hellingly Hailsham BN27 4DT
Hastings	Royal Victoria Hotel	Resort	70%	£75	0424 445544	51		The Marina St Leonards-on-Sea nr Hastings TN38 0BD
Lewes	Shelleys Hotel	MtCT	60%	£116	0273 472361	21		High Street Lewes BN7 1XS
Rye	George Hotel	Forte	62%	£91	0797 222114	22		High Street Rye TN31 7JP

Sussex, West

Town	Hotel	Group	Disc.	Price	Phone	Rooms		Address
Billingshurst	Forte Travelodge	Forte		£40	0403 782711	26		A29 Five Oaks Billingshurst RH14 9AE
Bognor Regis	Royal Norfolk	Forte	60%	£76	0243 826222	51		The Esplanade Bognor Regis PO21 2LH
Chichester	Dolphin & Anchor	Forte	63%	£96	0243 785121	49		West Street Chichester PO19 1QE
Crawley	George Hotel	Forte	64%	£96	0293 524215	86		High Street Crawley RH10 1BS
Fontwell	Forte Travelodge	Forte		£40	0243 543972	32		A27/A29 Fontwell BN18 0SB
Gatwick Airport - see under **London Airport Gatwick**								
Goodwood	Goodwood Park	Country Club	67%	£99	0243 775537	89	yes	Goodwood nr Chichester PO18 0QB
Horsham	Travel Inn	Travel Inns		£42	0403 50141	40		57 North Street Horsham RH12 1RB
Rusper	Ghyll Manor	Forte	68%	£116	0293 871571	27		High Street Rusper nr Horsham RH12 4PX

Location	Establishment	Group	Grade	Price	Tel	Rooms	Pool	Address
Tyne & Wear								
Gateshead	Forte Travelodge	Forte		£40	0748 3768	41		A194 Leam Lane Wardley Whitemare Pool nr Gateshead NE9
Gateshead	Springfield Hotel	Jarvis	63%	£95	091-477 4121	60		Durham Road Low Fell Gateshead NE9 5BT
Gateshead	Swallow Hotel	Swallow	60%	£82	091-477 1105	103	yes	High West Street Gateshead NE8 1PE
Newcastle-upon-Tyne	County Thistle	MtCT	68%	£98	091-232 2471	115		Neville Street Newcastle-upon-Tyne NE99 1AH
Newcastle-upon-Tyne	Forte Crest	Forte	61%	£87	091-232 6191	166		New Bridge Street Newcastle-upon-Tyne NE1 8BS
Newcastle-upon-Tyne	Holiday Inn	Holiday Inns	70%	£121	091-236 5432	150	yes	Great North Road Seaton Burn Newcastle-upon-Tyne
Newcastle-upon-Tyne	Moat House	QMH	59%	£68	091-262 8989	147	yes	Coast Road Wallend Newcastle-upon-Tyne NE28 1HP
Newcastle-upon-Tyne	Novotel	Novotel	63%	£81	091-214 0303	126	yes	Ponteland Road Kenton Newcastle-upon-Tyne
Newcastle-upon-Tyne	Swallow Gosforth Park	Swallow	73%	£115	091-236 4111	178	yes	High Gosforth Park Newcastle-upon-Tyne NE3 5HN
Newcastle-upon-Tyne	Swallow Hotel	Swallow	63%	£82	091-232 5025	94		2 Newgate Arcade Newcastle-upon-Tyne NE1 5SX
Newcastle-upon-Tyne	Airport Moat House	QMH	62%	£92	091-529 2041	100		Woolsington Newcastle-upon-Tyne NE13 8DJ
Sunderland	Swallow Hotel	Swallow		£79	0661 24911	66	yes	Queen's Parade Seaburn Sunderland SR6 8DB
Washington	Campanile Hotel	Campanile	59%	£36	091-416 5010	77		Emerson Road Washington nr Newcastle-upon-Tyne
Washington	Forte Posthouse	Forte		£64	091-416 2264	138		Emerson District 5 Washington NE37 1LB
Washington	Granada Lodge	Granada		£43	091-410 0076	35		A1M Washington DH3 2SJ
Washington	Moat House	QMH	66%	£94	091-417 2626	106	yes	Stone Cellar Road District 12 Washington NE37 1PH
Warwickshire								
Brandon	Brandon Hall	Forte	65%	£101	0203 542571	60		Brandon nr Coventry CV8 3FW
Charlecote	Charlecote Pheasant	QMH	62%	£85	0789 470333	67		Charlecote nr Warwick CV35 9EN
Kenilworth	De Montfort Hotel	De Vere	63%	£91	0926 55944	96		Kenilworth CV8 1ED
Leamington Spa	Courtyard by Marriott	Holiday Inns	65%	£75	0926 425522	97		Olympus Avenue Europa Way Leamington Spa CV34 6RJ
Nuneaton	Forte Travelodge	Forte		£40	0203 382541	40		A444 Bedworth Nuneaton Coventry CV12 0BN
Nuneaton	Travel Inn	Travel Inns		£42	0203 343584	30		Coventry Road Nuneaton CV10 7PJ
Stratford-upon-Avon	Alveston Manor	Forte	65%	£112	0789 204581	108		Clopton Bridge Stratford-upon-Avon CV37 7HP
Stratford-upon-Avon	Billesley Manor	QMH	76%	£128	0789 400888	41	yes	Billesley Alcester nr Stratford-upon-Avon B49 6NF

Location	Hotel	Group		Price	%	Phone	Rooms	Address
Stratford-upon-Avon	Falcon Hotel	QMH		£94	63%	0789 205777	73	Chapel Street Stratford-upon-Avon CV37 6HA
Stratford-upon-Avon	Forte Posthouse	Forte		£64	59%	0789 266761	60	Bridgefoot Stratford-upon-Avon CV37 7LT
Stratford-upon-Avon	Moat House International	QMH	yes	£120	71%	0789 414411	247	Bridgefoot Stratford-upon-Avon CV37 6YR
Stratford-upon-Avon	Shakespeare Hotel	Forte		£116	69%	0789 294771	63	Chapel Street Stratford-upon-Avon CV37 6ER
Stratford-upon-Avon	White Swan	Forte		£101	62%	0789 297022	42	Rother Street Stratford-upon-Avon CV37 6NH
Warwick	Hilton National	Hilton	yes	£139	66%	0926 499555	181	Stratford Road Warwick CV34 6RE
Wishaw	Belfry Hotel	De Vere	yes	£150	73%	0675 470301	219	Lichfield Road Wishaw B76 9PR

West Midlands

Location	Hotel	Group		Price	%	Phone	Rooms	Address
Birmingham	Campanile Hotel	Campanile		£36	70%	021-622 4925	50	Irving Street Lee Bank Birmingham B1 1DH
Birmingham	Copthorne Hotel	Copthorne	yes	£123	68%	021-200 2727	212	Paradise Circus Birmingham B3 3HJ
Birmingham	Forte Crest	Forte	yes	£97	60%	021-643 8171	254	Smallbrook Queensway Birmingham B5 4EW
Birmingham	Forte Posthouse	Forte	yes	£67		021-357 7444	192	Chapel Lane Great Barr Birmingham B43 7BG
Birmingham	Granada Lodge	Granada		£43	70%	021-550 3261	60	M5 Junction 3/4 Frankley Birmingham B32 4AR
Birmingham	Holiday Inn	Holiday Inns	yes	£124	61%	021-631 2000	288	Holiday Street Birmingham B1 1HH
Birmingham	Novotel	Novotel		£100	65%	021-643 2000	148	70 Broad Street Birmingham B1 2HT
Birmingham	Plough & Harrow	Forte		£101	65%	021-454 4111	44	135 Hagley Road Edgbaston Birmingham B16 8LS
Birmingham	Royal Angus Thistle	MtCT		£102	63%	021-236 4211	133	St Chads Queensway Birmingham B4 6HY
Birmingham	Strathallan Thistle	MtCT		£102	77%	021-455 9777	167	225 Hagley Road Edgbaston Birmingham B16 9RY
Birmingham	Swallow Hotel	Swallow	yes	£120		021-452 1144	98	12 Hagley Road Five Ways Birmingham B16 8SJ
Birmingham Airport	Forte Posthouse	Forte		£67	61%	021-782 8141	136	Coventry Road Birmingham Airport Birmingham
Birmingham Airport	Novotel	Novotel		£88	65%	021-782 7000	195	Birmingham Airport Birmingham B26 3QL
Coventry	Campanile Hotel	Campanile		£36		0203 622311	50	Wigston Road Walsgrave Coventry CV2 2SD
Coventry	Campanile Hotel	Campanile		£36		0203 639922	50	Abbey Road Whitley Coventry CV3 4BJ
Coventry	De Vere Hotel	De Vere		£176	69%	0203 633733	190	Cathedral Square Coventry CV1 5RP
Coventry	Forte Crest	Forte	yes	£70	66%	0203 613261	147	Hinckley Road Coventry CV2 2HP
Coventry	Forte Posthouse	Forte		£62	60%	0203 402151	184	Rye Hill Allesley Coventry CV5 9PH
Coventry	Novotel	Novotel		£78	62%	0203 365000	100	Wilsons Lane Longford Coventry CV6 6HL
Dudley	Forte Travelodge	Forte		£40		0384 481579	32	A461 Dudley Road Dudley DY5 1LQ
Dunchurch	Forte Travelodge	Forte		£40		0788 521528	40	A45 London Road, Thurlaston Dunchurch nr Rugby
Hagley	Travel Inn	Travel Inns		£42		0562 883120	40	Birmingham Road Hagley nr Stourbridge DY9 9JS

Location	Establishment	Group	Grade	Price	Tel	Rooms	Pool	Address
Meriden	Forest of Arden Hotel	Country Club	70%	£120	0676 22335	152	yes	Maxstoke Lane Meriden CV7 7HR
Meriden	Manor Hotel	De Vere	64%	£91	0676 22735	74		Main Road Meriden CV7 7NH
Oldbury	Forte Travelodge	Forte		£40	021-552 2967	33		A4123 Wolverhampton Road Oldbury Warly B69 2BH
Solihull	George Hotel	Jarvis	65%	£109	021-711 2121	78		The Square Solihull B91 3RF
Solihull	Moat House	QMH	69%	£115	021-711 4700	115	yes	Homer Road Solihull B91 3QD
Solihull	St John's Swallow Hotel	Swallow	63%	£108	021-711 3000	206	yes	651 Warwick Road Solihull B91 1AT
Solihull	Travel Inn	Travel Inns		£42	021-744 2942	40		Stratford Road Shirley Solihull B90 4PT
Sutton Coldfield	Forte Travelodge	Forte		£40	021-355 0017	32		Boldmere Road Sutton Coldfield B72 5UP
Sutton Coldfield	New Hall	MtCT	78%	£129	021-378 2442	60		Walmley Road Sutton Coldfield B76 8QX
Sutton Coldfield	Penns Hall	Jarvis	66%	£132	021-351 3111	114		Penns Lane Walmley Sutton Coldfield B76 8LH
Walsall	Forte Posthouse	Forte	61%	£62	0922 33555	101		Birmingham Road Walsall WS5 3AB
West Bromwich	Moat House	QMH	59%	£80	021-553 6111	172		Birmingham Road Bromwich B70 6RS
Wolverhampton	Mount Hotel	Jarvis	60%	£95	0902 752205	56		Mount Road Tettenhall Wolverhampton WV6 8HL
Wolverhampton	Victoria Park	Park Hotels	67%	£96	0902 29922	118		Lichfield Street Wolverhampton WV1 4DB

Wiltshire

Location	Establishment	Group	Grade	Price	Tel	Rooms	Pool	Address
Amesbury	Forte Travelodge	Forte		£40	0980 624966	32		A303 Amesbury SP4 7AS
Beanacre	Beechfield House	Hidden	72%	£110	0225 703700	20		Beanacre nr Melksham SN12 7PU
Chippenham	Granada Lodge	Granada	64%	£43	0666 837097	35		M4 Junction 17/18 Leigh Delamere Chippenham SN4 6LB
Malmesbury	Old Bell Hotel	Clipper	64%	£88	0666 822344	37		Abbey Row Malmesbury SN16 0BW
Salisbury	Rose & Crown	QMH	56%	£96	0722 327908	28		Harnham Road Harnham Salisbury SP2 8QJ
Salisbury	White Hart	Forte	63%	£106	0722 327476	68		1 St John Street Salisbury SP1 2SD
Swindon	De Vere Hotel	De Vere	62%	£110	0793 878785	154	yes	Shaw Ridge Leisure Park Whitehill Way Swindon SN5 7DW
Swindon	Forte Crest	Forte	62%	£88	0793 831333	97		Oxford Road Stratton St Margaret Swindon SN3 4TL
Swindon	Forte Posthouse	Forte	63%	£64	0793 524601	100		Marlborough Road Swindon SN3 6AQ
Swindon	Swindon Marriott Hotel	Marriott	71%	£121	0793 512121	153	yes	Pipers Way Swindon SN3 1SH
Swindon	Wiltshire Hotel	MtCT	62%	£100	0793 528282	95		Fleming Way Swindon SN1 1TN
Warminster	Granada Lodge	Granada		£43	0985 219639	31		A36/A350 Warminster BA12 7RU

Yorkshire, North

Location	Hotel	Group		Price	%	Phone	Rooms	Address
Harrogate	The Crown	Forte		£98	67%	0423 567755	121	Crown Place Harrogate HG1 2RZ
Harrogate	Hospitality Inn	MtCT		£93	61%	0423 564601	71	West Park Prospect Place Harrogate HG1 1LB
Harrogate	Imperial Hotel	Principal		£95	65%	0423 565071	85	Prospect Place Harrogate HG1 1LA
Harrogate	Majestic Hotel	Forte	yes	£114	64%	0423 568972	156	Ripon Road Harrogate HG1 2HU
Harrogate	Moat House	QMH		£119	64%	0423 500000	214	King's Road Harrogate HG1 1XX
Harrogate	Hotel St George	Swallow	yes	£99	63%	0423 561431	93	Ripon Road Harrogate HG1 2SY
Helmsley	Black Swan	Forte		£111	69%	0439 70466	44	Market Place Helmsley YO6 5BJ
Scarborough	The Crown	Forte		£91	63%	0723 373491	78	Esplanade Scarborough YO11 2AG
Scotch Corner	Forte Travelodge	Forte		£40		0748 3768	40	A1 Scotch Corner Skeeby nr Richmond DL10 5EQ
Skipton	Forte Travelodge	Forte		£40		0756 798091	32	A65/A59 Roundabout Gargrave Road Skipton BD23 1UD
York	Abbey Park Resort Hotel	Resort		£86	57%	0904 658301	85	The Mount York YO2 2BN
York	Forte Posthouse	Forte		£64	65%	0904 707921	139	Tadcaster Road York YO2 2QF
York	Forte Travelodge	Forte		£40		0973 531823	40	A64 Eastbound Bilbrough nr York
York	Holiday Inn	Holiday Inns		£129	68%	0904 648111	128	Tower Street York YO1 1SB
York	Novotel	Novotel	yes	£80	62%	0904 611660	124	Fishergate York YO1 4AD
York	Royal York Hotel	Principal		£100		0904 653681	148	Station Road York YO2 2AA
York	Swallow Hotel	Swallow	yes	£99	64%	0904 701000	113	Tadcaster Road York YO2 2QQ
York	Viking Hotel	QMH		£105	69%	0904 659822	188	North Street York YO1 1JF

Yorkshire, South

Location	Hotel	Group		Price	%	Phone	Rooms	Address
Barnsley	Ardsley Moat House	QMH		£90	65%	0226 289401	73	Doncaster Road Ardsley Barnsley S71 5EH
Barnsley	Forte Travelodge	Forte		£40		0226 298799	32	A633/635 Stairfoot Roundabout Barnsley
Bawtry	The Crown	Forte		£81	64%	0302 710341	57	High Street Bawtry DN10 6JW
Carcroft	Forte Travelodge	Forte		£40		0302 330841	40	A1 Great North Road Carcroft nr Doncaster
Doncaster	Campanile Hotel	Campanile		£36		0302 370770	50	Doncaster Leisure Park Bawtry Doncaster DN4 7PD
Doncaster	Danum Swallow Hotel	Swallow		£88	64%	0302 342261	66	High Street Doncaster DN1 1DN
Doncaster	Moat House	QMH	yes	£88	68%	0302 310331	100	Warmsworth Doncaster DN4 9UX
Rotherham	Campanile Hotel	Campanile		£36		0709 700255	50	Lowton Way, off Denby Way Hellaby Ind Est Rotherham
Rotherham	Moat House	QMH		£86	69%	0709 364902	83	Moorgate Road Rotherham S60 2BG

Location	Establishment	Group	Grade Price	Tel	Rooms	Pool	Address
Rotherham	Travel Inn	Travel Inns		£42 0709 543216	37		Bawtry Road Rotherham S65 3JB
Sheffield	Forte Crest	Forte	65%	£88 0742 670067	136	yes	Manchester Road Sheffield S10 5DX
Sheffield	Grosvenor House	Forte	67%	£75 0742 720041	103		Charter Square Sheffield S1 3EH
Sheffield	Holiday Inn Royal Victoria	Holiday Inns	67%	£108 0742 768822	100		Station Approach Sheffield S4 7XE
Sheffield	Moat House	QMH	71%	£100 0742 375376	95	yes	Chesterfield Road South Sheffield S8 8BW
Sheffield	St George Swallow Hotel	Swallow	64%	£92 0742 583811	141	yes	Kenwood Road Sheffield S7 1NQ

Yorkshire, West

Location	Establishment	Group	Grade Price	Tel	Rooms	Pool	Address
Bingley	Bankfield Hotel	Jarvis	61%	£105 0274 567123	103		Bradford Road Bingley BD16 1TV
Bradford	Novotel	Novotel	60%	£70 0274 683683	132		Merrydale Road Bradford BD4 6SA
Bradford	Stakis Norfolk Gardens	Stakis	65%	£106 0274 734734	120		Hall Ings Bradford BD1 5SH
Bradford	Victoria Hotel	Forte	61%	£77 0274 728706	59		Bridge Street Bradford BD1 1JX
Bramhope	Forte Crest	Forte	66%	£98 0532 842911	126	yes	Bramhope nr Leeds LS16 9JJ
Bramhope	Parkway Hotel	Jarvis	63%	£119 0532 672551	103	yes	Otley Road Bramhope nr Leeds LS16 8AG
Brighouse	Forte Crest	Forte	68%	£98 0484 400400	94	yes	Coalpit Lane Clifton Village Brighouse HD6 4HW
Ferrybridge	Granada Lodge	Granada		£43 0977 670488	35		M62/A1 Junction 33 Ferrybridge WF11 0AF
Garforth	Hilton National	Hilton	61%	£108 0532 866556	144	yes	Wakefield Road Garforth nr Leeds LS25 1LH
Hartshead Moor	Forte Travelodge	Forte		£40 0274 851706	40		Hartshead Moor Service Area Clifton Brighouse HD6 4RJ
Huddersfield	George Hotel	Principal	62%	£80 0484 515444	60		St George's Square Huddersfield HD1 1JA
Huddersfield	Pennine Hilton National	Hilton	66%	£100 0422 375431	118	yes	Ainley Top Huddersfield HD3 3RH
Leeds	Hilton International	Hilton	69%	£129 0532 442000	210		Neville Street Leeds LS1 4BX
Leeds	Leeds Marriott Hotel	Marriott	71%	£164 0532 442200	125	yes	Wellington Street Leeds LS1 4DL
Leeds	Merrion Hotel	MtCT		£91 0532 439191	120		Merrion Centre Leeds LS2 8NH
Leeds	Queen's Hotel	Forte	67%	£109 0532 431323	188		City Square Leeds LS1 1PL
Wakefield	Campanile Hotel	Campanile		£36 0924 201054	77		Monckton Road Wakefield WF2 7AL
Wakefield	Forte Posthouse	Forte	64%	£64 0924 276388	99		Queen's Drive Ossett Wakefield WF5 9BE
Wakefield	Granada Lodge	Granada		£43 0924 830569	31		M1 Junction 38/39 Woolley Edge Wakefield WF4 4LQ
Wakefield	Swallow Hotel	Swallow	58%	£86 0924 372111	64		Queen Street Wakefield WF1 1JU
Wentbridge	Forte Travelodge	Forte		£40 0977 620711	56		A1 Barnsdale Bar Wentbridge nr Pontefract WS8 3JB
Wentbridge	Wentbridge House	Select	63%	£71 0977 620444	12		Wentbridge nr Pontefract WF8 3JJ

SCOTLAND GROUP HOTELS

Location	Establishment	Group	Grade Price	Tel	Rooms	Pool	Address

Key: QMH (Queens Moat Houses), MtCT (Mount Charlotte Thistle). *Note:* Lodges (Forte Travelodge, Travel Inn, Granada, Campanile) and Inns are ungraded. We recommend that you call to confirm family facilities before staying at the hotels listed.

Borders

Location	Establishment	Group	Grade	Price	Tel	Rooms	Pool	Address
Peebles	Tontine Hotel	Forte	57%	£96	0721 20892	37		High Street Peebles EH45 8AJ

Central

Location	Establishment	Group	Grade	Price	Tel	Rooms	Pool	Address
Dunblane	Stakis Dunblane Hydro	Stakis	61%	£111	0786 822551	240	yes	Perth Road Dunblane FK15 0HG
Stirling	Granada Lodge	Granada		£43	0786 815033	37		M90/M80 Junction 9 Stirling FK7 8EU

Dumfries & Galloway

Location	Establishment	Group	Grade	Price	Tel	Rooms	Pool	Address
Gretna Green	Forte Travelodge	Forte		£40	0461 37566	41		A74 Trunk Road Gretna Green CA6 5HQ

Fife

Location	Establishment	Group	Grade	Price	Tel	Rooms	Pool	Address
Dunfermline	King Malcolm Thistle	MtCT	65%	£93	0383 722611	48		Queensferry Road Dunfermline KY11 5DS
St Andrews	Rusack's Hotel	Forte	74%	£134	0334 74321	50		Pilmour Links St Andrews KY16 9JQ

Grampian

Location	Establishment	Group	Grade	Price	Tel	Rooms	Pool	Address
Aberdeen	Bucksburn Moat House	QMH	69%	£104	0224 713911	144	yes	Oldmeldrum Road Bucksburn Aberdeen AB2 9LN
Aberdeen	Caledonian Thistle	MtCT	68%	£134	0224 640233	80		Union Terrace Aberdeen AB9 1HE
Aberdeen	Copthorne Hotel	Copthorne	68%	£122	0224 630404	89		122 Huntly Street Aberdeen AB1 1SU
Aberdeen	Stakis Tree Tops	Stakis	63%	£130	0224 313377	112	yes	161 Springfield Road Aberdeen AB9 2QH
Aberdeen	Travel Inn	Travel Inns		£42	0224 821217	40		Murcar Bridge of Don Aberdeen AB2 8BP

Location	Establishment	Group	Grade	Price	Tel	Rooms	Pool	Address
Aberdeen Airport	Aberdeen Marriott Hotel	Marriott	72%	£135	0224 770011	154	yes	Riverview Drive Fairburn, Dyce Aberdeen AB2 0AZ
Aberdeen Airport	Skean Dhu Hotel	MtCT	65%	£96	0224 725252	148		Argyll Road Dyce Aberdeen AB2 0DU

Highland

Location	Establishment	Group	Grade	Price	Tel	Rooms	Pool	Address
Aviemore	Aviemore Highlands Hotel	Principal	61%	£70	0479 810771	103		Aviemore Centre Aviemore PH22 1PJ
Aviemore	Stakis Aviemore Four Seasons	Stakis	70%	£96	0479 810681	89	yes	Aviemore PH22 1PF
Aviemore	Stakis Coylumbridge Resort	Stakis	61%	£99	0479 810661	175	yes	Aviemore PH22 1QN
Fort William	Mercury Hotel	MtCT	58%	£88	0397 703117	86		Achintore Road Fort William PH33 6RW
Inverness	Caledonian Hotel	Jarvis	69%	£111	0463 235181	100	yes	33 Church Street Inverness IV1 1DX
Inverness	Kingsmills Hotel	Swallow	67%	£105	0463 237166	84	yes	Culcabock Road Inverness IV2 3LP
Inverness	Mercury Hotel	MtCT	62%	£95	0463 239666	118		Millburn Road Inverness IV2 3TR
Nairn	Golf View Hotel	Rank	64%	£125	0667 52301	48		Seabank Road Nairn IV12 4HD

Lothian

Location	Establishment	Group	Grade	Price	Tel	Rooms	Pool	Address
Edinburgh	The Balmoral	Forte	83%	£185	031-556 2414	189	yes	Princes Street Edinburgh EH2 2EQ
Edinburgh	Barnton Thistle	MtCT	63%	£113	031-339 1144	50		Queensferry Road Edinburgh EH4 6AS
Edinburgh	Caledonian Hotel	QMH	79%	£192	031-225 2433	240		Princes Street Edinburgh EH1 2AB
Edinburgh	Forte Posthouse	Forte	62%	£64	031-334 0390	208		Corstorphine Road Edinburgh EH12 6UA
Edinburgh	Forte Travelodge	Forte		£40	031-441 4296	40		A720 Dreghorn Link City By-Pass Edinburgh EH13 9QR
Edinburgh	Granada Lodge	Granada	68%	£43	031-653 2427	44		A1 Musselburgh By-Pass Musselburgh Edinburgh EH21 8RE
Edinburgh	Hilton National	Hilton	65%	£150	031-332 2545	144		69 Belford Road Edinburgh EH4 3DG
Edinburgh	Holiday Inn Garden Court	Holiday Inns	75%	£91	031-332 2442	119		107 Queensferry Road Edinburgh EH4 3HL
Edinburgh	Howard Hotel	Select	70%	£160	031-557 3500	16		36 Great King Street Edinburgh EH3 6QH
Edinburgh	King James Thistle	MtCT	64%	£128	031-556 0111	147		St James Centre 107 Leith Street Edinburgh EH1 3SW
Edinburgh	Stakis Grosvenor Hotel	Stakis	65%	£106	031-226 6001	136		Grosvenor Street Edinburgh EH12 5EF
Edinburgh	Swallow Royal Scot	Swallow	78%	£118	031-334 9191	259	yes	111 Glasgow Road Edinburgh EH12 8NF
Kirknewton	Dalmahoy Hotel	Country Club	62%	£120	031-333 1845	115	yes	Kirknewton EH27 8EB
North Berwick	Marine Hotel	Forte	61%	£100	0620 2406	84	yes	Cromwell Road North Berwick EH39 4LZ
South Queensferry	Forth Bridges Moat House	QMH		£114	031-331 1199	108	yes	South Queensferry EH30 9SF

Strathclyde

Location	Hotel	Group		%	£	Phone	Rooms	Address
Abington	Forte Travelodge	Forte			£40	086 42782	54	A74/M74 Welcome Break Service Area Abington Biggar
Ayr	Caledonian Hotel	Jarvis	yes	64%	£110	0292 269331	114	Dalblair Road Ayr KA7 1UG
Cumbernauld	Travel Inn	Travel Inns			£42	0236 725339	37	4 South Muirhead Road Cumbernauld nr Glasgow G67 1AX
Dumbarton	Forte Travelodge	Forte			£40	0389 65202	32	A82 Milton Dumbarton G82 2TY
East Kilbride	Bruce Swallow Hotel	Swallow		59%	£72	035 52 29771	79	Cornwall Street East Kilbride G74 1AF
Erskine	Forte Posthouse	Forte	yes	62%	£62	041-812 0123	166	by Erskine Bridge PA8 6AN
Giffnock	Macdonald Thistle	MtCT		64%	£102	041-638 2225	58	Eastwood Toll Giffnock nr Glasgow G48 6RA
Glasgow	Copthorne Hotel	Copthorne		64%	£118	041-332 6711	140	George Square Glasgow G2 1DS
Glasgow	Forte Crest	Forte		74%	£98	041-248 2656	254	Bothwell Street Glasgow G2 7EN
Glasgow	Glasgow Marriott Hotel	Marriott	yes	72%	£136	041-226 5577	298	Argyle Street Anderston Glasgow G3 8RR
Glasgow	Hospitality Inn	MtCT		67%	£109	041-332 3311	307	36 Cambridge Street Glasgow G3 3HN
Glasgow	Kelvin Park Lorne Hotel	QMH		63%	£79	041-334 4891	99	923 Sauchiehall Street Glasgow G3 7TE
Glasgow	Moat House International	QMH	yes	69%	£128	041-204 0733	300	Congress Road Glasgow G3 8QT
Glasgow	Stakis Grosvenor	Stakis		66%	£111	041-339 8811	95	Grosvenor Terrace Glasgow G12 0TA
Glasgow	Swallow Hotel	Swallow	yes	61%	£88	041-427 3146	119	517 Paisley Road West Glasgow G51 1RW
Glasgow	Tinto Firs Hotel	MtCT		62%	£98	041-637 2353	30	470 Kilmarnock Road Glasgow G43 2BB
Glasgow Airport	Forte Crest	Forte		67%	£88	041-887 1212	300	Abbotsinch nr Paisley PA3 2TR
Glasgow Airport	Stakis Normandy	Stakis		61%	£102	041-886 4100	141	Inchman Road Renfrew Glasgow Airport PA4 5EJ
Gourock	Stakis Gantock Hotel	Stakis	yes	64%	£96	0475 34671	101	Cloch Road Gourock PA15 1AR
Irvine	Hospitality Inn	MtCT	yes	68%	£101	0294 74272	128	46 Annick Road Irvine KA11 4LD
Milngavie	Black Bull Thistle	MtCT		59%	£87	041-956 2291	27	Main Street Milngavie G62 6BH
Newhouse	Travel Inn	Travel Inns			£42	0698 860277	40	Glasgow Road Newhouse nr Motherwell ML1 5SY

Tayside

Location	Hotel	Group		%	£	Phone	Rooms	Address
Dundee	Angus Thistle	MtCT		69%	£108	0382 26874	58	Marketgait Dundee DD1 1QU
Dundee	Travel Inn	Travel Inns			£42	0382 561115	40	Kingsway West Invergowrie Dundee DD2 5JU
Kinross	Granada Lodge	Granada			£43	0577 64646	35	M90 Junction 6 Kinross KY13 7NQ
Perth	Royal George Hotel	Forte		62%	£91	0738 24455	42	Tay Street Perth PH1 5LD
Perth	Stakis City Mills Hotel	Stakis		59%	£86	0738 28281	76	West Mill Street Perth PH1 5QP

WALES GROUP HOTELS

Key: QMH (Queens Moat Houses), MtCT (Mount Charlotte Thistle). *Note:* Lodges (Forte Travelodge, Travel Inn, Granada, Campanile) and Inns are ungraded. We recommend that you call to confirm family facilities before staying at the hotels listed.

Location	Establishment	Group	Grade	Price	Tel	Rooms	Pool	Address
Bridgend	Forte Travelodge	Forte		£40	0656 659218	40		M4 J36 Service Area Sarn Park nr Bridgend Mid Glamorgan
Cardiff	Angel Hotel	QMH	66%	£124	0222 232633	91		Castle Street Cardiff South Glamorgan CF1 2QZ
Cardiff	Campanile Hotel	Campanile		£36	0222 549044	50		Caxton Place Pentwyn Cardiff South Glamorgan CF2 7HA
Cardiff	Cardiff Marriott Hotel	Marriott	69%	£125	0222 399944	182	yes	Mill Lane Cardiff South Glamorgan CF1 1EZ
Cardiff	Forte Crest	Forte	69%	£87	0222 388681	157		Castle Street Cardiff South Glamorgan CF1 2XB
Cardiff	Forte Posthouse	Forte	63%	£64	0222 731212	136	yes	Pentwyn Road Cardiff South Glamorgan CF2 7XA
Cardiff	Forte Travelodge	Forte		£40	0222 549564	32		Circle Way East (off A48M) Llancederyn Cardiff'S Glamorgan
Cardiff	Moat House	QMH	70%	£99	0222 732520	135	yes	Circle Way East Llanederyn Cardiff South Glamorgan CF3 7XF
Cardiff	Park Hotel	MtCT	70%	£107	0222 383471	119		Park Place Cardiff South Glamorgan CF1 3UD
Cardiff	Travel Inn	Travel Inns		£42	0633 680070	49		Newport Road Castleton nr Cardiff South Glamorgan
Carmarthen	Ivy Bush Royal	Forte	59%	£86	0267 235111	80		Spilman Street Carmarthen Dyfed SA31 1LG
Cross Hands	Forte Travelodge	Forte		£40	0269 845700	32		A48 Cross Hands nr Llanelli Dyfed SA14 6NW
Halkyn	Forte Travelodge	Forte		£40	0352 780952	31		A55 Halkyn Clwyd CH8 8RF
Llangollen	Hand Hotel	MtCT	55%	£65	0978 860303	57		Bridge Street Llangollen Clywd LL20 8PL
Llangollen	Royal Hotel	Forte	59%	£81	0978 860202	33		Bridge Street Llangollen Clywd LL20 8PG
Newport	Hilton National	Hilton	61%	£112	0633 412777	119	yes	The Coldra Newport Gwent NP6 2YG
Newport	Stakis Country Court	Stakis	69%	£107	0633 413733	141	yes	Chepstowe Road Newport Gwent NP6 2LX
Northop Hall	Forte Travelodge	Forte		£40	0244 816473	40		A55 Northop Hall Mold Clwyd CH7 6HB
Pencoed	Forte Travelodge	Forte		£40	0656 864404	40		Old Mill Felindre Road Pencoed nr Bridgend Mid Glamorgan
Port Talbot	Travel Inn	Travel Inns		£42	0639 813017	40		Baglan Road Port Talbot West Glamorgan SA12 8ES
Presteigne	Radnorshire Arms	Forte	61%	£86	0544 267406	16		High Street Presteigne Powys LD8 2BE
Swansea	Forte Crest	Forte	69%	£87	0792 651074	99	yes	39 The Kingsway Swansea West Glamorgan SA1 5LS
Swansea	Hilton National	Hilton	65%	£83	0792 310330	120	yes	Phoenix Way Ent Park Llansamlet Swansea W Glamorgan
Swansea	Swansea Marriott Hotel	Marriott	67%	£122	0792 642020	118	yes	Maritime Quarter Swansea West Glamorgan SA1 3SS
Tintern	Beaufort Hotel	Jarvis	60%	£92	0291 689777	24		Tintern Abbey Chepstow Gwent NP6 6SF
Wrexham	Forte Travelodge	Forte		£40	0978 365705	32		A483/A5152 Wrexham By-pass Rhostyllen Wrexham Clwyd

Maps

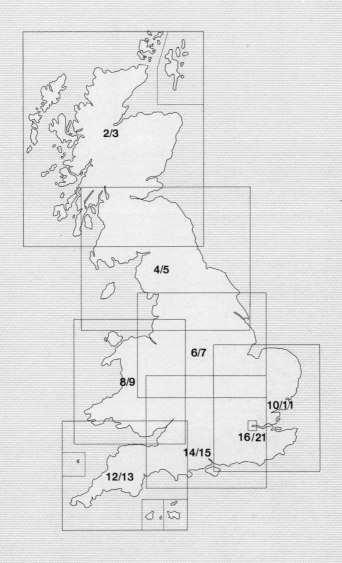

2/3

4/5

6/7

8/9

10/11

16/21

14/15

12/13

Motorways	●	Food
Primary Routes	□	Accommodation
Other Roads	▣	Accommodation and Food
County Boundaries	○	Family Pub

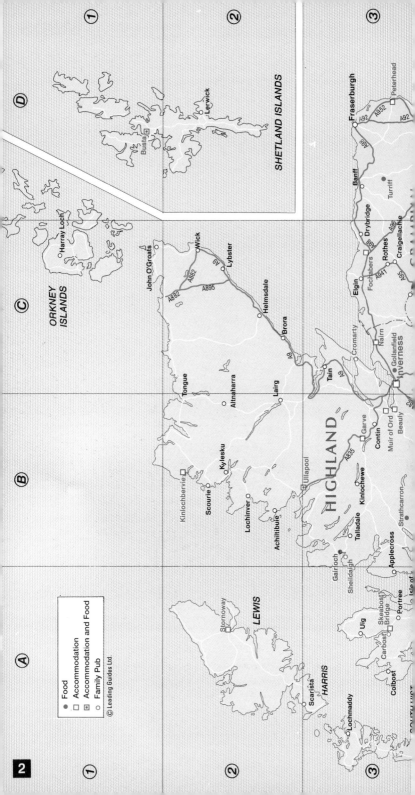

2

Food ●
Accommodation □
Accommodation and Food ⊡
Family Pub ○

© Leading Guides Ltd.

ORKNEY ISLANDS

Harray Loch ○

SHETLAND ISLANDS

Busta ⊡
Lerwick ●

John O'Groats ○
Wick
Lybster
A882
A895
A9
Helmsdale
Brora

Tongue
Altnaharra ○
Lairg ○

Kinlochbervie □
Scourie ○
Kylesku ○
Lochinver ○
Achiltibuie ○
Ullapool ⊡

HIGHLAND

Tain ○
A9
Cromarty
Nairn □
Gollanfield ⊡
Inverness ⊡
Garve □
Contin □
Beauly □
Muir of Ord □
A835
Kinlochewe
Talladale
Strathcarron
Gairloch ○
Shieldaig
Applecross ●
Isle of

LEWIS
Stornoway □

HARRIS
Scarista ○

Lochmaddy ○
Colbost ●
Carbost ○
Skeabost Bridge □
Uig ○
Portree □
SOUTH UIST

Elgin ○
Fochabers
A941
A96
Rothes □
Craigellachie
A95
Drybridge ○
Banff
A98
Turriff ●
Fraserburgh ●
A952
A90
Peterhead ●
A92
GRAMPIAN

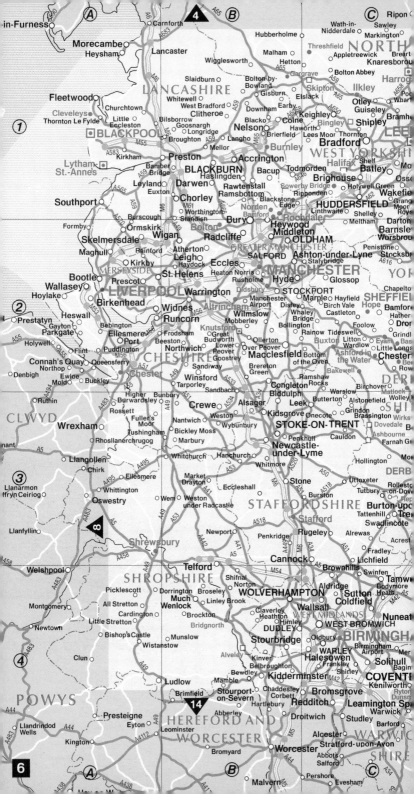

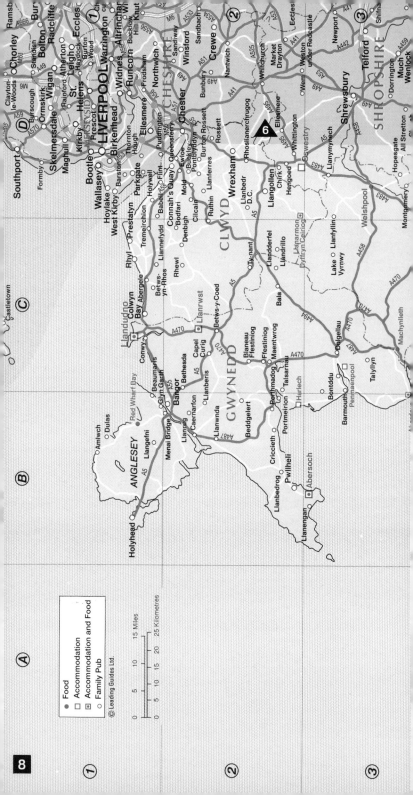

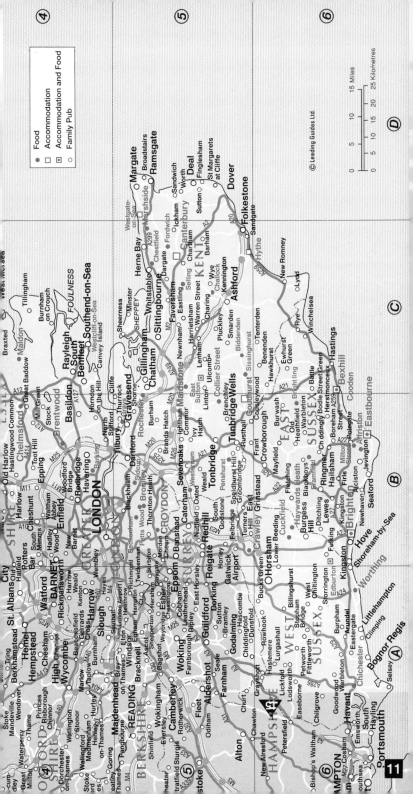

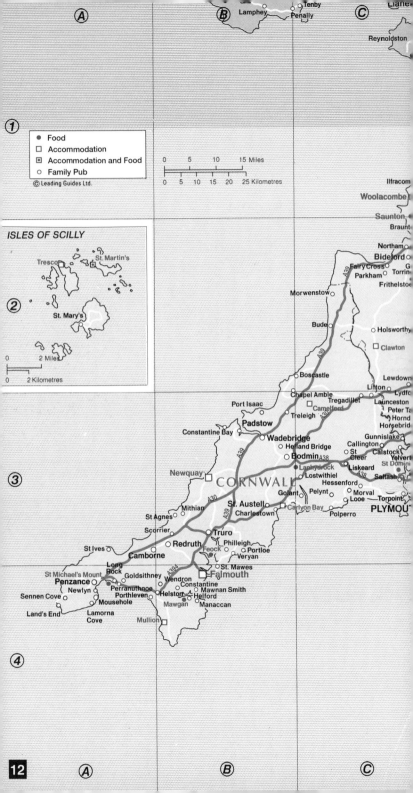

Food ●
Accommodation □
Accommodation and Food ⊡
Family Pub ○

© Leading Guides Ltd.

0   5   10   15 Miles
0 5 10 15 20 25 Kilometres

ISLES OF SCILLY

Tresco
St. Martin's
St. Mary's

0   2 Miles
0   2 Kilometres

Ⓐ Ⓑ Ⓒ Llane...

Lamphey Tenby
Penally

Reynoldston

Ilfracom...
Woolacombe
Saunton
Braunt...
Northam
Bideford
Fairy Cross G...
Parkham Torrin...
Frithelsto...

Morwenstow

Bude Holsworthy
Clawton

Boscastle
Lewdown
Chapel Amble Lifton
Tregadillet Lydfo...
Port Isaac Camelford Launceston
Treleigh Peter Ta...
Padstow Hornd...
Horsebrid...
Constantine Bay Wadebridge Gunnislake
Helland Bridge Callington Calstock
Bodmin St Yelvert...
Cleer St Domini...
Newquay Lanhydrock Liskeard Saltash
Lostwithiel Hessenford
CORNWALL Golant Pelynt Morval
Mithian St. Austell Looe Torpoint
Charlestown Carlyon Bay Polperro PLYMOU...
St Agnes
Scorrier Truro Phlleigh Portloe
St Ives Redruth Feock Veryan
Camborne St. Mawes
Long Falmouth
St Michael's Mount Rock
Penzance Goldsithney Wendron Constantine
Newlyn Perranuthnoe Helston Mawnan Smith
Sennen Cove Porthleven Helford
Mousehole Mawgan Manaccan
Land's End Lamorna
Cove Mullion

Ⓐ Ⓑ Ⓒ

12

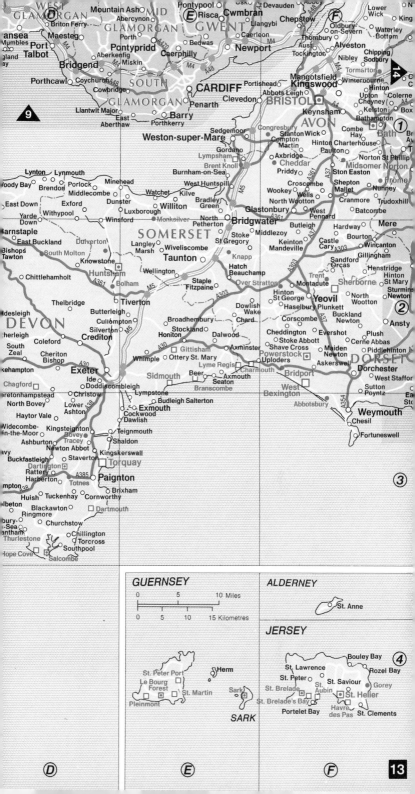

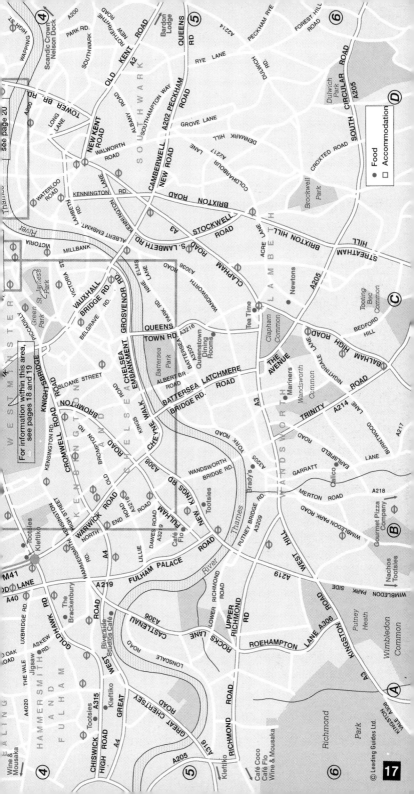

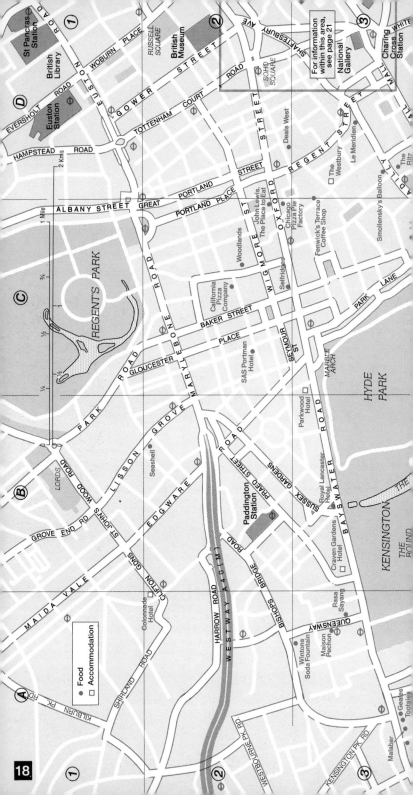

For information within this area, see page 21

Legend:
- Food (●)
- Accommodation (□)

St Pancras Station
British Library
Euston Station
Russell Square
British Museum
National Gallery
Charing Cross Station

EVERSHOLT
WOBURN PLACE
EUSTON ROAD
HAMPSTEAD ROAD
GOWER STREET
TOTTENHAM COURT ROAD
SOHO SQUARE
SHAFTESBURY AVE
THE MALL
WHITE

Deals West
The Westbury
Le Meridien
The Ritz
Smollensky's Balloon

REGENTS PARK
ALBANY STREET
GREAT PORTLAND STREET
PORTLAND PLACE
REGENT STREET
PORTLAND PLACE

Woodlands
John Lewis, The Place to Eat
Chicago Pizza Pie Factory
Fenwick's Terrace Coffee Shop

California Pizza Company
Selfridges
OXFORD STREET
WIGMORE ST
SEYMOUR ST
PARK LANE

MARYLEBONE ROAD
GLOUCESTER PLACE
BAKER STREET
PLACE

SAS Portman Hotel
MARBLE ARCH
Parkwood Hotel

PARK ROAD
LISSON GROVE
EDGWARE ROAD
LORDS
WOOD ROAD
ST JOHN'S WOOD ROAD
GROVE END RD

Seashell

HYDE PARK

Royal Lancaster Hotel
SUSSEX GARDENS
Paddington Station
PRAED STREET
BAYSWATER ROAD
KENSINGTON
THE ROUND

MAIDA VALE
CLIFTON GDNS
Colonnade Hotel
SHIRLAND ROAD
KILBURN PK RD

HARROW ROAD
WESTWAY A40 (M)
BISHOPS BRIDGE ROAD
WESTBOURNE PK RD
KENSINGTON PK RD

Craven Gardens Hotel
Rasa Sayang
Maison Pechon
Wintons Soda Fountain
QUEENSWAY

Malabar
Geales
Tootsies

2 Kms
1 Mile
¾
½
¼

18

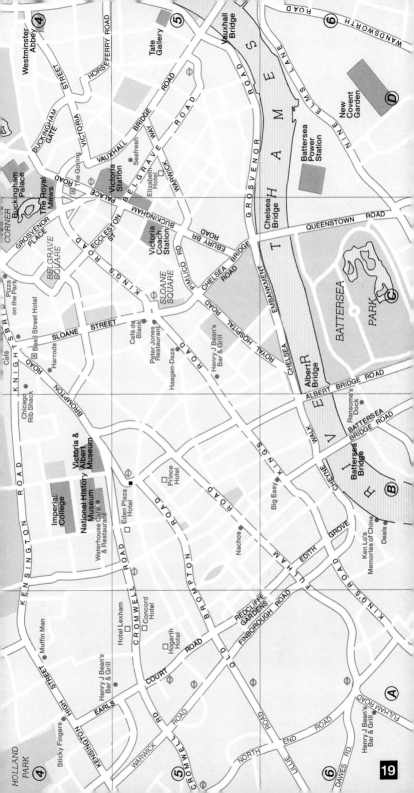

Index

READERS' COMMENTS

Please use this sheet, and the continuation overleaf, to recommend restaurants of **really outstanding quality.**

   Complaints about any of the Guide's entries will be treated seriously and passed on to our inspectorate, but we would like to remind you always to take up your complaint with the management at the time.

   We regret that owing to the volume of readers' communications received each year we will be unable to acknowledge these forms, but your comments will certainly be seriously considered.

Please post to: **Egon Ronay's Guides, 73 Uverdale Road, London SW10 0SW**

Please use an up-to-date Guide. We publish annually. (... And Baby Comes Too 1993)

Name and address of establishment	Your recommendation or complaint

320

Readers' Comments continued

Name and address of establishment	Your recommendation or complaint

Your Name (BLOCK LETTERS PLEASE)

Address